BRAIN STEM CONTROL OF SPINAL MECHANISMS

FERNSTRÖM FOUNDATION SERIES
VOLUME 1

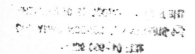

BRAIN STEM CONTROL OF SPINAL MECHANISMS

Proceedings of the 1st Eric K. Fernström Symposium
held in Lund (Sweden) on 10–13 November, 1981

Editors

BENGT SJÖLUND
ANDERS BJÖRKLUND

1982

ELSEVIER BIOMEDICAL PRESS
AMSTERDAM · NEW YORK · OXFORD

ISSN Series: 0167 7004
ISBN Volume: 0 444 80429 3

Published by:
Elsevier Biomedical Press
P.O. Box 211
1000 AE Amsterdam, The Netherlands

Sole distributors for the USA and Canada:
Elsevier Science Publishing Company Inc.
52 Vanderbilt Avenue
New York, N.Y. 10017

Library of Congress Cataloging in Publication Data

Eric K. Fernström Symposium (1st : 1981 : Lund, Sweden)
    Brain stem control of spinal mechanisms.

    (Fernström Foundation series, ISSN 0167-7004 ; v. 1)
    Bibliography: p.
    Includes index.
    1. Brain stem--Congresses. 2. Spinal cord--Congresses. 3. Sensory-motor intregration--Congresses. I. Sjölund, B. H. (Bengt H.) II. Björklund, Anders, 1945-   . III. Title. IV. Series. [DNLM: Brain stem--Physiology--Congresses. 2. Spinal cord--Physiology--Congresses. W1 FE746s v.1 / WL 310 E68 1981b]
QP376.8.E74 1981   612'.826   82-16429
ISBN 0-444-80429-3 (U.S.)

Printed in The Netherlands

List of Contributors

M. ABDELMOUMENE, N.I.D.R., National Institutes of Health, Bethesda, Maryland, U.S.A.

B. ALLEN, N.I.D.R., National Institutes of Health, Bethesda, Maryland, U.S.A.

A.I. BASBAUM, Departments of Anatomy and Physiology, School of Medicine, University of California, San Francisco, California, U.S.A.

G.J. BENNETT, N.I.D.R., National Institutes of Health, Bethesda, Maryland, U.S.A.

J.-M. BESSON, Unité de Recherches de Neurophysiologie Pharmacologique de l'INSERM, 2 rue d'Alésia, Paris, France

A. BJÖRKLUND, Department of Histology, University of Lund, Lund, Sweden

C.S. CHANDLER, Department of Anatomy, University of Newcastle upon Tyne, U.K.

C.J. DALSGAARD, Department of Anatomy, Karolinska Institutet, Stockholm, Sweden

A.H. DICKENSON, Department of Neurophysiology and Neuropharmacology, National Institute for Medical Research, The Ridgeway, Mill Hill, London, U.K.

A.W. DUGGAN, Department of Pharmacology, John Curtin School of Medical Research, Australian National University, Canberra, Australia

H. FORSSBERG, Dept. of Physiology III, Karolinska Institutet, Stockholm, Sweden

K. FUKUSHIMA, Department of Physiology, Hokkaido University School of Medicine, Sapporo, Japan

S. GOBEL, N.I.D.R., National Institutes of Health, Bethesda, Maryland, U.S.A.

S. GRILLNER, Department of Physiology III, Karolinska Institutet, Stockholm, Sweden

D.L. HAMMOND, Departments of Neurosurgery and Pharmacology, Mayo Foundation, Rochester, Minnesota, U.S.A.

G.R. HAMMOND, Department of Anatomy, University of Newcastle upon Tyne, U.K.

H. HAYASHI, N.I.D.R., National Institutes of Health, Bethesda, Maryland, U.S.A.

J.R. HEWIT, Department of Mechanical Engineering, University of Newcastle upon Tyne, U.K.

M.J. HOFFERT, N.I.D.R., National Institutes of Health, Bethesda, Maryland, U.S.A.

T. HÖKFELT, Department of Histology, Karolinska Institutet, Stockholm, Sweden

A.M. HUISMAN, Department of Anatomy II, Erasmus University Medical School, Rotterdam, The Netherlands

E. HUMPHREY, N.I.D.R., National Institutes of Health, Bethesda, Maryland, U.S.A.

S.P. HUNT, MRC Neurochemical Pharmacology Unit, Medical School, Hills Road, Cambridge, U.K.

G. JANSCO, Department of Anatomy, University of Szeged, Hungary

O. JOHANSSON, Department of Histology, Karolinska Institutet, Stockholm, Sweden

H.G.J.M. KUYPERS, Department of Anatomy II, Erasmus University Medical School, Rotterdam, The Netherlands

B.R. KOMISARUK, Institute of Animal Behavior, Rutgers University, Newark, New Jersey, U.S.A.

D. LE BARS, Unité de Recherches de Neurophysiologie Pharmacologique de l'INSERM, 2 rue d'Alésia, Paris, France

A. LUNDBERG, Department of Physiology, University of Göteborg, Göteborg, Sweden

J.M. LUNDBERG, Departments of Histology and Pharmacology, Karolinska Institutet, Stockholm, Sweden

A. McCLELLAN, Dept. of Physiology III, Karolinska Institutet, Stockholm, Sweden

S. MILLER, Department of Anatomy, University of Newcastle upon Tyne, U.K.

J.I. NAGY, MRC Neurochemical Pharmacology Unit, Medical School, Hills Road, Cambridge, U.K.

M. NINKOVIC, MRC Neurochemical Pharmacology Unit, Medical School, Hills Road, Cambridge, U.K.

G. NORELL, Neuroendocrine Unit, Laboratory of Clinical Sciences, Fogarty International Center, Biological Psychiatry Branch, National Institutes of Mental Health, Bethesda, Maryland, U.S.A.

B.W. PETERSON, Department of Physiology, Northwestern University Medical School, Chicago, Illinois, U.S.A.

P.M. ROBERTSON, Department of Anatomy, University of Newcastle upon Tyne, U.K.

Z. SELTZER, Neurobiology and Anesthesiology Branch, N.I.D.R., National Institutes of Health, Bethesda, Maryland, U.S.A.

K. SIGVARDT, Dept. of Physiology III, Karolinska Institutet, Stockholm, Sweden

B.H. SJÖLUND, Departments of Physiology and Neurosurgery, University of Lund, Sweden

G. SKAGERBERG, Department of Histology, University of Lund, Sweden

L. SKIRBOLL, Section of Biochemistry and Pharmacology, Biological Psychiatry Branch, National Institutes of Mental Health, Bethesda, Maryland, U.S.A.

D.J. STELZNER, Department of Anatomy, S.U.N.Y. Upstate Medical Center, Syracuse, New York, U.S.A.

N. TAN, Department of Mechanical Engineering, University of Newcastle upon Tyne, U.K.

L. TERENIUS, Department of Pharmacology, University of Uppsala, Sweden

F. WALBERG, Anatomical Institute, University of Oslo, Norway

P. WALLÉN, Department of Physiology III, Karolinska Institutet, Stockholm, Sweden

D.C. WEST, Department of Physiology, Medical School, University of Birmingham, U.K.

T. WILLIAMS, Department of Physiology III, Karolinska Institutet, Stockholm, Sweden

W.D. WILLIS, Marine Biomedical Institute, Departments of Anatomy and of Physiology and Biophysics, University of Texas Medical Branch, Galveston, Texas, U.S.A.

J.H. WOLSTENCROFT, Department of Physiology, Medical School, University of Birmingham, U.K.

T.L. YAKSH, Departments of Neurosurgery and Pharmacology, Mayo Foundation, Rochester, Minnesota, U.S.A.

W. ZIEGLGÄNSBERGER, Max-Planck-Institute for Psychiatry, Kraepelinstrasse 2, München, F.R.G.

Preface

The present monograph on Brain Stem Control of Spinal Mechanisms has been made possible through the sponsorship of the Eric K. Fernström Foundation. It has been written by scientists contributing to the vast increase of knowledge in this field during the last decades. The topic is covered from structural as well as from functional, both motor and sensory, points of view.

The volume forms the proceedings of a symposium held at Örenäs Castle outside Lund, Sweden, to bring together researchers studying various aspects of bulbospinal control systems. The aim was to create a dialogue between scientists involved in the study of motor mechanisms on the one hand, and segmental transmission of sensory, particularly nociceptive, information on the other, and to relate these functions to anatomical structures, particularly to evaluate the participation of monoaminergic and peptidergic neuron systems. It was felt that the interaction in such a symposium would facilitate the formation of conceptual models including both "motor" and "sensory" control systems or even models, joining them into a single concept. As can be seen from the proceedings now presented, fruitful attempts have already been made in this direction. It is our hope that the scientific community will find the present volume of interest and value and will be as fascinated as we are by the neuronal systems descending from the brain stem to the spinal cord to control such diverse actions as locomotion and the transmission of nociception.

We wish to thank the Eric K. Fernström Foundation for generous economic support and its chairman, Professor Håkan Westling, Dean of the Medical Faculty, University of Lund, for a never-failing interest in the organization of this symposium, to be the first in a series of Eric. K. Fernström Symposia in Medical Science held at the University.

Special thanks go to Mrs Ingegärd Lindqvist, Secretary of the Eric K. Fernström Foundation, for invaluable assistance during all phases of the symposium, including the publication of this book. Thanks are also due to Miss Karin Jönsson and to Mrs AnnChristin Rynell for assistance during the symposium, and to Mrs MaryLynn Gage for excellent scrunity of the English text and for collation of the references.

x

The support of Astra Pharmaceutical Company, Södertälje, Sweden, and the Swedish Medical Research Council (Projects nos. 5658 and 4493) is also acknowledged.

Bengt Sjölund
Anders Björklund

The Eric K. Fernström Foundation

The foundation was established in 1977 through a donation from the retired ship-owner, Eric K. Fernström, Med.dr.h.c., to the Medical Faculty at the University of Lund, Sweden. Part of the annual returns is used to sponsor scientific symposia in the biomedical field, arranged by medical institutions belonging to the University of Lund. The proceedings of these symposia will in the future appear in the Eric K. Fernström Foundation Series, published by Elsevier Biomedical Press. The foundation also awards scientific prizes for medical research. The main Eric K. Fernström Prize is given yearly to the most outstanding and able medical scientist in the Nordic countries. In addition, each of the six Medical Faculties in Sweden is given the opportunity to award a yearly prize to one or two of its most promising young scientists.

Contents

Anatomical Organization

Physiology of Descending Systems: Motor Aspects

Physiology of Descending Systems: Sensory Aspects

Section I

Anatomical Organization

Brain Stem Control of Spinal Mechanisms
– B. Sjölund and A. Björklund, editors
© 1982 Elsevier Biomedical Press

1

Paths Descending from the Brain Stem – An Overview

FRED WALBERG

Anatomical Institute, University of Oslo, Oslo, Norway

I. Introduction

The spinal cord is influenced through several fiber tracts which originate in the brain stem. Best known of these are the rubrospinal, the vestibulospinal and the reticulospinal tracts, but recent research has shown that the spinal cord receives fibers from many other nuclei and cell groups within the brain stem. In this review a survey will be given of the anatomical studies on the descending pathways from the brain stem; the functional aspects of these fiber systems will be considered in other chapters of this volume.

II. The Rubrospinal Tract

Experimental studies based on retrograde and anterograde degeneration have shown that, in mammals, the red nucleus has a prominent projection to the spinal cord (Fig. 1A) and that small as well as large cells participate in the projection (Pompeiano and Brodal, 1957b; Kuypers and Lawrence, 1967). These observations have recently been confirmed in studies where horseradish peroxidase has been used as a retrograde tracer (Kuypers and Maisky, 1975, cat; Kneisley et al., 1978, monkey; Maisky and Kuypers, 1978a, cat; Basbaum and Fields, 1979, cat and rat; Murray and Gurule, 1979, rat).

There is, furthermore, a somatotopical pattern within the projection (Pompeiano and Brodal, 1957b; Nyberg-Hansen and Brodal, 1964; Murray and Haines, 1975; Castiglioni et al., 1978; Kneisley et al., 1978; Murray and Gurule, 1979; Zemlan et al., 1979; Hayes and Rustioni, 1981; Watkins et al., 1981). The rubrospinal fibers ending in the cervical cord originate in the dorsomedial part of the red nucleus, those ending in the lumbosacral cord origi-

2

nate in the ventrolateral part, with an intermediate area representing the "trunk" region (Fig. 1B). This somatotopy appears not to be present in lower mammals (Martin et al., 1981b, opossum). However, it is interesting that some rubral cells in the cat (Hayes and Rustioni, 1981) as well as in the opossum (Martin et al., 1981b), branch to supply the cervical and lumbar intumescence.

The anterograde degeneration studies have shown that the rubrospinal tract is almost entirely crossed, with the crossing occurring immediately below the red nucleus. The fibers proceed caudally somewhat lateral to the lateral corticospinal tract, and in mammals can be followed to the lumbosacral level (Orioli and Mettler, 1956; Hinman and Carpenter, 1959; Kuypers et al., 1962;

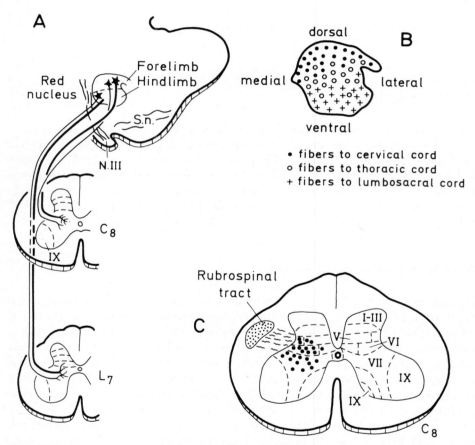

Figure 1. Diagram of the rubrospinal projection in the cat. A, the origin and course of the rubrospinal fibers. B, the somatotopic pattern in the red nucleus as this appears in a transverse section at the middle level of the nucleus. C, the site of termination for the rubrospinal fibers in relation to Rexed's laminae of the spinal cord. (Diagram based on the findings of Pompeiano and Brodal (1957a) and Nyberg-Hansen and Brodal (1964).) For abbreviations, see separate list.

Nyberg-Hansen and Brodal, 1964; Poirier and Bouvier, 1966; Miller and Strominger, 1973; Brown, 1974; Martin et al., 1974; Murray and Haines, 1975). This course of the rubrospinal fibers has recently been confirmed in studies with neuronal markers (Edwards, 1972; Kuypers and Maisky, 1977).

In the cat, the terminal site for the rubrospinal fibers appears to be the lateral part of Rexed's lamina V, lamina VI and the dorsal and central parts of lamina VII (Fig. 1C), an area corresponding largely to that for the termination of the corticospinal fibers from the "motor" cortex. This pattern of termination has been revealed in degeneration (Nyberg-Hansen and Brodal, 1964) as well as in autoradiographic tracing studies (Edwards, 1972), and it appears to be the same in the monkey (Murray and Haines, 1975). Most of the fibers are distributed to dendrites of the spinal cord cells (Brown, 1974; Kostyuk and Skibo, 1975; Goode and Sreesai, 1978).

III. The Vestibulospinal Tracts

In mammals there are three major vestibulospinal projections: a lateral, a medial, and a caudal vestibulospinal tract.

The well-known lateral vestibulospinal tract has been shown to originate in the lateral vestibular nucleus (nucleus of Deiters) (Fig. 2A). With the modified Gudden method (Brodal, 1940), Pompeiano and Brodal (1957a) showed that in the cat the fibers of this tract are derived not only from giant cells, but also from other cells within the nucleus. This observation has recently been confirmed in studies with neuronal tracers (Kuypers and Maisky, 1975, cat; Henkel and Martin, 1977, opossum; Peterson and Coulter, 1977, cat; Crutcher et al., 1978, opossum; Kneisley et al., 1978, monkey; Zemlan et al., 1979, rat), and fits with the presence of thick as well as thin fibers in the tract.

Similar to what has been found for the rubrospinal projection, there is also a somatotopical pattern within the projection from the lateral vestibular nucleus (Fig. 2B). This pattern was first demonstrated in retrograde and anterograde degeneration studies in the cat (Pompeiano and Brodal, 1957a; Nyberg-Hansen and Mascitti, 1964) and was later shown to be present in other mammals (Kneisley et al., 1978; Zemlan et al., 1979). Studies where horseradish peroxidase has been used as a retrograde tracer have, in addition, revealed that a similar organization exists in birds (Wold, 1978, domestic hen). Since the lateral vestibulospinal tract in mammals extends to the lumbosacral level of the cord, this means that one may speak of a "neck and forelimb region", a "trunk region" and a "hindlimb region" of the lateral vestibular nucleus. It should, however, be mentioned that the borders between these nuclear regions are not sharply delimited.

The termination for the lateral vestibulospinal fibers differs from that of the rubrospinal tract (Fig. 2C). Rexed's lamina VIII and the ventral and central parts of lamina VII receive the bulk of the afferents; only a few fibers termi-

4

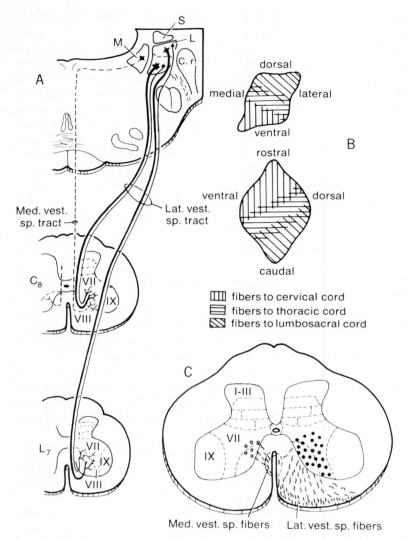

Figure 2. Diagram of the origin, course and termination of the lateral and medial vestibulospinal tracts. A, the course of the fibers. B, the somatotopic pattern in the projection from the lateral vestibular nucleus as seen in a transverse (above) and sagittal (below) reconstruction of the nucleus. C, the termination of the two vestibulospinal tracts in the spinal cord in relation to Rexed's laminae. (Diagram based on the findings of Pompeiano and Brodal (1957a), Nyberg-Hansen and Mascitti (1964) and Nyberg-Hansen (1964a).) For abbreviations, see separate list.

nate within lamina IX, the area containing motoneurons (Nyberg-Hansen and Mascitti, 1964).

The medial vestibulospinal tract (Fig. 2A) is relatively modest and takes its origin only from the medial vestibular nucleus (Nyberg-Hansen, 1964a). Unlike the lateral vestibulospinal tract, which after leaving the lateral vestibular nucleus passes in a ventral direction to descend in the ipsilateral ventrolateral funiculus, the medial vestibulospinal tract consists of a small number of fibers which descend in the medial longitudinal fasciculus to proceed bilaterally in the ventral funiculus close to the midline. Nyberg-Hansen found that, in contrast to the former fibers, the medial vestibulospinal tract terminates at mid-thoracic levels. This difference in distribution indicates that the medial vestibular nucleus and its tract are chiefly concerned in the transmission of vestibular impulses to the neck and forelimb muscles, while the lateral vestibular nucleus and its descending fibers may influence the entire body. It should, however, be mentioned that the fibers of the lateral and medial spinovestibular tracts appear to share the same terminal area within the spinal cord (Nyberg-Hansen, 1964a).

A caudal vestibulospinal tract (Fig. 3) has recently been demonstrated in a study where horseradish peroxidase was used as a retrograde tracer (Peterson and Coulter, 1977). In the cat this tract originates in the caudal poles of the medial and descending vestibular nucleus and in cell group f of Brodal and Pompeiano (1957). It descends at least as far as to the lumbar intumescence. Subsequent studies by Peterson et al. (1978) have provided evidence that the fibers of the caudal vestibulospinal tract descend bilaterally within the ventral as well as the dorsolateral funiculi. Apart from this, virtually nothing is known about the anatomy of this tract. (The reader is referred to the publica-

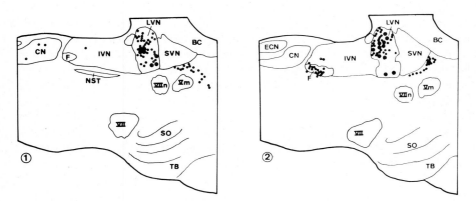

Figure 3. Location of retrogradely labeled neurons in the vestibular nuclei and adjacent brain stem in parasagittal sections following a unilateral injection of horseradish peroxidase at L_6. (From Peterson and Coulter, 1977, with permission.) For abbreviations, see separate list.

tion by Peterson et al. (1978) for details concerning the functional properties of the fibers.) A final point to mention is that Hayes and Rustioni (1981) describe a branching to the cervical and lumbar intumescence of axons from single cells in the medial, descending and lateral vestibular nucleus.

IV. Reticulospinal Tracts

The reticular formation of the brain stem sends a heavy fiber projection to the spinal cord. This projection had already been demonstrated by the classical neuroanatomists. During the last decades a wealth of new details has been added to our knowledge of the anatomy of the reticulospinal tracts. In these studies, degeneration as well as tracer techniques have been used (see especially Pitts, 1940; Bodian, 1946; Torvik and Brodal, 1957; Kuypers et al., 1962; Kuypers, 1964; Nyberg-Hansen, 1965; Petras, 1967; Holstege et al., 1979; Beran and Martin, 1971; Martin and Dom, 1971; Edwards, 1975; Kuypers and Maisky, 1975; Martin et al., 1975; Castiglioni et al., 1977; Gallaway et al., 1977; Glazer et al., 1977; Basbaum et al., 1978; Kneisley et al., 1978; Maisky and Kuypers, 1978a, b; Basbaum and Fields, 1979; Martin et al., 1979a, b; Tohyama et al., 1979a; Zemlan and Pfaff, 1979; Zemlan et al., 1979; Goode et al., 1980; Bowker et al., 1981).

Before a review is given of the origin, course and termination of the reticulospinal fibers, it is appropriate to give a short survey of the anatomy of the nuclei of the reticular formation. Since the pioneering experimental studies of the connections of these nuclei have been made in the cat (Brodal and coworkers, see below), the description of the nuclei will be based on the observations made in this animal.

The reticular formation of the brain stem is usually considered to comprise the areas of the medulla, pons and mesencephalon, which structurally are characterized by diffuse aggregations of cells of different types and sizes, and separated by nerve fibers traversing the region in all directions. However, the experimental studies have given evidence that the reticular formation should not be considered an entity, but that it is built up by groups of more or less well circumscribed nuclei*. From caudal to rostral within the reticular formation (RF), one can distinguish between a nucleus reticularis ventralis, a nucleus reticularis lateralis, a nucleus reticularis parvicellularis, a nucleus reticularis gigantocellularis, a nucleus reticularis pontis caudalis, a nucleus reticularis pontis oralis, and the reticular formation of the mesencephalon. The delimitations of the nuclei are shown in Figure 4**.

---

* In this review the nomenclature introduced by Brodal (see especially Brodal, 1957) is used.
** Three rather well circumscribed nuclei, the lateral reticular nucleus, the nucleus reticularis paramedianus and the nucleus reticularis tegmenti pontis (of Bechterew), will not be dealt with here. None of these nuclei has been shown to send fibers to the spinal cord.

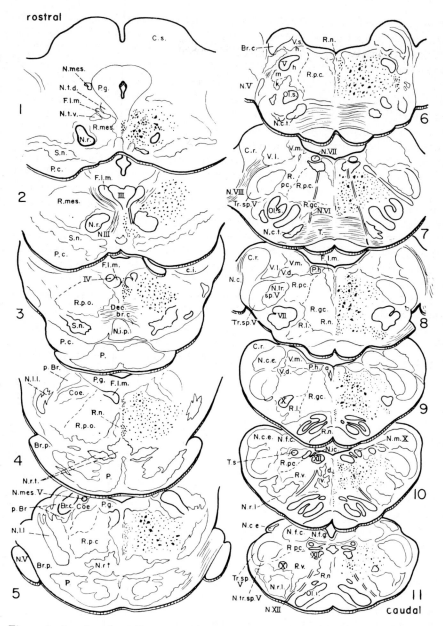

Figure 4. A series of equally spaced drawings of transverse Nissl sections through the brain stem of the cat illustrating the cell groups of the reticular formation. The drawings of dots of different sizes in the right half of the diagram indicate the distribution of cell types according to size. On the left side the broken lines give the approximate borders between the various reticular nuclei. (From Brodal, 1957, with permission.) For abbreviations, see separate list.

With the modified Gudden method (Brodal, 1940), Torvik and Brodal (1957) demonstrated that, in the cat, reticulospinal fibers are derived from small as well as large cells scattered at all levels of the medullary and pontine RF. They found, however, two clearly maximal areas of origin: one in the pons and the other in the medulla. Both were restricted to approximately the medial two-thirds of the RF, where large cells occur (Fig. 4). The fibers from the pons descend ipsilaterally, those from the medulla are ipsilateral as well as contralateral. The majority of the medullary fibers come from nucleus reticularis gigantocellularis, the fibers from the pons emerge from the nucleus reticularis parvicellularis and the caudal part of the nucleus reticularis pontis oralis. Furthermore, it is interesting that the experimental study by Torvik and Brodal (1957) indicated that there is no somatotopical pattern in the reticulospinal projection. They estimated that more than half of the large cells of the nucleus reticularis parvicellularis send their fibers to the spinal cord.

The efferent pontine fibers descend almost exclusively ipsilaterally in the ventral funiculus, the medullary fibers run bilaterally in the lateral funiculus and the fibers from both regions proceed to the lowermost levels of the cord (Nyberg-Hansen, 1965). A recent autoradiographic study (Basbaum et al., 1978) provides evidence that some of the descending fibers from the medulla also pass in the dorsolateral funiculus.

The termination of the reticulospinal fibers has been studied in detail by Nyberg-Hansen (1965), who found that, in the cat, the fibers from the pontine RF terminate ventrally within lamina VIII and the adjacent part of lamina

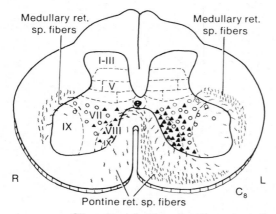

▲ Sites of termination of pontine ret. sp. fibers
• Sites of termination of medullary ret. sp. fibers

Figure 5. Diagram of a transverse section of the cervical spinal cord indicating the position of the reticulospinal fibers from medullary and pontine reticular regions, and the sites of termination of the fibers in relation to Rexed's laminae. (From Nyberg-Hansen, 1965, with permission.) For abbreviations, see separate list.

VII. The medullary RF fibers have a different termination. They end chiefly in lamina VII, with a few fibers passing to laminae VIII and IX (Fig. 5). In other mammalian species, largely similar results have been obtained concerning the origin (Kuypers et al., 1962; Kuypers, 1964; Castiglioni et al., 1977; Gallaway et al., 1977, monkey; Beran and Martin, 1971, opossum), course (Kneisley et al., 1978, monkey) and termination (Martin and Dom, 1971, opossum) of the fibers. A projection to the intermediolateral cell column has also been described (Amendt et al., 1979).

A detailed account of the reticulospinal projection as this appears when the new tracer techniques are applied is given by Kuypers (this volume). Suffice it here, therefore, to stress a few of the new observations. Firstly, although Torvik and Brodal (1957) were unable to show that reticulospinal fibers also originate in the mesencephalic RF, this has now been established (Kuypers and Maisky, 1975, 1977; Basbaum and Fields, 1979; Tohyama et al., 1979a; Martin et al., 1979a). Secondly, with tracer techniques and immunocytochemical methods it has been possible to indicate the location within the RF of the spinal projecting catecholaminergic cells (Glazer et al., 1977; Kneisley et al., 1978; Basbaum and Fields, 1979; Goode et al., 1980; Blessing et al., 1981; Bowker et al., 1981; Loewy et al., 1981). An especially interesting feature is that there appears to be a segmental segregation in the projection, with dopamine fibers arising from the diencephalon, noradrenaline fibers from the pons and adrenaline fibers from the medulla (Ross et al., 1981; Westlund et al., 1981; see the former authors for other references). A final point of interest is that studies with double-labeling techniques have shown that single reticular cells may innervate the cervical as well as the lumbar part of the spinal cord (Hayes and Rustioni, 1981; Martin et al., 1981a). Martin and his coworkers have also provided details regarding development of the reticulospinal tracts (Cabana and Martin, 1981).

V. The Spinal Projection from Locus Coeruleus, Nucleus Subcoeruleus and the Parabrachial Nucleus

The nucleus locus coeruleus (LC), which is located near the floor of the rostral part of the fourth ventricle, has attracted considerable interest in recent years, as has the nucleus subcoeruleus, a rather diffuse cell group ventrolateral to the nucleus LC. A similar situation exists regarding the parabrachial nucleus (PBN), an ill-defined cell group surrounding the brachium conjunctivum, and rostrally fusing with the LC. The reason for this interest is that it has been found that these cell groups belong to brain stem regions rich in noradrenaline (NA) (for details, see other chapters of this volume). The first demonstration of this finding came from the study by Dahlström and Fuxe (1964).

Tracer studies have demonstrated that some cells in all three of these nuclei send their fibers to the spinal cord (Fig. 6, level 6) (Holstege et al., 1979; Maeda

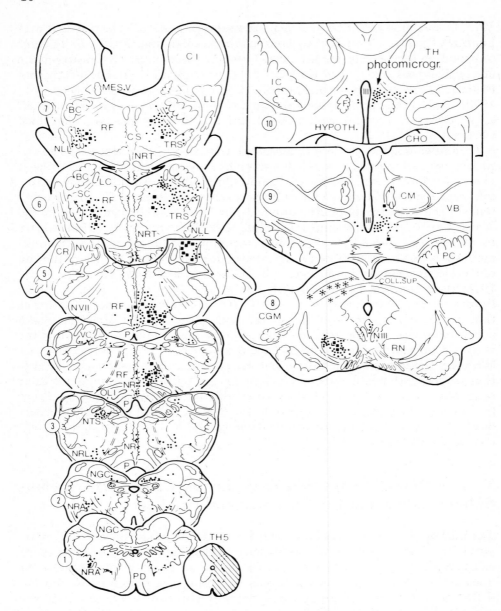

Figure 6. Distribution of retrogradely labeled neurons (dots and squares) at various brain stem levels (1–10) after a unilateral injection of horseradish peroxidase at Th₅. Asterisks at level 8 indicate the position of labeled collicular neurons after contralateral injections in C₂. For details, see text. (From Kuypers and Maisky, 1975, with permission.) For abbreviations, see separate list.

et al., 1973; Ross and Reis, 1974; Kuypers and Maisky, 1975; Hancock and Fougerousse, 1976; McBride and Sutin, 1976; Nygren and Olson, 1977; Peterson and Coulter, 1977; Satoh et al., 1977; Commissiong et al., 1978; Kneisley et al., 1978; Maisky and Kuypers, 1978a, b; Ader et al., 1979; Basbaum and Fields, 1979; Martin et al., 1979a; Mason and Fibiger, 1979; Tohyama et al., 1979b; Zemlan et al., 1979; Commissiong, 1981; Guyenet, 1980; Karoum et al., 1980; Saper and Loewy, 1980). The coeruleospinal fibers pass in the ipsilateral ventral funiculus (Pickel et al., 1974)* to terminate within the intermediate zone of the spinal gray as far caudally as the sacral cord (Holstege et al., 1979)**. Furthermore, Nygren and Olson (1977) have shown that lesions of LC give a loss of catecholamine terminals in laminae I–IV and IV–IX of the spinal cord. The descending PBN fibers course within the lateral funiculus to enter the cervical segments (Saper and Loewy, 1980). Recent observations indicate that some of the catecholamine LC cells have branching axons, with one fiber reaching the spinal cord and the other reaching the cerebellum (Nagai et al., 1981). Divergent axon collaterals, with one branch to the spinal cord and the other to the cerebral cortex or thalamus, have also been described (Room et al., 1981). Furthermore, axons of some cells surrounding the brachium conjunctivum branch to reach the cervical and lumbar enlargements (Hayes and Rustioni, 1981).

VI. The Spinal Projection from the Periaqueductal Gray, the Interstitial Nucleus of Cajal and the Edinger–Westphal Nucleus

Recent tracer studies have shown that there is a spinal projection from the central gray (Kuypers and Maisky, 1975; Castiglioni et al., 1978; Maisky and Kuypers, 1978a; Basbaum and Fields, 1979; Zemlan et al., 1979; Watkins et al., 1981). Watkins et al. (1981) claim that the fibers descend in the dorsolateral funiculus of the spinal cord. Likewise, the interstitial nucleus of Cajal has been shown to send some of its fibers to the spinal cord (Nyberg-Hansen, 1966; Carpenter et al., 1970; Kuypers and Maisky, 1975; Castiglioni et al., 1978; Maisky and Kuypers, 1978a; Zemlan et al., 1979). According to Nyberg-Hansen (1966), the latter fibers descend to the sacral level in the medial longitudinal fasciculus to terminate chiefly in lamina VIII and the adjoining part of lamina VII, an area coinciding approximately with that of the vestibulospinal

---

* According to Kuypers and Maisky (1977), the fibers from the nucleus LC and nucleus subcoeruleus pass in the ipsilateral ventrolateral funiculus. Nygren and Olson (1977) mention the ventral funiculus and the ventral part of the lateral funiculus as pathways for the fibers from the LC, and Watkins et al. (1981) traced a few descending fibers in the dorsoventral funiculus.
** The recent observations by Commissiong (1981) indicate that the nucleus LC innervates the motoneurons in the spinal cord.

12

fibers. There is, furthermore, a conspicuous projection from the Edinger–Westphal nucleus (Castiglioni et al., 1978; Loewy and Saper, 1978; Basbaum and Fields, 1979). According to Loewy and Saper (1978), there are two descending pathways from this nucleus (Fig. 7): one branch courses along the ventral edge of the spinal trigeminal nucleus to terminate in lamina I and possibly in and near lamina V, and the other branch descends into the dorsal columns.

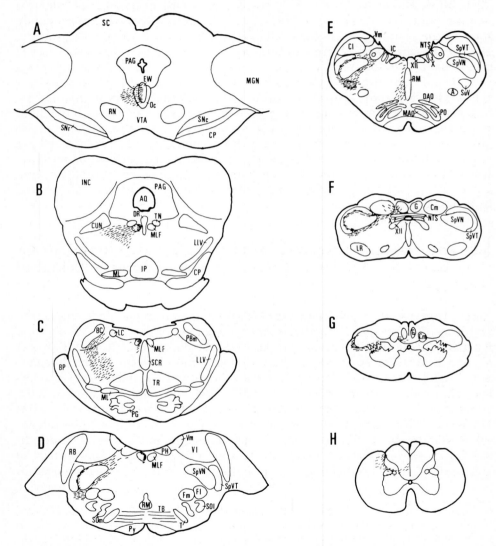

Figure 7. Diagram of the origin, course and termination of the descending projection from the Edinger–Westphal nucleus. (From Loewy and Saper, 1978, with permission.) For abbreviations, see separate list.

Castiglioni et al. (1978) have, in addition, found evidence of a spinal projection from the nucleus of Darkschewitsch and the supratrochlear and oculomotor nuclei. These demonstrations of descending fibers from the periaqueductal gray should be kept in mind in future studies concerning pathways active in the depression of noxious stimuli. The observation of a spinal projection from the Edinger–Westphal nucleus indicates that, contrary to current thinking, this cell group is obviously not only a parasympathetic relay nucleus. It is also of interest to note that some cells in the nucleus have branching axons, with one branch supplying the cervical cord and the other supplying the lumbar cord (Hayes and Rustioni, 1981).

VII. The Descending Projection from the Raphe Nuclei

The raphe nuclei form a narrow, continuous collection of cells along the midline of the brain stem. The nuclei originate at the caudal end of the medulla and end in the rostral mesencephalon. The different nuclei fuse with each other and are not easily delimited from the reticular formation. In mammals, eight nuclei can be distinguished (Fig. 8). From caudal to rostral they are: the nuclei raphe obscurus, raphe pallidus, raphe magnus, raphe pontis, centralis superior, raphe dorsalis, linearis intermedius and linearis rostralis. Dahlström and Fuxe (1964), in their pilot study, gave evidence that the majority of the brain stem serotoninergic (5-HT) neurons were concentrated in these nuclei.

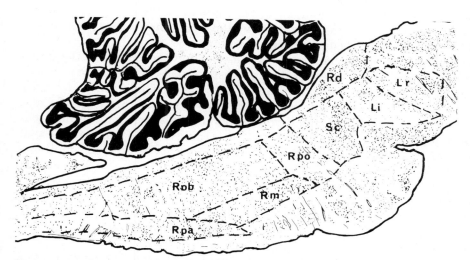

Figure 8. Drawing of a parasagittal section through the brain stem of the cat showing the location and extent of the various raphe nuclei. (From Pierce et al., 1977, with permission.) For abbreviations, see separate list.

This observation has initiated numerous investigations of the connections of the raphe nuclei.

In their experimental study with the modified Gudden method (Brodal, 1940), Brodal et al. (1960) concluded that, in the cat, the descending fibers come chiefly from nucleus raphe magnus, with a small contribution from the nucleus raphe pallidus and the nucleus raphe obscurus and pontis, and that the fibers descend in the dorsal half of the lateral funiculus to reach the cervical and thoracic cord. Recent tracer studies have confirmed this origin for the descending fibers, and some of them have also revealed that the fibers can be followed to the lumbar level of the cord (see especially Kuypers and Maisky, 1975; Bobillier et al., 1976; Pierce et al., 1976; Martin, 1977; Crutcher et al., 1978; Kneisley et al., 1978; Maisky and Kuypers, 1978a; Basbaum and Fields, 1979; Zemlan et al., 1979; Watkins et al., 1980; Bowker et al., 1981). Tohyama et al. (1979b) have recently found evidence of a spinal projection from the nucleus raphe dorsalis.

The tracer studies have provided divergent results as regards the course of the fibers. Basbaum et al. (1976, 1978), Basbaum and Ralston (1978), G.F. Martin et al. (1978), R.F. Martin et al., (1978) and Basbaum and Fields (1979) found that the nucleus raphe magnus sends its spinal fibers via the dorsolateral funiculus, whereas the nucleus raphe obscurus and pallidus send their fibers predominantly via the ventral funiculus. However, Kuypers and Maisky (1977) claim that the fibers from the raphe nuclei descend especially in the ventral and ventrolateral funiculi. Basbaum et al. (1976) indicate that the axons of the raphe neurons terminate in laminae I, II and V, and it appears that the same raphe neuron may innervate both the cervical and lumbar spinal cord (Hayes and Rustioni, 1981; Martin et al., 1981a). As concerns nucleus raphe pallidus and obscurus, Loewy (1981) has shown that these nuclei send fibers to the intermediolateral cell column.

The tracer studies have also provided evidence that the location of the spinal projecting raphe cells agrees with the distribution of the serotoninergic perikarya observed by Dahlström and Fuxe (1964) (Oliveras et al., 1977; Kneisley et al., 1978; Watkins et al., 1980; Bowker et al., 1981). It has also been demonstrated that the spinal projecting raphe neurons contain substance P and enkephalin (Bowker et al., 1981). In this context we should mention that it has been shown that 5-HT and substance P appear to be present simultaneously in some raphe cells (Hökfelt et al., 1978; Chan-Palay, 1979), and that 5-HT- and enkephalin-containing raphe neurons have also been described (Glazer et al., 1981). Hökfelt and coworkers (Johansson et al., 1981) have recently found, with immunocytochemical techniques, that some spinal projecting raphe neurons may even have three putative transmitters: 5-HT, substance P and the thyrotropin-releasing hormone.

In this chapter the functional roles attributed to the raphe nuclei will not be reviewed. However, it is appropriate to recall that the raphe nuclei, particularly the nucleus raphe magnus, have been shown to be involved in the transmission of pain (cf. what is said above for the periaqueductal gray). The raphe nuclei also appear to be engaged in the mechanisms of sleep. Referring to this latter function, it is interesting that Scheibel et al. (1975) have given evidence of a special relationship between the raphe nerve cells and their surrounding vessels, an anatomical relationship which might point to a possible function of raphe neurons and chemosensors for circulating substances.

VIII. The Tectospinal Tract

All students appear to agree that the tectospinal tract originates in the superior colliculus. The projection has been described with degeneration methods (Rasmussen, 1936; Verhaart and van Beusekom, 1958; Altman and Carpenter, 1961; Nyberg-Hansen, 1964b; Petras, 1967) and with tracer techniques (Kuypers and Maisky, 1975; Castiglioni et al., 1978; Zemlan et al., 1979). The experimental studies demonstrate that the tract originates in the deep layers of the contralateral superior colliculus, descends to the cervical segments, and terminates chiefly in laminae VII and VI, with some endings in lamina VIII.

IX. Descending Fibers from the Hypothalamus

Fifty years ago, Beattie et al. (1930) demonstrated with anterograde degeneration methods that there are direct fibers from the hypothalamus to the sacral segments of the spinal cord. This early observation has now been confirmed in tracer studies (Kuypers and Maisky, 1975; Hancock, 1976; Saper et al., 1976; Kneisley et al., 1978; Maisky and Kuypers, 1978a, b; Basbaum and Fields, 1979; Blessing and Chalmers, 1979; Hosoya and Matsushita, 1979; Zemlan et al., 1979; Rapisarda and Simonelli, 1981; Sawchenko and Swanson, 1981). Cells in the paraventricular nucleus and in the dorsal, posterior, medial and lateral hypothalamic areas have been shown to participate in the projection (Hosoya, 1980). The fibers have been shown to pass in the dorsolateral funiculus and to terminate in the intermediolateral cell column (Saper et al., 1976; Swanson, 1977) and in laminae I–III of the spinal cord (Nilaver et al., 1980). Studies where combined catecholamine and horseradish peroxidase (Blessing and Chalmers, 1979), or combined monoamine histofluorescence and fluorescent retrograde tracing (Björklund and Skagerberg, 1979), techniques have been applied have shown that a conspicuous portion of the cells in the dorsal and posterior hypothalamus projecting to the spinal cord are catecholaminergic*. Since Lindvall et al. (1974; see their Fig. 8) have described

---

* The reader is referred to other studies by Björklund and his group for details concerning the regenerating capacity of these fibers after administration of neurotoxins (see especially Björklund et al., 1973; Nobin et al., 1973).

bifurcation of axons of some of these cells, Björklund and Skagerberg (1979) suggest that some of the spinal projecting cells could send collaterals to diencephalic regions. Clearly, studies where the double-labeling technique is used could clarify this question and show further details of projections of the periventricular catecholaminergic cells.

X. Descending Connections from Other Brain Stem Nuclei

Experimental anatomical studies have shown that there is a clearcut spinal projection from the *nucleus of the solitary tract* (Torvik, 1957; Norgren and Leonard, 1971; Kuypers and Maisky, 1975; Burton and Loewy, 1977; Peterson and Coulter, 1977; Satoh et al., 1977; Crutcher et al., 1978; Kneisley et al., 1978; Loewy and Burton, 1978; Norgren, 1978; Amendt et al., 1979). Loewy and Burton (1978) followed the fibers to the motoneurons of the phrenic nerve, to the ventral horn in the thoracic segments, and to the intermediolateral cell column. Likewise, fibers from the *dorsal column nuclei* (Fig. 9) to all levels of the spinal cord have recently been described (Kuypers and Maisky, 1975*; Burton and Loewy, 1977). In the rat, cat and monkey, these fibers descend ipsilaterally, primarily from the ventral portion of the dorsal column nuclei at about the middle of their rostrocaudal extent, and terminate in the dorsal horn where the cells of origin for the spinothalamic, spinocervical and cervicothalamic tracts are located (Burton and Loewy, 1977). Many of the spinal projecting cells send a branch rostrally to the thalamus (Bromberg et al., 1981). *Trigeminospinal* fibers have previously been shown to exist (Szentágothai, 1948) and their presence has been verified in other studies (Stewart and King, 1963; Mizuno and Sauerland, 1970; Tiwari and King, 1974; Burton and Loewy, 1977; Craig, 1978; Crutcher et al., 1978; Satoh, 1979; Matsushita et al., 1980, 1981). The most detailed of these is the study of Matsushita et al. (1981), who have demonstrated that the descending projection originates from all three subdivisions of the spinal trigeminal nucleus and from the mesencephalic nucleus. Since the study shows that cells of different sizes participate in the trigeminospinal projection, the authors speculate that this projection may have not only a trigeminospinal reflex, but other unknown functions as well.

A spinal projection from the nucleus of the *posterior commissure* has likewise been described (Kuypers and Maisky, 1975), as have fibers from the *zona incerta* (Basbaum and Fields, 1979; Ricardo, 1981) and *Forel's field* H_1 (Ricardo, 1981).

A final tract to consider is the descending fibers from the *cerebellar nuclei*. This projection was first demonstrated by Thomas et al. (1956) in an anterograde degeneration study. They showed that the fibers were derived from the fastigial nucleus and reached the cervical spinal cord. Retrograde tracer

---

* See also Maisky and Kuypers (1978a, b).

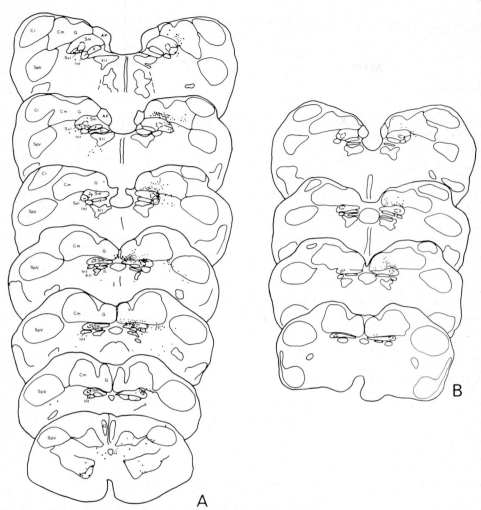

Figure 9. Position of labeled neurons in the dorsal column nuclei and adjacent regions of two cats after injections of horseradish peroxidase into the right half of the spinal cord at: A, the C_3–C_8 segments and B, the L_2 segment. Every cell seen on ten adjoining serial sections is plotted on each drawing. (From Burton and Loewy, 1977, with permission.) For abbreviations, see separate list.

studies (Fukushima et al., 1977; Matsushita and Hosoya, 1978) have confirmed this observation** and demonstrated that the fibers also originate in the posterior interposite nucleus, including cells lying between the two nuclei, and in the lateral nucleus (Bharos et al., 1981). According to the latter authors, the spinal projecting axons from a certain portion of the cells in the fastigial

---

** The reader is referred to Wilson et al. (1977) for a consideration of the functional properties of this projection.

and lateral nucleus are collaterals from fibers projecting to various brain stem nuclei.

Summary

A review is given of the anatomy of the paths descending to the spinal cord from the brain stem. Reference is made to the classical observations with retrograde and anterograde degeneration techniques, and to the recent studies where tracer, fluorescence and immunocytochemical methods have been applied. The experimental anatomical investigations have shown that, in addition to the classical rubrospinal, vestibulospinal, reticulospinal and tectospinal tracts, there are spinal projections from several other nuclei and cell groups in the brain stem. The spinal projecting regions are the raphe nuclei, the periaqueductal gray with the Edinger–Westphal nucleus and the interstitial nucleus of Cajal, the nucleus locus coeruleus, nucleus subcoeruleus and the parabrachial nucleus, the hypothalamus, the nucleus of the solitary tract, the dorsal column nuclei, the nucleus of the Vth nerve, the nucleus of the posterior commissure, and the cerebellar nuclei. The reader is referred to other chapters of this volume for functional considerations concerning the spinal projection from the above-mentioned nuclear regions.

Abbreviations

a	accessory group of paramedian reticular nucleus
A	ambiguus nucleus
AO	aqueduct
AP	area postrema
BC	brachium conjunctivum
BP	brachium pontis
Br.c.	superior cerebellar peduncle (brachium conjunctivum)
Br.p.	middle cerebellar peduncle (brachium pontis)
C.r.	inferior cerebellar peduncle (restiform body)
C.s.	superior colliculus
CGM	medial geniculate body
CHO	optic chiasm
CI, c.i.	inferior colliculus
Cl	lateral cuneate nucleus
CM	center medium
Cm	medial cuneate nucleus
CN	cuneate nucleus
Coe.	nucleus coeruleus
COLL.SUP	superior colliculus
CP	cerebral peduncle
CR	restiform body
CS	nucleus centralis superior
CUN	cuneiform nucleus

d.	dorsal group of paramedian reticular nucleus
Dec.br.c.	decussation of superior cerebellar peduncle (brachium conjunctivum)
DR	dorsal raphe nucleus
ECN	external cuneate nucleus
EW	Edinger–Westphal nucleus
F	vestibular group f; fasciculus retroflexus
F.l.m.	medial longitudinal fasciculus
Fl	lateral facial nucleus
Fm	medial facial nucleus
G	gracile nucleus
h	region poor in cells (Meessen and Olszewski) surrounding the motor trigeminal nucleus
HYPOTH.	hypothalamic area
IC, Ic	intercalatus nucleus
INC	inferior colliculus
Int	intermediate nucleus
IP	interpeduncular nucleus
IVN	inferior vestibular nucleus
k	cell group "k" of Meesen and Olszewski
L	lateral vestibular nucleus (Deiters')
LC	locus coeruleus
Li	nucleus linearis intermedius
LL	lateral lemniscus
LLV	ventral nucleus of the lateral lemniscus
LR	lateral reticular nucleus
Lr	nucleus linearis rostralis
LVN	lateral (Deiters') vestibular nucleus
m	cell group "m" of Meessen and Olszewski
M	medial vestibular nucleus
MAO	medial accessory nucleus of the inferior olive
MES.V	mesencephalic nucleus of trigeminal nerve
MGN	medial geniculate body
ML	medial lemniscus
MLF	medial longitudinal fasciculus
N.c.	cochlear nuclei
N.c.e.	external (accessory) cuneate nucleus
N.c.t.	nucleus of the corpus trapezoideum
N.f.c.	nucleus cuneatus
N.f.g.	nucleus gracilis
N.i.p.	nucleus interpeduncularis
N.ic.	nucleus intercalatus
N.l.l.	nuclei of lateral lemniscus
N.m.X	dorsal motor (parasympathetic) nucleus of vagus
N.mes.	mesencephalic nucleus of trigeminal nerve
N.mes.V	mesencephalic trigeminal nucleus
N.r.	red nucleus
N.r.l.	lateral reticular nucleus (nucleus of lateral funiculus)
N.r.t.	nucleus reticularis tegmenti pontis
N.t.d.	dorsal tegmental nucleus
N.t.v.	ventral tegmental nucleus
N.tr.sp.V	spinal nucleus of trigeminal nerve

NGC	nuclei cuneatus and gracilis
NLL	nucleus of the lateral lemniscus
NR	raphe nucleus
NRA	retroambiguus nucleus
NRL	nucleus reticularis lateralis
NRT	nucleus reticularis tegmenti pontis
NST	nucleus of solitary tract
NTS	solitary nucleus
NVL	lateral vestibular nucleus
NIII	oculomotor nucleus
N.III,V,VI,VII,VIII,X,XII	root fibers of cranial nerves
NVII	motor nucleus of facial nerve
Oc	oculomotor nucleus
Ol.i., OLI	inferior olive
Ol.s.	superior olive
P, Py	pyramidal tract
P.	pontine nuclei
p.Br.	nucleus parabrachialis
P.c.	basis pedunculi (crus cerebri)
P.g.	periaqueductal gray
P.h.	nucleus praepositus hypoglossi
PAG	periaqueductal gray
PBm	medial parabrachial nucleus
PC	pedunculus cerebri
pc.	nucleus reticularis parvicellularis
PD	pyramidal decussation
PG	pontine gray
PH	perihypoglossal nucleus
PO	principal nucleus of the inferior olive
R.	right
R.gc.	nucleus reticularis gigantocellularis
R.l.	nucleus reticularis lateralis (Meessen and Olszewski)
R.mes.	reticular formation of the mesencephalon
R.n.	nucleus of the raphe
R.p.c.	nucleus reticularis pontis caudalis
R.p.o.	nucleus reticularis pontis oralis
R.pc.	nucleus reticularis parvicellularis
R.v.	nucleus reticularis ventralis
RB	restiform body
Rd	nucleus raphe dorsalis
RF	reticular formation
Rm, RM	nucleus raphe magnus
RN	red nucleus
Rob	nucleus raphe obscurus
Rpa	nucleus raphe pallidus
Rpo	nucleus raphe pontis
S	superior vestibular nucleus
S.n.	substantia nigra
Sc	nucleus raphe centralis superior
SC	nucleus subcoeruleus; superior colliculus
SCR	superior central raphe nucleus
Sm	medial nucleus of the solitary tract

SNc	substantia nigra, pars compacta
SNr	substantia nigra, pars reticulia
SO	superior olive
SOl	lateral nucleus of the superior olive
SOm	medial nucleus of the superior olive
SpV, SpVN	spinal trigeminal nucleus
SpVT	spinal trigeminal tract
SuV	subtrigeminal nucleus
Svl	ventrolateral nucleus of the solitary tract
SVN	superior vestibular nucleus
T	trapezoid nucleus
T.	trapezoid body
T.s.	tractus solitarius surrounded by nucleus of solitary tract
TB	trapezoid body
TH	thalamus
TN	trochlear nucleus
TR	medial tegmenta reticular nucleus
Tr.sp.V	spinal tract of trigeminal nerve
TRS	rubrospinal tract
v.	ventral group of paramedian reticular nucleus
V.d.	inferior (descending) vestibular nucleus
V.l.	lateral vestibular nucleus
V.m.	medial vestibular nucleus
V.s.	superior vestibular nucleus
VB	thalamus
VC	vestibular complex
Vl	lateral vestibular nucleus
Vm	trigeminal motor nucleus; medial vestibular nucleus
VTA	ventral tegmental area
I-IX	Rexed's laminae I–IX
III,IV,V,VII,X,XII	motor nuclei of cranial nerves
VIIn	facial nerve

References

Ader, J.P., Postema, F. and Korf, J. (1979) Contribution of the locus coeruleus to the adrenergic innervation of the rat spinal cord. A biochemical study, *J. neural Transm.*, 44: 159-173.

Altman, J. and Carpenter, M.B. (1961) Fiber projections of the superior colliculus in the cat, *J. comp. Neurol.*, 116: 157-178.

Amendt, K., Czachurski, J., Dembowsky, K. and Seller, H. (1979) Bulbospinal projections to the intermediolateral cell column; a neuroanatomical study, *J. Auton. Nerv. Syst.*, 1: 103-117.

Basbaum, A.I. and Fields, H.L. (1979) The origin of descending pathways in the dorsolateral funiculus of the spinal cord of the cat and rat: Further studies on the anatomy of pain modulation, *J. comp. Neurol.*, 187: 513-532

Basbaum, A.I. and Ralston III, H.J. (1978) Projections from nucleus raphe magnus in the primate, *Pain*, Suppl. 1: 259 (Abstract).

Basbaum, A.I., Clanton, C.H. and Fields, H.L. (1976) Opiate and stimulus-produced analgesia: functional anatomy of a medullospinal pathway, *Proc. nat. Acad. Sci. U.SA.*, 73: 4685-4688.

Basbaum, A.I., Clanton, C.H. and Fields, H.L. (1978) Three bulbospinal pathways from the rostral medulla of the cat. An autoradiographic study of pain modulating systems. *J. comp. Neurol.*, 178: 209-224.

Beattie, J., Brow, G.R. and Long, C.N.H. (1930) Physiological and anatomical evidence for the existence of nerve tracts connecting the hypothalamus with spinal sympathetic centres, *Proc. roy. Soc. B*, 106: 253-275.

Beran, R.L. and Martin, G.F. (1971) Reticulo-spinal fibers of the opossum, *Didelphis virginiana*. I. Origin, *J. comp. Neurol.*, 141: 453-466.

Bharos, T.B., Kuypers, H.G.J.M., Lemon, R.N. and Muir, R.B. (1981) Divergent collaterals from deep cerebellar neurons to thalamus and tectum, and to medulla oblongata and spinal cord: retrograde fluorescent and electrophysiological studies, *Exp. Brain Res.*, 42: 399-410.

Björklund, A. and Skagerberg, G. (1979) Evidence for a major spinal cord projection from the diencephalic A11 dopamine cell group in the rat using transmitter-specific fluorescent retrograde tracing, *Brain Res.*, 177: 170-175.

Björklund, A., Nobin, A. and Stenevi, U (1973) Regeneration of central serotonin neurons after axonal degeneration induced by 5,6-dihydroxytryptamine, *Brain Res.*, 50: 214-220.

Blessing, W.W. and Chalmers, J.P. (1979) Direct projection of catecholamine (presumably dopamine)-containing neurons from hypothalamus to spinal cord, *Neurosci. Lett.*, 11: 35-40

Blessing, W.W., Goodchild, A.K., Dampney, R.A.L. and Chalmers, J.P. (1981) Cell groups in the lower brain stem of the rabbit projecting to the spinal cord, with special reference to catecholamine-containing neurons, *Brain Res.*, 221: 35-55.

Bobillier, P., Seguin, S., Petitjean, F., Salbert, D., Touret, M. and Jouvet, M. (1976) The raphe nuclei of the cat brain stem: a topographical atlas of their efferent projections as revealed by autoradiography, *Brain Res.*, 113: 449-486.

Bodian, D. (1946) Spinal projections of brainstem in rhesus monkey, deduced from retrograde chromatolysis, *Anat. Rec.*, 94: 512-513 (Abstract).

Bowker, R.M., Steinbusch, H.W.M. and Coulter, J.D. (1981) Serotonergic and peptidergic projections to the spinal cord demonstrated by a combined retrograde HRP histochemical and immunocytochemical staining method, *Brain Res.*, 221: 412-417.

Brodal, A. (1940) Modification of Gudden method for study of cerebral localization, *Arch. Neurol Psychiat.*, 43: 46-58.

Brodal, A. (1957) *The Reticular Formation of the Brain Stem. Anatomical Aspects and Functional Correlations, The Henderson Trust Lecture*, Oliver and Boyd, Edinburgh.

Brodal, A. and Pompeiano, O. (1957) The vestibular nuclei in the cat, *J. Anat. (Lond.)*, 91: 438-454.

Brodal, A., Taber, E. and Walberg, F. (1960) The raphe nuclei of the brain stem in the cat. II. Efferent connections, *J. comp. Neurol.*, 114: 239-259.

Bromberg, M.B., Burnham, J.A. and Towe, A.L. (1981) Doubly projecting neurons of the dorsal column nuclei, *Neurosci. Lett.*, 25: 215-220.

Brown, L.T. (1974) Rubrospinal projections in the rat, *J. comp. Neurol.*, 154: 169-188.

Burton, H. and Loewy, A.D. (1977) Projections to the spinal cord from medullary somatosensory relay nuclei, *J. comp. Neurol.*, 173: 773-792.

Cabana, T. and Martin, G.F. (1981) The origin of brain stem-spinal projections at different stages of development in the North American opossum, *Develop. Brain Res.*, 2: 163-168.

Carpenter, M.B., Harbison, J.W. and Peter, P. (1970) Accessory oculomotor nuclei in the monkey: projections and effects of discrete lesions, *J. comp. Neurol.*, 140: 131-154.

Castiglioni, A.J., Gallaway, M.C. and Coulter, J.D. (1977) Origins of descending spinal projections from the brainstem in the monkey, *Soc. Neurosci. Abstr.*, 3: 268.

Castiglioni, A.J., Gallaway, M.C. and Coulter, J.D. (1978) Spinal projections from the midbrain in the monkey, *J. comp. Neurol.*, 178: 329-346.

Chan-Palay, V. (1979) Combined immunocytochemistry and autoradiography after in vivo injections of monoclonal antibody to substance P and ^{3}H-serotonin: co-existence of two putative transmitters in single raphe cells and fiber plexuses, *Anat. Embryol.*, 156: 241-254.

Commissiong, J.W. (1981) Evidence that the noradrenergic coerulospinal projection decussates at the spinal level, *Brain Res.*, 212: 145-151.

Commissiong, J.W., Hellström, S.O. and Neff, N.H. (1978) A new projection from locus coeruleus to the spinal ventral columns: histochemical and biochemical evidence, *Brain Res.*, 148: 207-213.

Saper, C.B. and Loewy, A.D. (1980) Efferent connections of the parabrachial nucleus in the rat, *Brain Res.*, 197: 291-317.

Saper, C.B., Loewy, A.D., Swanson, L.W. and Cowan, W.M. (1976) Direct hypothalamo-autonomic connections, *Brain Res.*, 117: 305-312.

Satoh, K. (1979) The origin of reticulospinal fibers in the rat: a HRP study, *J. Hirnforsch.*, 20: 313-332.

Satoh, K., Tohyama, M., Yamamoto, K., Sakumoto, T. and Shimizu, N. (1977) Noradrenaline innervation of the spinal cord studied by the horseradish peroxidase method combined with monoamine oxidase staining, *Exp. Brain Res.*, 30: 175-186.

Sawchenko, P.E. and Swanson, L.W. (1981) A method for tracing biochemically defined pathways in the central nervous system using combined fluorescence retrograde transport and immunohistochemical techniques, *Brain Res.*, 210: 31-51.

Scheibel, M.E., Tomiyasu, U. and Scheibel, A.B. (1975) Do raphe nuclei of the reticular formation have a neurosecretory or vascular sensor function? *Exp. Neurol.*, 47: 316-329.

Stewart, W.A. and King, R.B. (1963) Fiber projections from the nucleus caudalis of the spinal trigeminal nucleus, *J. comp. Neurol.*, 121: 271-286.

Swanson, L.W. (1977) Immunohistochemical evidence for a neurophysin-containing autonomic pathway arising in the paraventricular nucleus of the hypothalamus, *Brain Res.*, 128: 346-353.

Szentágothai, J. (1948) Anatomical considerations of monosynaptic reflex arcs, *J. Neurophysiol.*, 11: 445-454.

Thomas, D.M., Kaufman, R.P., Sprague, J.M. and Chambers, W.W. (1956) Experimental studies of the vermal cerebellar projections in the brain stem of the cat (fastigiobulbar tract), *J. Anat. (Lond.)* 90: 371-385.

Tiwari, R.K. and King, R.B. (1974) Fiber projections from trigeminal nucleus caudalis in primate (squirrel monkey and baboon), *J. comp. Neurol.*, 158: 191-206.

Tohyama, M., Sakai, K., Salvert, D., Touret, M. and Jouvet, M. (1979a) Spinal projections from the lower brain stem in the cat as demonstrated by the horseradish peroxidase technique. I. Origins of the reticulospinal tracts and their funicular trajectories, *Brain Res.*, 173: 383-403.

Tohyama, M., Sakai, K., Touret, M., Salvert, D. and Jouvet, M. (1979b) Spinal projections from the lower brain stem in the cat as demonstrated by the horseradish peroxidase technique. II. Projections from the dorsolateral pontine tegmentum and raphe nuclei, *Brain Res.*, 176: 215-231.

Torvik, A. (1957) The spinal projection from the nucleus of the solitary tract. An experimental study in the cat, *J. Anat. (Lond.)*, 91: 314-322.

Torvik, A. and Brodal, A. (1957) The origin of reticulospinal fibers in the cat. An experimental study, *Anat. Rec.*, 128: 113-137.

Verhaart, W.J.C. and van Beusekom, G.T. (1958) Fiber tracts in the cord in the cat, *Acta psychiat. neurol. scand.*, 33: 359-376.

Watkins, L.R., Griffin, G., Leichnetz, G.R. and Mayer, D.J. (1980) The somatotopic organization of the nucleus raphe magnus and surrounding brain stem structures as revealed by HRP slow-release gels, *Brain Res.*, 181: 1-15.

Watkins, L.R., Griffin, G., Leichnetz, G.R. and Mayer, D.J. (1981) Identification and somatotopic organization of nuclei projecting via the dorsolateral funiculus in rats: a retrograde tracing study using HRP slow-release gels, *Brain Res.*, 223: 237-255.

Westlund, K.N., Bowker, R.M., Ziegler, M.G. and Coulter, J.D. (1981) Origins of spinal noradrenergic pathways demonstrated by retrograde transport of antibody to dopamine-β-hydroxylase, *Neurosci. Lett.*, 25: 243-249.

Wilson, V.J., Uchino, Y., Susswein, A. and Fukushima, K. (1977) Properties of direct fastigiospinal fibers in the cat, *Brain Res.*, 126: 543-546.

Wold, J.E. (1978) The vestibular nuclei in the domestic hen (*Gallus domesticus*). IV. The projection to the spinal cord, *Brain Behav. Evol.*, 15: 41-62.

Zemlan, F.P. and Pfaff, D.W. (1979) Topographical organization in medullary reticulospinal systems as demonstrated by the horseradish peroxidase technique, *Brain Res.*, 174: 161-166.

Zemlan, F.P., Kow, L.-M., Morrell, J.I. and Pfaff, D.W. (1979) Descending tracts of the lateral columns of the rat spinal cord: a study using the horseradish peroxidase and silver impregnation techniques, *J. Anat. (Lond.)* 128: 489-512.

Brain Stem Control of Spinal Mechanisms
– B. Sjölund and A. Björklund, editors
© 1982 Elsevier Biomedical Press

2

The New Anatomy of the Descending Brain Pathways

H.J.G.M. KUYPERS and A.M. HUISMAN

Department of Anatomy II, Erasmus University Medical School, P.O. Box 1738, 3000 DR Rotterdam, The Netherlands

I. Anatomical Findings

Since the beginning of this century anterograde and retrograde degeneration techniques have been used to study anatomically the descending pathways to the spinal cord. The retrograde degeneration technique (Brodal, 1940) was used to demonstrate the cells of origin of these descending pathways, while the anterograde degeneration technique using several staining procedures (Rasdolsky, 1923; Szentagothai-Schimert, 1941; Kuypers et al., 1962; Nyberg-Hansen, 1966a; Petras, 1967; Martin et al., 1975) was employed to demonstrate the trajectory and the terminal distribution area of the descending pathways in the spinal gray.

The descending pathways are derived from both the cerebral cortex and the brain stem. The corticospinal fibers in virtually all mammals terminate mainly contralaterally in the spinal gray. Anterograde degeneration findings (Kuypers, 1960; Nyberg-Hansen and Brodal, 1963; Schoen, 1964; Petras, 1967; Martin et al., 1975) showed that the corticospinal fibers in the spinal gray display different distribution patterns in different species (Fig. 1). Thus, in opossum the corticospinal fibers only reach the upper half of the cord, and in the spinal gray are distributed mainly to the spinal dorsal horn, i.e. Rexed's lamina IV and the medial parts of lamina V, and to a limited extent also to the dorsal part of the intermediate zone (Martin et al., 1975). In the cat the corticospinal fibers descend throughout the length of the spinal cord. As compared to the opossum they show a wider distribution in the intermediate zone and terminate in laminae V–VII (Nyberg-Hansen and Brodal, 1963). Moreover, the distribution of the cortical fibers to the medioventral parts of lamina VII occurs bilaterally (Flindt-Egebak, 1977), as demonstrated by means of the anterograde axonal transport technique using labeled amino acid (Lasek et al., 1968; Cowan et al., 1972). In the rhesus monkey the distribution of the corticospinal fibers in the spinal gray shows a further expansion. Thus, in monkey, the corticospinal fibers are also distributed to lamina VIII, and the distribution to lamina VIII and the adjoining parts of lamina VII occurs bilaterally (Kuypers, 1960; Petras, 1968). Moreover, in monkeys some corticospinal fibers are distributed contralaterally to the dorsolateral portion of the lateral motoneuronal cell groups of the enlargements, i.e. to motoneurons innervating distal extremity muscles (Kuypers, 1960; Petras, 1968). This distribution pat-

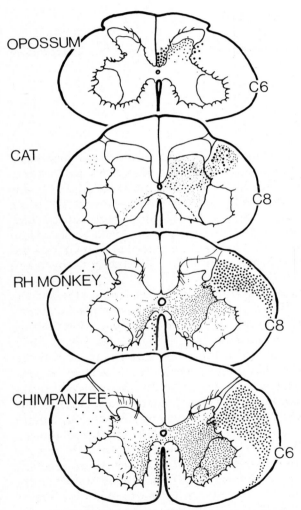

Figure 1. Differences in the distribution of the corticospinal fibers to the dorsal horn, the intermediate zone and the motoneuronal cell groups in opossum, cat, Rhesus monkey and chimpanzee. (From Kuypers, 1981, with permission.)

tern is confirmed by the findings obtained by means of the anterograde axonal transport technique (Coulter and Jones, 1977; Tigges et al., 1979). Finally in champanzee and man (Kuypers, 1964; Schoen, 1964) the corticospinal fibers show a distribution similar to that in the monkey except for the fact that in chimpanzee and man the corticospinal fibers are distributed diffusely throughout the lateral motoneuronal cell group, i.e. to motoneurons of distal muscles as well as to motoneurons of proximal muscles.

The differences in the distribution of the corticospinal fibers appear to have a functional meaning such that they parallel differences in the motor capacities of the various animals. For example, findings after transection of the pyramidal tract (Lawrence and Kuypers, 1968a) in monkey indicate that the direct corticomotoneuronal connections, which exert a powerful grip on motoneurons (Phillips and Porter, 1964), provide the capacity to execute highly fractionated movements, as exemplified by individual finger movements. In this respect it is of interest to note that also in the raccoon, which displays a striking agility in the execution of hand and finger movements, some direct corticomotoneuronal connections exist (Petras and Lehman, 1966). Moreover, in the newborn rhesus monkey, in which corticomotoneuronal connections are largely lacking (Kuypers, 1962; Felix and Wiesendanger, 1971), the capacity to execute individual finger movements does not exist. However, this capacity gradually develops during the first postnatal year (Lawrence and Hopkins, 1976), in parallel with the postnatal development of the direct corticomotoneural connections (Kuypers, 1962) (Fig. 2).

With respect to the differences in the distribution of the corticospinal fibers in the spinal gray, it is of importance to emphasize that the duration and the severity of the flaccid pareses, which occur after lesions of the precentral motor cortex or transection of the pyramidal tract in various mammals, parallel the development of the corticomotoneuronal connections. Thus, in cat the flaccid paresis is minimal (Liddel and Phillips, 1944). In monkey it is much more pronounced and mainly affects distal extremity muscles (Tower, 1940; Denny-Brown and Botterell, 1948; Lawrence and Kuypers, 1968a), while in chimpanzee it also affects the proximal muscles, such that the arm hangs loosely from the shoulder (Tower, 1944). These defects probably reflect a dysfunction in the interneurons and motoneurons due to the destruction of their corticospinal terminals, and probably results in 'pyramidal shock' as described by Denny-Brown and Botterell (1948).

The corticospinal pathway is paralleled by the descending brain stem pathways. According to the anterograde degeneration findings (Kuypers et al., 1962; Nyberg-Hansen, 1966a; Petras, 1967; Martin et al., 1975), these brain stem pathways are distributed in all animals in roughly the same way and terminate almost exclusively in the intermediate zone. However, recent findings indicate that the degree of collateralization of individual fiber systems may differ in different species (see later). Following brain stem lesions some degenerating brain stem fibers are present in the spinal medial motoneuronal

32

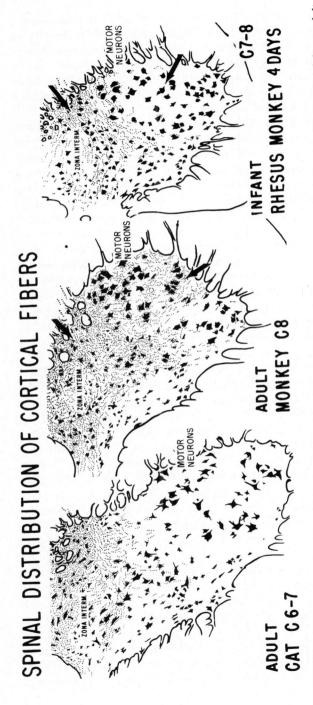

Figure 2. Differences in the distributions of the corticospinal fibers to the intermediate zone and the motoneuronal cell groups in adult cat, adult monkey and newborn monkey. (Modified after Kuypers, 1962, with permission).

cell groups, especially in the cervical cord, and some are present in the lateral motoneuronal cell groups. The distribution of the latter fibers, however, strongly suggests that the vast majority of them passes through the motoneuronal cell groups on their way to the intermediate zone (Petras, 1967).

The failure to observe a pronounced brain stem projection to the somatic motoneuronal cell groups of the spinal cord in anterograde degeneration experiments is most clearly shown by the findings of Nyberg-Hansen in cat (1969) because, after hemisection of the cats' spinal cord at upper cervical levels, virtually no degenerating fibers were observed in the motoneuronal cell groups of the cervical and lumbosacral enlargements. With respect to the distribution of the descending brain stem pathways to the spinal cord, earlier anterograde degeneration findings also failed to show the existence of direct brain stem connections to the motoneurons in monkey (Kuypers et al., 1962). In monkey, cortical connections to the motoneurons of distal extremity muscles exist. The difference in the distributions of the cortical and brain stem pathways to the motoneurons, as demonstrated by the anterograde degeneration findings, therefore was taken to explain the fact that, in monkey, the corticospinal fibers provide the capacity to execute highly fractionated movements, as exemplified by individual finger movements.

Retrograde degeneration and anterograde degeneration findings indicated that the descending brain stem pathways are derived from the interstitial nucleus of Cajal (Nyberg-Hansen, 1966b), the red nucleus (Pompeiano and Brodal, 1957a; Nyberg-Hansen and Brodal, 1964), the pontine and medullary medial reticular formation (Torvik and Brodal, 1957; Nyberg-Hansen, 1965), the lower brain stem raphe nuclei (Brodal et al., 1960), the vestibular complex (Pompeiano and Brodal, 1957b) and the ventrolateral subnucleus of the solitary nucleus (Torvik, 1957). However, in the early 1970s the retrograde neuronal labeling technique was developed. This is based on the fact that proteins, and in particular horseradish peroxidase (HRP), are taken up by axon terminals and by damaged axons and are then transported retrogradely through the axons to the parent cell bodies, in which they can be demonstrated histochemically (Kristensson and Olsson, 1971, 1974; LaVail and LaVail, 1972; Kuypers et al., 1974; Mesulam, 1978).

Following HRP hemi-infiltration of upper cervical or thoracic spinal segments in cat (Kuypers and Maisky, 1975), all the brain stem cell groups which, according to the retrograde degeneration findings give rise to descending pathways, were retrogradely labeled. However, many retrogradely labeled neurons also occurred in other cell groups (Fig. 3), i.e. in the contralateral nucleus retroambiguus, the ipsilateral dorsal column nuclei, the contralateral area of the ventrolateral pontine tegmentum adjoining the rubrospinal tract, and the ipsilateral dorsal pontine tegmental area comprising the nucleus locus coeruleus, the nucleus subcoeruleus and the nucleus of Kölliker–Fuse. In addition, retrograde labeled neurons occurred in the ipsilateral mesencephalic reticular formation and the adjoining parts of the central gray, in the midline

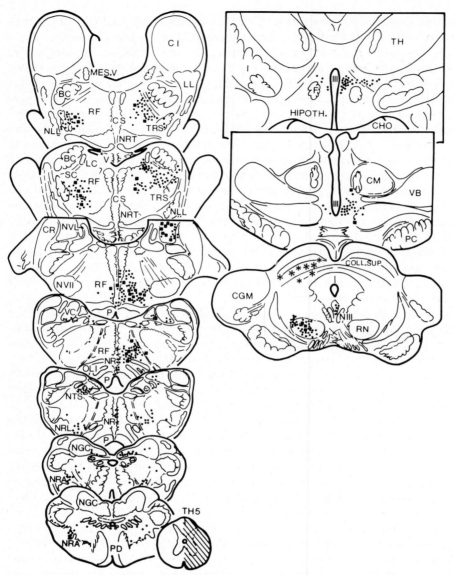

Figure 3. Distribution of retrogradely labeled HRP-positive neurons (dots and squares) in cat brain stem after unilateral injection of HRP at Th5. Note labeled neurons in the locus coeruleus (LC) and the nucleus subcoeruleus (SC) at levels 6 and 7 and in the hypothalamus at levels 9 and 10 ipsilaterally, as well as in the upper pontine tegmentum (levels 6 and 7) adjoining the rubrospinal tract (TRS) contralaterally. Asterisks at level 8 indicate the position of labeled collicular neurons after contralateral injections in C2. Abbreviations: NGC, nuclei cuneatus and gracilis; P, pyramidal tract; OLI, oliva inferior; VC, vestibular complex; CS, nucleus centralis superior; NRT, nucleus reticularis tegmenti pontis; NLL, nucleus of the lateral lemniscus (LL); F, fornix; TH, thalamus; CM, center medium. (From Kuypers and Maisky, 1975, with permission.)

area between the oculomotor nuclei, as well as in the hypothalamus, including the nucleus paraventricularis. These retrograde HRP findings in cat are supported by other findings in other animals. Thus, the findings indicate that, in addition to the well-known descending brain stem pathways, several others also exist.

The funicular trajectory of the descending brain stem pathways from the various cell groups has also been studied by means of the retrograde HRP labeling technique. This was done in two ways: either by injecting HRP in different funiculi (Leichnetz et al., 1978; Tohyama et al., 1979a, b), or by partial transection of the spinal cord at C6–C7, unilaterally leaving certain portions of the funiculi intact, followed by HRP injections at more caudal levels (Kuypers and Maisky, 1977; Martin et al., 1979b; Basbaum and Fields, 1979). The findings in these experiments confirmed earlier degeneration findings and indicated that in C6–C7 the rubrospinal tract is located in the dorsolateral funiculus and that the vestibular and interstitiospinal tracts are located mainly in the ventral funiculus and the adjoining parts of the lateral funiculus, while the pontine and medullary reticulospinal tracts are located in the ventral, the ventrolateral and the most ventral portion of the dorsolateral funiculus (Kuypers and Maisky, 1977). However, in these experiments the coeruleo- and subcoeruleospinal tracts were found to be located mainly in the ventrolateral funiculus, while the hypothalamospinal fibers, which are concentrated in the dorsolateral funiculus, were found to be also present to some degree in the ventrolateral and the ventral funiculi. Further, the crossed pontospinal tract, which descends from neurons in the ventrolateral pontine tegmentum, was found to be located mainly in the dorsal parts of the lateral funiculus, i.e. in roughly the same area as the rubrospinal tract. Many of these findings are supported by the other retrograde HRP transport findings. However, with respect to the funicular trajectory of the raphespinal fibers, some discrepancies occurred. Thus, in our experiments with partial transection of the spinal cord at C6–C7 followed by HRP injections at more caudal levels (Kuypers and Maisky, 1977), no raphespinal fibers were found in the dorsal parts of the dorsolateral funiculus. This is in contrast to several other observations (Leichnetz et al., 1978; Basbaum and Fields, 1979; Martin et al., 1979b) which indicate that neurons in the rostral parts of the medullary raphe nuclei, i.e. the nucleus raphe magnus, descend mainly through the dorsolateral funiculus, while the fibers from the caudal parts of the raphe nuclei, i.e. the nuclei raphe pallidus and obscurus, are mainly located in the ventral and ventrolateral funiculi. Our failure to observe a pronounced accumulation of HRP-labeled neurons in the nucleus raphe magnus following HRP transport through fibers in the dorsal parts of the dorsolateral funiculus was probably due to the fact that in our cases the brain stem was customarily transected at the level of the nucleus raphe magnus and then frequently postfixed overnight. This postfixation tends to suppress the HRP reaction in the tissue adjacent to the cut surface. This may explain why, in several of our cases, relatively few neurons of the nucleus raphe magnus were HRP-labeled. Our failure to detect descending raphe magnus fibers in the dorsolateral funiculus by means of the above HRP method should not, therefore, be regarded as contradictory to the findings of the other investigators. As a consequence, in Figure 4 the solid line, labeled R, which represents the funicular distribution of the raphe spinal fibers, has been continued as an interrupted line into the dorsal parts of the dorsolateral funiculus. This arrangement is supported by recent anterograde aminoacid transport findings (Holstege and Kuypers, 1982a, b).

As pointed out in the beginning of this chapter, according to the anterograde degeneration findings obtained since the early parts of this century the descending brain stem pathways terminate mainly in the intermediate zone. In the late 1960s an anterograde tracing method was developed. This technique is based on the fact that tritiated amino acids injected into the brain are taken up by local neurons and incorporated into proteins, which are then transported

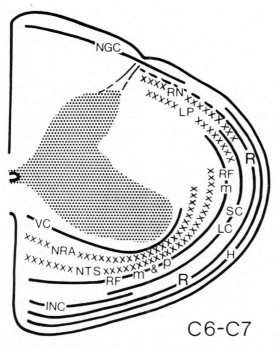

C6-C7

Figure 4. Diagram summarizing the distribution of the descending fibers from the various brain stem cell groups over the different C6–C7 funiculi (××××, fibers from contralateral brain stem cell groups; ————, fibers from ipsilateral brain stem cell groups). Abbreviations: NGC, nuclei gracilis and cuneatus; RN, red nucleus; LP, lateral pontine area adjoining the rubrospinal tract; RFm, medullary medial reticular formation; RFp, pontine medial reticular formation; LC, nucleus locus coeruleus; SC, nucleus subcoeruleus; VC, vestibular complex; NRA, nucleus retroambiguus; NTS, nucleus of the tractus solitarius; INC, interstitial nucleus of Cajal; R, medullary raphe nuclei; H, dorsal hypothalamus. (Modified after Kuypers and Maisky, 1977, with permission.)

anterogradely through the axons to their terminals. The trajectory of these radioactively labeled fibers and the location of their terminals can then be demonstrated by means of light microscopy and electron microscopy autoradiography (Lasek et al., 1968; Hendrikson, 1969; Cowan et al., 1972). The distribution of the descending brain stem pathways to the spinal cord in opossum (Martin et al., 1979a, 1981a) and cat (Basbaum et al., 1978; Holstege et al., 1979; Holstege and Kuypers, 1982a, b) has been reinvestigated using this anterograde amino acid transport technique.

According to the earlier anterograde degeneration findings (Kuypers et al., 1962; Nyberg-Hansen, 1966; Petras, 1967; Martin et al., 1975), the descending brain stem pathways terminate mainly in the intermediate zone and may be subdivided into a medial and a lateral group on the basis of their differential distribution in the intermediate zone (Kuypers, 1964). The lateral group of brain stem pathways, according to the anterograde degeneration findings, descends laterally through the lower brain stem and terminates mainly in the dorsal and lateral parts of the intermediate zone throughout the spinal cord. These parts of the intermediate zone, according to retrograde HRP transport findings (Molenaar and Kuypers, 1978; Molenaar, 1978), contain mainly short propriospinal neurons. On the basis of retrograde degeneration findings (Kuypers and Lawrence, 1967), the crossed descending rubrospinal tract represents the most prominent component of this lateral group of brain stem pathways. The medial group of brain stem pathways descends through the medial and ventromedial parts of the lower brain stem and, according to the anterograde degeneration findings, characteristically terminates in the ventromedial part of the intermediate zone, while only relatively few fibers are distributed to the dorsal and lateral parts. This ventromedial part of the intermediate zone (lamina VIII and the adjoining parts of lamina VII) characteristically contains many long propriospinal neurons which distribute their fibers throughout the length of the spinal cord (Molenaar and Kuypers, 1978). The medial group of brain stem fibers, according to anterograde degeneration findings, comprises the interstitiospinal tract, the tectospinal tract and the vestibulospinal tract, as well as the reticulospinal tracts from both the pontine and the medullary medial reticular formation (Nyberg-Hansen, 1966a; Petras, 1967).

The anterograde labeled amino acid transport findings in the cat (Holstege et al., 1979; Holstege and Kuypers, 1982a, b; Huerta and Harting, 1982) and opossum (Martin et al., 1979a, 1981b) confirmed several of the earlier anterograde degeneration findings, and indicated that the tectospinal tract and the mesencephalic and the pontine reticulospinal tracts, as well as the Deiterospinal tract, from the lateral vestibular nucleus are distributed preferentially to the ventromedial parts of the intermediate zone, while the rubrospinal tract distributes mainly to the dorsal and lateral parts of the intermediate zone. However, the anterograde amino acid transport findings also demonstrated the existence of several unknown fiber connections. Thus they showed that neurons in the midline area between the oculomotor nuclei (Loewy and Saper, 1978) and neurons in the nucleus raphe magnus in the upper medulla oblongata (Basbaum et al., 1978; Martin et al., 1979a, 1981a; Holstege and Kuypers, 1982a, b) project by way of the dorsolateral funiculus to the dorsal horn, especially to laminae I and II and to the dorsal parts of the intermediate zone (Fig. 5, left). The anterograde amino acid transport findings further indicated that the crossed pontospinal tract, which is derived from neurons in the ventrolateral pontine tegmentum in cat, is distributed to the dorsal parts of the intermediate zone, and also to the outer layers of the dorsal horn (Holstege and Kuypers, 1982).

In addition to the brain stem projections to the dorsal horn, anterograde amino acid transport findings demonstrated the existence of descending brain stem projections to the motoneuronal cell groups throughout the spinal cord in opossum, cat and monkey (Martin et al., 1979a, 1981a; Westlund and Coulter, 1980; Holstege and Kuypers, 1982). Some of these brain stem projections to the somatic motoneuronal cell groups have also been demonstrated in birds (Cabot et al., 1982). The brain stem projections to the somatic motoneuronal cell groups are derived from the dorsolateral pontine tegmentum (nucleus coeruleus, nucleus subcoeruleus, nucleus of Kölliker–Fuse) and from the raphe nuclei and the adjoining medial reticular formation in the medulla oblongata between the facial and the hypoglossal nuclei (Fig. 5, right). In fact, neurons in these areas project to both the motoneuronal cell groups and the intermediate zone.

The raphe nuclei in the medulla oblongata, that is, both at the level of the facial nucleus and at more caudal levels, i.e. between the facial and the hypoglossal nuclei, also project to the thoracolumbar and the sacral autonomic lateral horn (Martin et al., 1979a, 1981a; Holstege and Kuypers, 1982). Moreover, the dorsal part of the dorsolateral pontine tegmentum also gives rise to a pronounced projection to the autonomic motoneuronal cell group of the sacral cord (Holstege and Kuypers, 1982).

The existence of medullary reticular projections to the somatic motoneuronal cell groups in the spinal cord could be confirmed by anterograde amino acid transport findings in rat using electron microscope autoradiography (Holstege and Kuypers, 1982). In this material a good many heavily labeled terminals could be observed in lumbar lateral motoneuronal cell groups after labeled leucine injections in the ventromedial part of the reticular formation of the medulla oblongata followed by a 6 months autoradiographic exposure time (Fig. 6).

The existence of the brain stem pathway to the somatic and autonomic motoneuronal cell groups escaped detection by the earlier anterograde degeneration technique (Nyberg-Hansen, 1969). However, their existence was indicated already by the histofluorescent findings in rat (Dahlström and Fuxe, 1964, 1965; Nygren and Olson, 1977), which also showed that the descending projections from the dorsolateral pontine tegmentum, comprising the area of the nucleus subcoeruleus and coeruleus and the nucleus of Kölliker–Fuse

to the motoneuronal cell groups in the cat, seem to be of a larger diameter than those in rat.

II. Functional Aspects

In our earlier functional studies (Lawrence and Kuypers, 1968a, b), the motor defects resulting from the transection of the various descending pathways in monkey were investigated. These studies revealed that, after transection of both pyramidal tracts, the monkey regains a considerable motor control during the postoperative recovery period, but that the capacity to execute individual finger movements is permanently abolished. The motor control, which is regained during the recovery period, appears to be subserved by the descending brain stem pathways since transection of different brain stem pathways abolishes certain aspects of this motor control. Thus, after bilateral transection of the medial *brain stem pathways* at the level of the VI nucleus in bilaterally pyramidotomized monkey, the animal cannot right itself for several weeks and shows a pronounced flexion bias of the extremities. Yet, soon after the operation it is able to pick up food morsels with the hands in roughly the same manner as before, i.e. after recovery from the pyramidotomy. When the animal ultimately is able to right itself and walk it frequently veers from its course and has difficulties circumventing obstacles. It also shows a striking poverty of orienting movements. Thus, such animals sitting in the examining chair behave very differently when approached with food than do animals with only a bilateral pyramidotomy. Pyramidotomized monkeys immediately turn towards the food and reach for it with an outstretched arm and an open hand, while the animals with an additional transection of the medial brain stem pathways at the level of the VI nucleus do not turn towards the food, but follow it only with their eyes and pick it up only when it is brought within the reach of their hands.

Unilateral transection of the lateral brain stem pathways at different pontine and medullary levels in bilaterally pyramidotomized monkeys consistently produces an entirely different defect than is observed after transection of the medial brain stem pathways. The animals with lesions of the lateral brain stem system do not show any defect in righting, but the extremities ipsilateral to the transection show a motor defect. Thus, immediately after the operation the ipsilateral arm, and especially the hand, shows some weakness, such that in picking up morsels of food the hand is placed limply on the food and is then raked towards the animal. After one to two weeks the animals can use the hand in picking up morsels of food, but this is achieved by synergistic movements of arm and hand, such that the hand is opened and closed as a part of an extension and flexion movement of the whole arm. This defect appeared to be related to the transection of the rubrospinal tract, since it did not occur when the lateral brain stem lesions at different pontine medullary levels spared the area of the rubrospinal tract. Other findings showed that the defect did not reflect a somatosensory impairment (Lawrence and Kuypers, 1968b).

In view of these findings it was concluded that in monkey *the medial brain stem system* (at least as it derives from the mesencephalon and pontine medial tegmental field, i.e. rostral to the transection at the level of the VI nucleus) represents the basic system by which the brain controls movements. This control is mainly concerned with body and integrated limb–body movements, such as orienting movements and with synergistic movements of the whole limb. It is also concerned with the direction of progression. The *lateral brain stem system*, and in particular the rubrospinal tract, adds some resolution to this brain stem control and provides the capacity to execute independent movements of the individual limbs, especially their distal parts. The corticospinal pathway amplifies these various brain stem controls and, by means of its direct connections to motoneurons, also provides the capacity to execute highly fractionated distal extremity movements, as exemplified by relatively independent finger movements. These conclusions are supported by several recent electrophysiological findings. In particular, with respect to the medial brain stem system, they are in agreement with the findings of Peterson and Fukushima (this volume).

With respect to the above findings it is, however, of importance to emphasize that the profuse projections from the area of the nucleus coeruleus and subcoeruleus, and especially from the medullary raphe nuclei, to the spinal somatic motoneuronal cell groups were spared in these experiments. The contribution to motor control provided by these projections is still obscure. In view of the fact that the direct corticomotoneuronal connections in the monkey provide the capacity to execute highly fractionated movements, it was tempting to assume that the direct brain stem connections to the motoneurons may also contribute to this capacity. However, this seems unlikely since bilateral pyramidotomy both in adult and newborn rhesus monkeys permanently abolishes the capacity to execute highly fractionated distal extremity movements (Lawrence and Kuypers, 1968a; Lawrence and Hopkins, 1976), despite the fact that under these circumstances the direct brain stem projections to motoneurons, including those innervating distal extremity muscles, remain intact (Martin et al., 1979a, 1981a; Holstege and Kuypers, 1982). In this respect it is of importance to recall that the raphespinal, as well as the reticulospinal, pathways represent rather diffuse systems, with a high degree of collateralization (Peterson et al., 1975; Huisman et al., 1981, 1982; Hayes and Rustioni, 1981; Martin et al., 1981b). This may explain why these systems, despite their direct connections to the motoneurons, cannot activate a restricted number of motoneurons, as required for the execution of highly fractionated movements.

The function of the brain stem projections to the motoneurons – which projections tend to be regarded as the third component of the motor system (Fig. 10) – may in part be clarified by considering the influence of serotonin and noradrenaline on motor control, since at least parts of these brain stem projections to the motoneurons and the intermediate zone carry serotonin or noradrenaline as a putative transmitter, probably in combination with substance P and enkephalin (Hökfelt et al., 1978, 1979; Bowker et al., 1981). Intravenous injections of serotonin precursors increase the discharge of alpha- and gamma-motoneurons (Anderson and Shibuya, 1966; Clineschmidt et al., 1971; Myslinsky and Anderson, 1978). Moreover, injections of noradrenaline precursors increase the amplitude of the lumbar monosynaptic reflex (Baker and Anderson, 1970; Barnes et al., 1980; Strahlendorf et al., 1980). This suggests that both putative transmitters and, by the same token, the serotonergic and noradrenergic components of the descending brain stem pathways to the motoneurons, exert a direct facilitatory influence. This is in keeping with the fact that pharmacological treatment, which increases stimulation of postsynaptic serotonin receptors, produces in several species a syndrome of motor

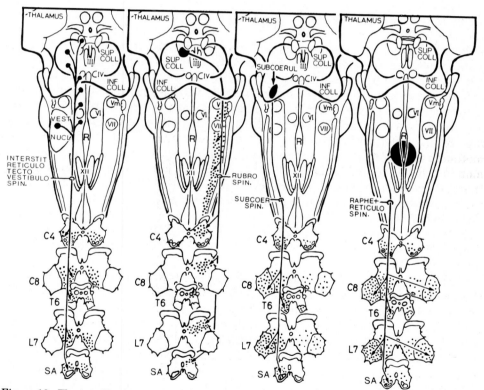

Figure 10. The two diagrams on the left show the contrasting terminal distributions in the intermediate zone of component pathways of the medial and the lateral brain stem systems. The two diagrams on the right show the distribution of the subcoeruleospinal and raphe- and reticulospinal pathways to the spinal motoneuronal cell groups. (From Kuypers, 1981, with permission.)

unrest (Jacobs, 1976). Since this syndrome is dependent on fiber connections from the pons and the medulla oblongata to the spinal cord (Jacobs and Kleinfuss, 1975), it probably reflects the activity of the bulbospinal serotonergic system.

Recent studies of the effects of serotonin and noradrenaline on motoneurons in the lumbosacral cord and the facial nucleus in combination with other types of motoneuronal stimulation (McCall and Aghajanian, 1979; White and Neuman, 1980), showed that both serotonin and noradrenaline, when applied to the motoneurons, bring about a pronounced and long-lasting decrease in the threshold for motoneuronal activity elicited by application of glutamate or stimulation of the motor cortex and red nucleus. These findings are reminiscent of those obtained in invertebrates in which serotonergic neurons modulate the release of sensorineurons transmitter to interneurons and motoneurons (Kandel, 1979). The changes in the excitability of the motoneurons in rat produced by serotonin and noradrenaline presumably mimic those produced by the activity of long descending brain stem pathways (Fung and Barnes, 1981). It has therefore been suggested that these pathways function as gain setting systems (McCall and Aghajanian, 1979) which determine the overall responsiveness of the motoneurons and probably also of the interneurons, both of which represent key elements in motor control. In this respect it is quite striking to note that, in patients with a vital depression, treatment with tricyclic antidepressants may improve motor responsiveness and that chronic treatment with these drugs enhances the responsiveness of motoneurons to serotonin and noradrenaline (Menkes et al., 1980). The idea that the above descending brain stem pathways to the intermediate zone and the somatic motoneuronal cell groups enhance the responsiveness of interneurons and motoneurons is further supported by the fact that, in monkey, bilateral upper thoracic transection of the ventral and ventrolateral funiculi, which contain these pathways, abolishes the responses of lumbosacral motoneurons to stimulation of the contralateral precentral motor cortex. This occurs despite the fact that the lateral corticospinal tract remains intact and, caudal to the transection, still conducts the signals elicited by the motor cortex stimulation (Bernhard et al., 1955).

If activation of the serotonergic and noradrenergic brain stem pathways to the motoneurons produces an increase in responsiveness of the final common pathway, it would seem likely that these brain stem pathways are especially active under circumstances which require a high level of motor activity, as in fight and flight. This hypothesis may be extended one step further by assuming that, under these circumstances, an increase in activity of the descending brain stem system to the dorsal horn may occur simultaneously. This system depresses pain transmission by suppressing the activity of spinothalamic dorsal horn neurons, which are responsive to noxious stimuli (Proudfit and Anderson, 1975; Beall et al., 1976; Basbaum et al., 1976; Willis et al., 1977). However, these assumptions seem to be in conflict with a vast literature which indicates that serotonin has an inhibitory effect on behavior (cf. Chase and Murphy, 1973; Costa et al., 1974). Yet, this paradox may be more apparent than real since, for example, activation of serotonin receptors in motoneurons apparently has a facilitatory effect on these cells, while the activation of such receptors in other neurons, e.g. in mesencephalon and forebrain, may produce an inhibitory effect (Wang and Aghajanian, 1977; Aghajanian and Wang, 1978). The above paradox may therefore be resolved by realizing that it is probably incorrect to assume that all serotonergic systems are active within the same behavioral context. In other words, behavioral changes produced by serotonin and its precursors do not necessarily constitute a behavioral entity.

The extensive noradrenergic and serotonergic brain stem projections to the somatic motoneuronal cell groups – which projections tend to be regarded as a third component of the motor system (Fig. 10) – might in part be under limbic control, since the area of the nucleus subcoeruleus receives many descending fibers from the amygdala and since the nucleus coeruleus and subcoeruleus, as well as the lower brain stem raphe nuclei, receive descending afferents from the mesencephalic central gray and the lateral hypothalamus (Sakai et al., 1977; Hopkins and Holstege, 1978; Wolstencroft, 1980; Hosoya and Matsushita, 1981). This descending bulbospinal gain setting system, as the third component of the motor system, therefore might be instrumental in providing motivational drive in the execution of movements, an aspect of motor control which has seldom been considered in connection with the descending pathways. This hypothesis would imply that the speed and forcefulness of the movements, as well as the disregard for pain displayed by a hungry monkey trying to retrieve food, may in part reflect an increase in activity of this third component of the motor system.

References

Abzug, C., Maeda, M., Peterson, B.W. and Wilson, V.J. (1974) Cervical branching of lumbar vestibulospinal axons, J. Physiol. (Lond.), 243: 499-522.

Aghajanian, G.K. and Wang, R.J. (1978) Physiology and pharmacology of central serotonergic neurons. In M.A. Liption, A. DiMascio and K.F. Killam (Eds.), Psychopharmacology: A Generation of Progress, Raven Press, New York, pp. 171-183.

Anderson, E.G. and Shibuya, T. (1966) The effect of 5-hydroxytryptophan and L-tryptophan on spinal synaptic activity, J. Pharmacol. exp. Ther., 153: 352-360.

Baker, R.G. and Anderson, E.G. (1970) The effect of L-3,4-dihydroxyphenylalanine on spinal reflex activity, J. Pharmacol. exp. Ther., 173: 212-223.

Barnes, C.D., Fung, S.J. and Gintantas, J. (1980) Brainstem noradrenergic system depression by cyclobenzaprine, Neuropharmacology, 19: 221-224.

Basbaum, A.I. and Fields, H.L. (1979) The origin of descending pathways in the dorsolateral funiculus of the spinal cord of the cat and rat: further studies on the anatomy of pain modulation, J. comp. Neurol., 187: 513-532.

Basbaum, A.I., Clanton, C.H. and Fields, H.L. (1976) Opiate and stimulus-produced analgesia: functional anatomy of a medullospinal pathway, Proc. nat. Acad. Sci. U.S.A., 72: 4685-4688.

Basbaum, A.I., Clanton, C.H. and Fields, H.L. (1978) Three bulbospinal pathways from the rostral medulla of the cat: an autoradiographic study of pain modulating systems, *J. comp. Neurol.*, 178: 209-224.

Beall, J.E., Martin, R.F., Applebaum, A.E. and Willis, W.D. (1976) Inhibition of primate spinothalamic tract neurons by stimulation in the region of the nucleus raphe magnus, *Brain Res.*, 114: 328-333.

Bentivoglio, M., Kuypers, H.G.J.M., Catsman-Berrevoets, C.E., Loewe, H. and Dann, O. (1980) Two new fluorescent retrograde neuronal tracers which are transported over long distances, *Neurosci. Lett.*, 18: 25-30.

Bernhard, C.G., Bohm, E. and Petersén, I. (1955) An analysis of causes of postoperative limb pareses following anterolateral chordotomy, *Acta psychiat. neurol. scand.*, 30: 779-792.

Bowker, R.M., Steinbusch, H.W.M. and Coulter, J.D. (1981) Serotonergic and peptidergic projections to the spinal cord demonstrated by a combined retrograde HRP histochemical and immunocytochemical staining method, *Brain Res.*, 211: 412-417.

Brodal, A. (1940) Modification of Gudden method for study of cerebral localization, *Arch. Neurol. Psychiat.*, 43: 46-58.

Brodal, A., Taber, E. and Walberg, F. (1960) The raphe nuclei of the brain stem in the cat. II. Efferent connections, *J. comp. Neurol.*, 114: 239-259.

Cabot, J.B. Reiner, A. and Bogen, N. (1982) Avian bulbospinal pathways: anterograde and retrograde studies of cells of origin, funicular trajectories and laminar terminations. In H.G.J.M. Kuypers and G.F. Martin (Eds.) *Descending Pathways to the Spinal Cord, Progress in Brain Research, Vol. 57* Elsevier Biomedical, Amsterdam.

Cajal, S. Ramón y (1952) *Histologie du Système Nerveux de l'Homme et des Vertébrés,* Instituto Ramón y Cajal, Madrid, 1952.

Chase, T.N. and Murphy, D.L. (1973) Serotonin and central nervous system function, *Ann. Rev. Pharmacol.*, 13: 181-197.

Chineschmidt, B.V., Pierce, J.E. and Sjoerdsma, A. (1971) Interactions of tricylic antidepressants and 5-hydroxyindolealkylamine precursors on spinal monosynaptic reflex transmission, *J. Pharmacol. exp. Ther.*, 179: 312-323.

Costa, E., Gessa, G.L. and Sandler, M. (1974) In *Advances in Biochemical Psychopharmacology: Serotonin: New Vistas, Vol. 11,* Raven Press, New York.

Coulter, J.D. and Jones, E.G. (1977) Differential distribution of corticospinal projections from individual cytoarchitectonic fields in the monkey, *Brain Res.*, 129: 335-340.

Cowan, W.M., Gottlieb, D.I., Hendrickson, A.E., Price, J.L. and Woolsey, T.A. (1972) The autoradiographic demonstration of axonal connections in the central nervous system, *Brain Res.*, 37: 21-51.

Crutcher, K.A., Humbertson, A.O. and Martin, G.F. (1978) The origin of brainstem–spinal pathways in the north american opossum (*Didelphis virginiana*). Studies using the horseradish peroxidase method, *J. comp. Neurol.*, 179: 169-194.

Dahlström, A. and Fuxe, K. (1964) Evidence for the existence of monoamine-containing neurons in the central nervous system. I. Demonstration of monoamines in the cell bodies of brain stem neurons, *Acta physiol. scand.*, 62: 5-55.

Dahlström, A. and Fuxe, K. (1965) Evidence for the existence of monoamine neurons in the central nervous system. II. Experimentally induced changes in the intraneuronal amine levels of bulbospinal neuron systems, *Acta physiol. scand.*, 64: 6-36.

Denny-Brown, D. and Botterell, E.H. (1948) The motor functions of the agranular frontal cortex, *Res. Publ. Assoc. nerv. ment. Dis.*, 27: 235-345.

Felix, D. and Wiesendanger, M. (1971) Pyramidal and non-pyramidal motor cortical effects on distal forelimb muscles of monkeys, *Exp. Brain Res.*, 12: 81-91.

Flindt-Egebak, P. (1977) Autoradiographical demonstration of the projections from the limb areas of the feline sensorimotor cortex to the spinal cord, *Brain Res.*, 136: 153-156.

Fung, S.J. and Barnes, C.D. (1981) Evidence of facilitatory coeruleospinal action in lumbar motoneurons of cats, *Brain Res.*, 216: 299-311.

exception of those cells which are right at the midline, the descending 5-HT projections are always strictly ipsilateral relative to their funicular trajectory. Injections restricted to the gray matter, however, sometimes result in labeling of a few 5-HT cells contralateral to the injection site, which must be interpreted as evidence that some crossing takes place at the segmental level.

A substantial population of non-serotoninergic neurons with spinal projectins are found intermingled with the serotoninergic ones (open symbols in Fig. 4). At the level of the inferior olive non-serotoninergic spinal cord-projecting neurons are seen in the reticular formation just dorsal to the olive, where they can be seen to form a "bridge" between the lateral B1 group and the medially located B1–B2 complex. No 5-HT-containing cells are found in this area (compare levels d and e in Fig. 1 with levels b and c in Fig. 4). Some non-serotoninergic spinal cord-projecting cells are also seen within the raphe obscurus, while very few non-5-HT cells with spinal projections are seen within the raphe pallidus. At levels rostral to the inferior olive the labeled non-serotoninergic cells become more numerous. Many of these neurons are found intermingled with the 5-HT-containing neurons in the nc. raphe magnus. The more laterally located labeled cells in the nc. reticularis magnocellularis tend to lie dorsal to the labeled 5-HT-containing neurons. Bowker et al. (1981) have reported that over 70% of the total number of 5-HT-containing neurons in the B1–B3 groups can be labeled retrogradely from the spinal cord. They also estimate that nearly 90% of the retrogradely labeled neurons are serotoninergic. This is consistent with our own observation that only few non-5-HT spinal cord-projecting neurons are found within nc. raphe pallidus and obscurus, while our data point to a much higher fraction of labeled non-serotonin neurons in nc. raphe magnus (about one-half of the total labeled neuronal population). Similar results have been reported by Satoh (1979).

The labeled non-5-HT neurons associated or intermingled with the 5-HT cells in the B1–B3 groups have, in general, the same projection patterns as the neighboring 5-HT neurons, but some differences are readily observed: while the spinal cord-projecting 5-HT neurons are almost completely ipsilateral, the non-5-HT system shows a clear bilateral distribution, although with an ipsilateral predominance. While the 5-HT-containing system is rather sharply divided into a caudal and a rostral part with differential projections (the B1 and B2 groups projecting to the ventral cord, and the B3 group projecting to the dorsal cord), the non-serotoninergic neurons show more overlapping projections. Thus, the non-serotoninergic cells in the B1–B2 area project to some degree also through dorsal areas of the spinal cord, and some of the non-serotoninergic neurons in the B3 area projects to more ventral parts of the spinal cord.

This rostral to caudal topography among the medullary neurons is consistent with the HRP studies of Martin et al. (1978) in the cat, and of Basbaum and Fields (1979), Zemlan et al. (1979) and Watkins et al. (1980) in rat and cat, showing that the raphe-spinal projection descending in the dorsolateral

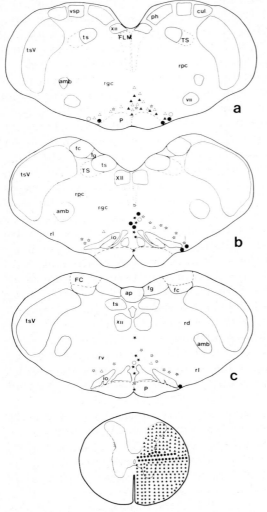

Figure 4. Principal projection patterns from the medullary B1–B3 cell groups to the spinal cord in the rat. The diagrams summarize the results from a large number of animals in which True Blue was injected unilaterally into different portions of the white and gray matter. The labeled 5-HT-containing and non-5-HT-containing cell bodies have been plotted according to the principles outlined in Fig. 3. (From Skagerberg and Björklund, 1982, with permission.) Symbols: filled stars, 5-HT-containing cells labeled from injections confined to the ventral quadrant of the cord; open stars, non-5-HT-containing cells labeled from the same injections; filled circles, 5-HT-containing cells labeled from injections confined to the intermediate portion of the cord (including the intermediolateral column); open circles, non-5-HT-cells labeled from the same injections; filled triangles, 5-HT-containing cells labeled from injections confined to the dorsal quadrant of the cord (the dorsolateral funiculus and the dorsal horn); open triangles, non-5-HT-cells labeled from the same injections. For abbreviations, see legend to Fig. 1.

funiculus originates chiefly in neurons in the rostral part of the medullary raphe, i.e. nc. raphe magnus and nc. reticularis magnocellularis, whereas the axons descending in the ventral quadrant originate mainly in cells of the caudal medullary raphe, i.e. the raphe pallidus and obscurus areas. With the autoradiographic technique, (Basbaum et al., 1978; Basbaum and Ralston, 1978; see also Basbaum, this volume) in the cat and monkey, and Loewy (1981) in the rat and cat, have shown: (i) that the major projection from the area of the nc. raphe magnus project via the dorsolateral funiculus to innervate (probably bilaterally) the dorsal horn (including lamina I and II), and (ii) that the major projection from the raphe pallidus and obscurus areas descend in the ventral and ventrolateral funiculi to innervate the ventral and intermediate gray and the intermediolateral column. Consistent with our findings is also the recent autoradiographic studies of Loewy et al. (1981) and Loewy and McKellar (1981) that cells in the area of the lateral B1 cells and the caudal part of the lateral B3 cells, project heavily to the intermediolateral cell column.

In summary (Fig. 5), three major components can be distinguished in the descending serotonin system: (i) *a dorsal pathway*, originating in the nc. raphe magnus and its lateral extension in nc. reticularis magnocellularis, and projecting ipsilaterally along the dorsolateral funiculus to innervate the dorsal horn (probably bilaterally); (ii) *a ventral pathway*, originating in the nc. raphe pallidus and obscurus and descending ipsilaterally in the ventral quadrant of the white matter to innervate the ventral and intermediate gray; and (iii) *an intermediate pathway* originating in nc. obscurus and in nc. paragigantocellularis pars alpha, and descending ipsilaterally in the lateral funiculus to innervate the intermediolateral cell column in the thoracic cord. The non-serotoninergic spinal cord-projecting neurons have a similar rostro-caudal topography, but apparently with a greater overlap between the neurons projecting to the dorsal and ventral cord regions. The non-serotoninergic neurons also have a distinct contralateral descending projection.

III. The Noradrenaline System

III.1. *Distribution of cell bodies*

The brain stem NA neurons are primarily located in the medulla oblongata and pons. On the basis of topography they can be divided into three major cell systems (cf. Dahlström and Fuxe, 1964; Lindvall and Björklund, 1978): *the locus coeruleus–subcoeruleus complex, the lateral tegmental cell system* (which has one medullary and one pontine part), and *the dorsal medullary cell group*. Figure 6 gives a schematic overview of the distribution of the noradrenergic perikary in the rat, as shown by the ALFA method. In their dopamine-β-hydroxylase (DBH)-immunofluorescence study, Swanson and Hartman (1975) report a total of about 4700 noradrenergic (i.e. DBH-positive) neurons on each

DESCENDING SEROTONIN PATHWAYS

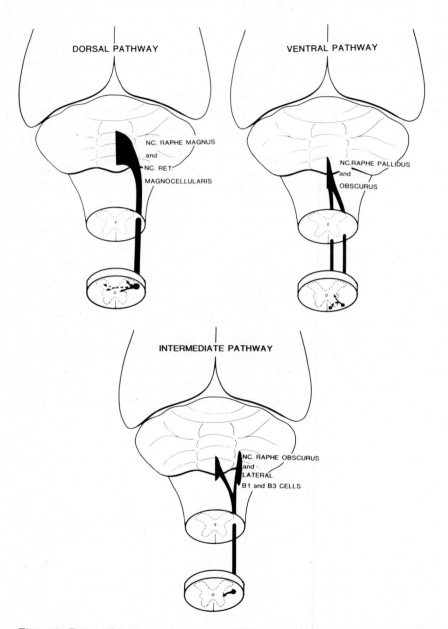

Figure 5. Principal arrangement of the dorsal, ventral and intermediate serotonin pathways to the cord, as outlined in the text.

CA cell bodies

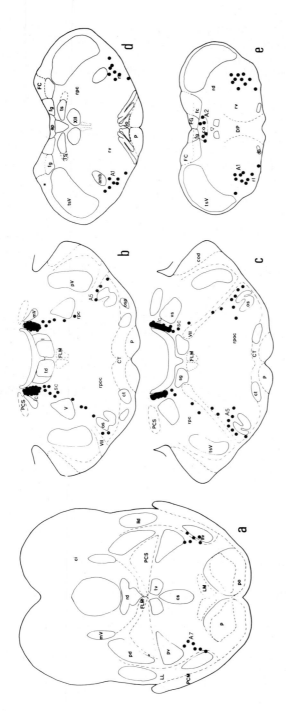

Figure 6. Distribution of NA-containing cell bodies in the pons and medulla oblongata of the rat, as revealed by the ALFA method. The density of the dots is roughly proportional to the number of fluorescent cell bodies visualized in each area. Abbreviations: amb, nucleus ambiguus; ap, postrema; cer, cerebellum; cod, nucleus cochlearis dorsalis; CT, corpus trapezoideum; ct, nucleus corporis trapezoidei; DP, pyramidal decussation; FC, fasciculus cuneatus; fc, nucleus fasciculus cuneatus; FG, fasciculus gracilis; fg, nucleus fasciculus gracilis; io, nucleus olivaris inferior; l, nucleus tegmenti dorsalis lateralis; LM, lemniscus medialis; llv, nucleus lemnisci lateralis ventralis; mV, nucleus tractus mesencephali nervi trigemini; os, nucleus olivaris superior; osp, nucleus parolivaris superioris; P, tractus corticospinalis; PCS, pedunculus cerebellaris superior; PCM, pedunculus cerebellaris medius; pd, nucleus parabrachialis dorsalis; pV, nucleus principalis nervi trigemini; pv, nucleus parabrachialis ventralis; rl, nucleus reticularis lateralis; rpc, nucleus reticularis parvicellularis; rpoc, nucleus reticularis pontis caudalis; rpoo, nucleus reticularis pontis oralis; sc, subcoeruleus; td, nucleus tegmenti dorsalis; TS, tractus solitarius; ts, nucleus tractus solitarius; tsV, nucleus tractus spinalis nervi trigemini; V, nucleus motorius nervi trigemini; VII, nervus facialis.

side in the rat's brain stem. Combining the data from this study and from the Falck–Hillarp histofluorescence study of Nygren and Olson (1977b), it appears that about 45–50% of the noradrenergic neurons occur in the locus coeruleus, about 10–15% in the subcoeruleus area, about 30% in the lateral tegmental cell system, and about 10% in the dorsal tegmental cell group. This means that about 70–75% of the brain's noradrenergic neurons are located in the pons and about 25–30% in medulla oblongata.

The locus coeruleus–subcoerulus complex. In the *rat*, the locus coeruleus is a compact cell group made up almost exclusively of NA-containing cells (Dahlström and Fuxe, 1964; Swanson, 1976). The nucleus, which contains a total of 1400–1600 cells in the rat (Descarries and Sucier, 1972; Ross et al., 1975, Swanson, 1976), is usually divided into a dorsal part composed of densely packed fusiform cells, and a ventral part containing somewhat larger multipolar neurons. These larger ventral neurons amount to about 200 on each side (Swanson, 1976). These latter neurons are morphologically similar to the NA neurons in the subcoeruleus area. In fact, the multipolar neurons in the ventral locus coeruleus are topographically continuous with the more ventrally located subcoeruleus cells, and they have similar projection patterns. This makes a sharp distinction between locus coeruleus and nc. subcoeruleus difficult (see Amaral and Sinnamon, 1977, for further discussion). According to Nygren and Olson (1977b) the subcoeruleus contains about 200 NA neurons on each side.

The locus coeruleus complex has also a dorsolateral extension of cells, along the medial aspect of the superior cerebellar peduncle into the roof of the fourth ventricle (the so-called A4 cell group of Dahlström and Fuxe, 1964). This subgroup is particularly prominent in primates and man (Braak, 1975; Demirjian et al., 1976).

The locus coeruleus–subcoeruleus complex in the *cat* is more loosely arranged and has a more complex topography (Maeda et al., 1973; Chu and Bloom, 1974; Jones and Moore, 1974; Léger et al., 1979). The locus coeruleus proper, which corresponds to the dorsal compact part of the locus coeruleus in the rat, is located in the periventricular gray and adjoining tegmentum, extending about 3 mm along the mesencephalic root of the trigeminal nerve. More scattered NA neurons extend ventrolaterally from the locus coeruleus proper in the nc. subcoeruleus, and dorsoventrally in the medial and lateral parabrachial nuclei, and the Kölliker–Fuse nucleus. Catecholamine neurons, probably corresponding to the A4 cell group, are also found in the white matter separating the vestibular and intracerebellar nuclei (Persson and Wiklund, 1981). According to Wiklund et al. (1981) the total locus coeruleus complex in the cat contains about 9000 NA neurons on each side, out of which about 5300 are located in the locus coeruleus proper. It should be pointed out that, in the cat, both locus coeruleus and subcoeruleus contain a significant number of serotoninergic cell bodies (Léger et al., 1979).

The lateral tegmental cell system. These cells are located in the ventrolateral tegmentum, from the caudal pole of the medulla oblongata up to the level of the motor nucleus of the trigeminal nerve in the pons (Dahlström and Fuxe, 1964; Palkovits and Jacobowitz, 1974; Swanson and Hartman, 1975; Blessing et al., 1980; Wiklund et al., 1981). Topographically (and on the basis of its ontogenetic development) (Seiger and Olson, 1973), this rather disseminated cell system can be divided into a medullary part (groups A1 and A3 in Dahlström's and Fuxe's teminology) and a pontine part (groups A5 and A7).

The cells in the *medullary part* extend, both in rat and cat, from the pyramidal decussation up to the rostral part of the inferior olivary nucleus. They occur mainly scattered around the lateral reticular nucleus, and in the rat some cell bodies are found also within this nucleus (Dahlström and Fuxe, 1964; Blessing et al., 1980; Wiklund et al., 1981). This cell group is the A1 group of Dahlström and Fuxe (1964). Hökfelt et al. (1974) report that a major portion of the PNMT-immunoreactive (i.e. most probably A-producing) neurons are located in the rostral part of this cell group.

The cells in the *pontine part* are distributed from the level of the rostral part of the facial nucleus up to the level of the trigeminal motor nucleus. Caudally, the cells occur caudal and medial to the outgoing fibers of the facial nerve, close to the superior olivary complex. This cell cluster is the A5 group of Dahlström and Fuxe (1964). Further rostrally, the cells extend into the area between the ventrolateral border of the superior cerebellar peduncle and the lateral lemniscus, forming the A7 group. The border between this A7 group and the subcoeruleus cell group is not well-defined. The topography of the lateral tegmental neurons are similar in rat and cat (see Dahlström and Fuxe, 1964; Swanson and Hartman, 1975 (rat); Blessing et al., 1980; Wiklund et al., 1981 (cat)).

The dorsal medullary cell group. These cells, designated A2, occur both in rat and cat in the nucleus of the solitary tract and the commissural nucleus, with some cells also in the dorsal motor nucleus of the vagus (Dahlström and Fuxe, 1964). Also this cell group contains putative A-producing neurons, as revealed by PNMT-immunohistochemistry (Hökfelt et al., 1974).

III.2. Organization of descending projections to the spinal cord

As summarized in Figure 7, NA fibers innervate the spinal cord gray matter at all levels of the cord (Carlsson et al., 1964; Dahlström and Fuxe, 1965). The highest density of terminals is found in the intermediolateral column. According to Dahlström and Fuxe (1965) the NA fibers are concentrated to the ventromedial part of this nucleus, where they intimately enclose the perikarya of the preganglionic sympathetic neurons. Strands of NA fibers can also be followed from the densely innervated intermediolateral cell column medially towards the central canal. This innervation pattern is seen also in the cat (McLachlan and Oldfield, 1981). A rich NA innervation is also found in the ventral horn throughout the cord (Fig. 8a). In the cervical and lumbar segments, Dahlström and Fuxe (1965) have reported that the NA innervation is

CA terminals

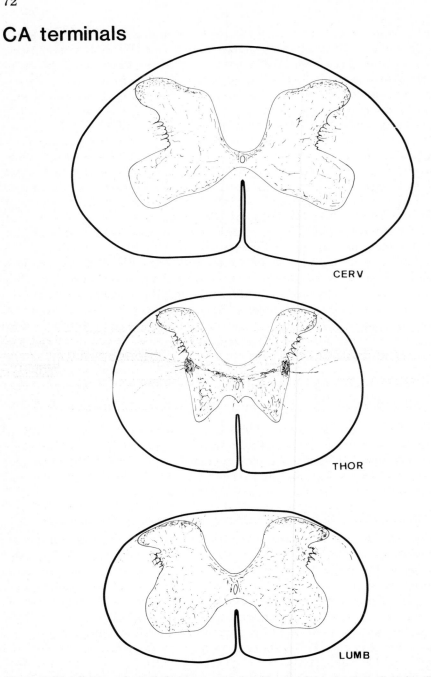

Figure 7. Distribution of catecholamine-containing fibers and terminals in three levels of the rat spinal cord, as revealed by the ALFA method.

the densest in the region of the ventrolateral and dorsolateral motor neurons. The intermediate gray and the dorsal horn have a more scattered NA fiber supply. Laminae I and II are traversed by a large number of longitudinally running catecholamine-containing fibers, oriented in the predominant direction of the dendrites in this zone (Fig. 8b and c).

This general distributional pattern is consistent with biochemical measures

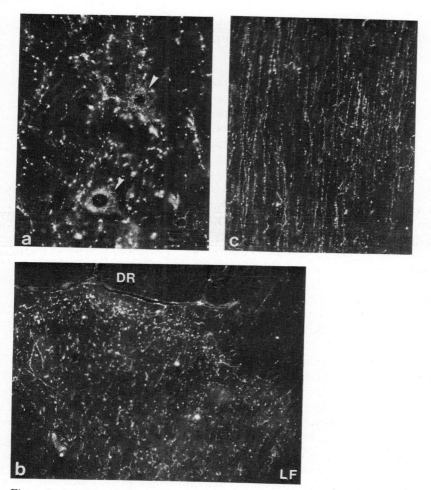

Figure 8. Appearance of the catecholamine-containing innervation in the rat spinal cord. a, detail from the ventral horn in the upper cervical cord. The large cell bodies (arrow heads) are the perikarya of α-motor neurons. b, transverse section through the dorsal horn in the upper thoracic cord. DR, dorsal root; LF, lateral funiculus. C, longitudinal section through the outer layers of the dorsal horn, illustrating the dense arrangement of longitudinally running fibers in this area. ALFA method.

of the distribution of NA in the cord, both in rats (Zivin et al., 1975) and cats (Fleetwood-Walker and Coote, 1981a).

The NA innervation of the spinal cord originates primarily in the locus coeruleus–subcoeruleus complex and the lateral tegmental cell system. Anatomically, the noradrenergic spinal afferents can thus be referred to two separate projection systems, a coeruleospinal pathway and a tegmento-spinal pathway. The dorsal medullary cell group was originally suggested by Dahlström and Fuxe (1965) to contribute to the spinal NA innervation, but this projection has so far not been well substantiated with the more recently introduced tract-tracing techniques (McKellar and Loewy, 1979; Smolen et al., 1979; Blessing et al., 1981).

III.3. The coeruleo-spinal noradrenaline pathway

Bilateral lesion of the locus coeruleus–subcoeruleus complex has been shown to cause an almost complete disappearance of the NA innervation in the ventral horn, the intermediate gray, and the ventral part of the dorsal horn (corresponding to laminae IV–IX), throughout the cord (Nygren and Olson, 1977a). Biochemically, bilateral locus coeruleus lesions (whose encroachment upon the subcoeruleus area are unclear) have been reported to cause 30–40% reductions in total NA or DBH content in the rat spinal cord (Ross and Resi, 1974; Commissiong et al., 1978; Adèr et al., 1979), and about 80% reduction of NA in the ventral horn in the cat (Fleetwood-Walker and Coote, 1981b). According to Karoum et al. (1980) and Commissiong (1981) the coeruleo-spinal projection is 50% crossed, the crossing most probably taking place at the segmental level.

HRP injections into the spinal cord in the rat label predominantly multipolar cells in the ventral subdivision of the locus coeruleus and in the subcoeruleus area, and only a few of the smaller fusiform cells in the dorsal subdivision (Satoh et al., 1977; Satoh, 1979; Adèr et al., 1979; Guynet, 1980). In Guynet's (1980) study, a maximum of 180 cells in the ipsilateral coeruleus–subcoeruleus area could be labeled from a large unilateral HRP injection into the cervical cord. This amounts to about one-half of the multipolar neurons in the area, but only to about 10% of the total number of NA neurons in the coeruleus–subcoeruleus complex.

The study of Zemlan et al. (1979), using restricted unilateral HRP injections into the white matter of the thoracic cord, indicate that the axons from the coeruleus–subcoeruleus neurons descend ipsilaterally in the ventral and ventral-lateral funiculi. This is consistent with the findings of Basbaum and Fields (1979), using HRP injections in combination with partial lesions of the cord, and with the fluorescence histochemical observations of Nygren and Olson (1977a) in rats with bilateral coeruleus–subcoeruleus lesions.

Guynet (1980) has provided electrophysiological evidence that a significant proportion of the coeruleo-spinal neurons (4 out of 8 tested) give off collaterals that ascend in the dorsal tegmental bundle. Double-labeling studies with fluorescent retrograde tracers support the existence of such collateral arrangements. Thus, a small proportion (perhaps some 10%) of the cells labeled by tracers injected into the spinal cord become double-labeled with a second tracer injected into either cerebral cortex, hippocampus or thalamus (Room et al., 1981), or into the cerebellum (Nagai et al., 1981).

HRP experiments in the cat (Kuypers and Maisky, 1975; Hancock and Fougerousse, 1976; Basbaum and Fields, 1979) have shown that the spinal cord-projecting neurons are located both in the locus coeruleus proper, the sub-coeruleus, the parabrachial nuclei and the Kölliker–Fuse nucleus. It is so far not clear, however, to what extent these retrogradely labeled cells represent noradrenergic or non-noradrenergic neurons. In the cat, Basbaum and Fields (1979) found that the coeruleo-spinal projection descended ipsilaterally in both the dorsolateral funiculus and in the ventral quadrant.

In summary (see Fig. 9), the coeruleo-spinal NA pathway originates in the ventral portion of the locus coeruleus and the nc. subcoeruleus, and descends ipsilaterally in the ventral and ventrolateral funiculi to innervate bilaterally

DESCENDING NA PATHWAYS

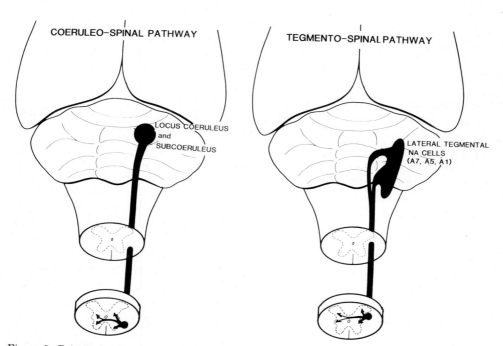

Figure 9. Principal arrangement of the coeruleo-spinal and tegmento-spinal NA pathways, as outlined in the text.

the ventral horn, the intermediate gray and the ventral part of the dorsal horn at all levels of the cord. The crossing is at the segmental level.

III.4. *The tegmento-spinal noradrenaline pathway*

The coeruleus-subcoeruleus area is responsible for about 30–40% of the spinal NA innervation in the rat. Remaining afferents, primarily going to: (i) the intermediolateral column, the area around the central canal, and the fiber strands interconnecting the two; and (ii) the outer layers of the dorsal horn, originate in the lateral tegmental cell system and possibly – to a minor extent – also in the dorsal medullary cell group. Observations of retrograde cell changes after spinal transection led Dahlström and Fuxe (1965) to emphasize the medullary part of the lateral tegmental cell system, i.e. the A1 group, as the source of NA fibers to the spinal cord. Later retrograde tracing studies (Satoh et al., 1977; Satoh, 1979; Loewy et al., 1979; McKellar and Loewy, 1979; Blessing et al., 1981; Skagerberg and Björklund, unpublished observations) indicate that, in the rat and rabbit, the spinal cord-projecting NA neurons in the lateral tegmental cell systems are primarily confined to the pontine groups (A5 and A7). The situation may, however, be somewhat different in other species. Thus, based on the effect of lesions on spinal cord catecholamine content, Fleetwood-Walker and Coote (1981b) have suggested a more important role for the medullary A1 cells in the cat. Likewise, there seems to be a prominent projection from catecholamine-containing neurons in the medullary A1 area to the thoracic spinal cord in the chicken (Smolen et al., 1979). In the rat, Hökfelt et al. (1980) have reported that the PNMT-positive neurons in the rostral part of the A1 area (named C1) can be retrogradely labeled from the spinal cord. This suggests the possibility that A-containing neurons may constitute a major portion of the spinal cord-projecting catecholaminergic neurons in the A1 area, at least in this species (cf. McKellar and Loewy, 1979; Blessing et al., 1981).

It is important to emphasize that, in the rat and rabbit at least, the vast majority of the cells in the area of the A1 cell group which can be retrogradely labeled from the spinal cord are non-catecholaminergic (McKellar and Loewy, 1979; Blessing et al., 1981; Skagerberg and Björklund, unpublished observations). Similarly, a significant portion of the retrogradely labeled neurons in the pontine A5 cell group (primarily in its dorsal part) is non-catecholaminergic (Loewy et al., 1979; Skagerberg and Björklund, unpublished observations).

The exact contribution of the dorsal medullary A2 neurons is unclear. Cells in this area are retrogradely labeled after tracer injections into the cord (Satoh et al., 1977; Kuypers and Maisky, 1975). However, combined techniques using HRP or fluorescent retrograde tracers in combination with catecholamine histofluorescence have failed to demonstrate any catecholamine-containing spinal cord-projecting neurons in this area (McKellar and Loewy, 1979; Smolen et al., 1979; Blessing et al., 1981; Skagerberg and Björklund, unpublished observations). Fleetwood-Walker and Coote (1981b) have reported a small (18%) reduction in NA in the region of the intermediolateral column after bilateral lesions of the A2 area in the cat. It seems possible, however, that this effect could have been due to lesions of fibers-of-passage, e.g. of axons coming from neurons located in the pons.

Some information is available as to the trajectory of the tegmento-spinal NA pathway. Thus, Nygren and Olson (1977a) reported that the catecholamine-containing axons remaining after a bilateral lesion of the locus coeruleus–subcoeruleus complex were confined to the dorsolateral funiculus. This is consistent with the observations of Basbaum and Fields (1979) that retrograde labeling of cells in the A1 and A5 areas remained in animals with sparing of the dorsolateral funiculus, but not after sparing of the ventral quadrant. Finally, Loewy et at. (1979) have autoradiographically traced axons from the pontine A5 area predominantly ipsilaterally in the medial part of the lateral funiculus. These axons terminated bilaterally in the intermediolateral column and adjoining parts of the intermediate zone.

In summary (see Fig. 9), available data indicate that the tegmento-spinal NA pathway originates in the pontine A5 and A7 cell groups, and to a varying degree probably also in the medullary A1 cells. The axons project predominantly ipsilaterally in the dorsolateral funiculus and terminate bilaterally in the intermediolateral column, and associated parts of the intermediate gray, of the thoracic cord, and in the dorsal horn at all spinal levels.

IV. The Diencephalo-Spinal Dopamine System

As mentioned in the Introduction, several biochemical studies have suggested that part of the DA found in the spinal cord should constitute a separate descending catecholamine system with DA as the transmitter rather than as a precursor for NA. The first morphological evidence for such a system came in 1979 when three groups (Björklund and Skagerberg, 1979b; Blessing and Chalmers, 1979; Hökfelt et al., 1979), using combined histochemistry and retrograde tracing techniques, independently showed that DA-containing neurons in the diencephalon in rat and rabbit have projections to the spinal cord. Due to the technical problems of visualizing a sparse DA innervation in the presence of a 10-fold richer NA innervation, the terminal distribution of the DA innervation has, however, been unresolved.

Biochemical assays have shown the highest DA levels in the dorsal and intermediate parts of the cord, both in rats and cats (Commissiong and Neff, 1979; Fleetwood-Walker and Coote, 1981a). By using a combined 6-hydroxydopamine (6-OHDA) and 5,7-dihydroxytryptamine (5,7-DHT) treatment (see Fig. 10), it has been possible to deplete 94–99% of NA in all parts of the cord, while only marginally affecting the DA levels (Skagerberg et al., 1982). In such pretreated rats the DA/NA ratio is increased in the dorsal and intermediate cord, from a normal of about 0.1 to between 1.5 and 6.0, indicating

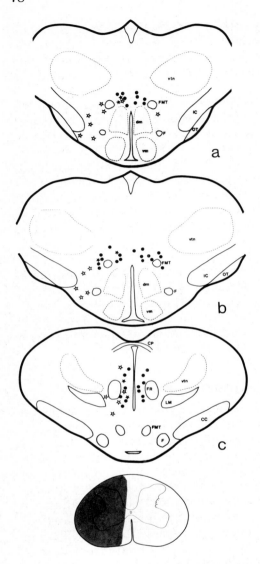

Figure 10. Retrograde labeling of cell bodies in the caudal diencephalon from a unilateral injection of True Blue into the cervical spinal cord. In this animal the entire spinal NA system had been eliminated by a combined 6-OHDA and 5,7-DHT treatment (2×100 mg/kg, s.c. of 6-OHDA given at birth, plus 150 µg 5,7-DHT, intraventricularly, given at about 2 months of age). DA-containing cell bodies (filled stars) as well as non-DA-containing cell bodies (open stars) are labeled ipsilaterally in the A11 cell group. The non-labeled DA-containing cells are marked with filled circles. (From Skagerberg et al., 1982, with permission.) Abbreviations: CC, crus cerebri; CP, commissura posterior; dm, nucleus dorsomedialis; IC, capsula interna; F, fornix; FMT, fasciculus mammilothalamicus; FR, fasciculus retroflexus; LM, lemniscus medialis; OT, tractus opticus; vm, nucleus ventromedialis; vtn, nucleus ventralis thalami.

that the vast majority of the fluorescence histochemically detectable catecholamine fibers are DA-containing in the neurotoxin-pretreated animals. The combined 6-OHDA and 5,7-DHT treatment thus offers a possibility for relatively selective visualization of the spinal DA innervation. Some NA remains, however, particularly in the intermediate thoracic cord (amounting to about 30% of the total catecholamine content in this area). It is highly improbable that any of the fibers visualized in the neurotoxin-pretreated rats are A-containing, since the concentrations of A in the cord is at least 5–10 times lower than that of DA (van der Gugten et al., 1976; Versteeg et al., 1976), and since it is unlikely that any A-containing fibers can be visualized with the ALFA method (Björklund et al., 1980).

IV.1. Distribution of dopamine neurons projecting to the spinal cord

In rats subjected to the combined neurotoxin treatment, we have used the transmitter-specific retrograde tracing technique to study the distribution of tracer-labeled DA-containing cell bodies after injections of fluorescent tracer in the cervical spinal cord (Skagerberg et al., 1982). The distribution of labeled cells is shown in Figure 10. The spinal cord-projecting DA neurons are found in the caudal diencephalon, in the so-called A11 cell group. These neurons are found along the dorsal and medial aspects of the fasciculus mammillo-thalamicus and, more caudally, in between the fasciculus retroflexus and the third ventricle. This arrangement is in agreement with the results reported by Hökfelt et al. (1979), while Blessing and Chalmers (1979) referred their retro-gradely labeled neurons in the rabbit to the A13-cell group, which is located in the medial zona incerta rostral to the A11 group. However, as Björklund and Nobin (1973) have pointed out, there is no sharp border between the A11 and A13 groups, but cells are referred to either group on basis of cell morphology and fluorescence intensity. The distribution of the diencephalic DA neurons projecting to the spinal cord (which in the rat are not found in the A13 group) may thus vary somewhat between species.

IV.2. Distribution of presumed dopamine fibers in the spinal cord

The distribution of presumed DA fibers, as revealed in 6-OHDA + 5,7-DHT pretreated rats, is schematically illustrated in Figure 11. Fluorescent structures are visualized along the whole extent of the spinal cord in the most dorsal and lateral parts of the dorsal horn, including the reticular nucleus of the dorsal horn, and in the areas dorsal and lateral to the central canal. The ventral horn is virtually free of presumed DA-containing fibers.

At thoracic and upper lumbar levels there is an increased density of fibers in the intermediolateral cell column and in the area surrounding the central

DA terminals

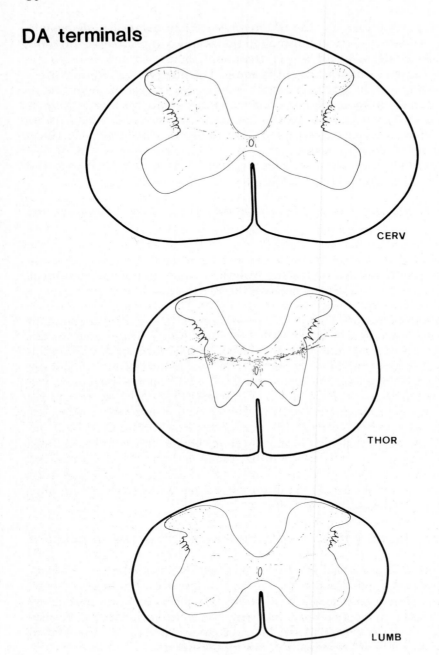

CERV

THOR

LUMB

Figure 11. Distribution of presumed DA-containing fibers in the rat spinal cord after removal of the NA innervations through combined 6-OHDA and 5,7-DHT pretreatment (cf. Fig. 10). (From Skagerberg et al., 1982, with permission.)

canal. These latter fibers can, especially in longitudinal sections, be seen to be part of a continuous system of fibers between the area around the central canal and the intermediolateral cell column. In longitudinal sections it is clearly seen that the innervation of the intermediolateral column is not evenly distributed along the longitudinal plane but forms clusters of innervation which no doubt correspond to the clustering of preganglionic neurons (Fig. 12). Some coarse fibers of fiber bundles are often seen to radiate out laterally from the intermediolateral cell column into the white matter, sometimes almost reaching out to the lateral surface of the cord.

IV.3. Organization of the descending dopamine system

As can be seen in Figure 10, the system seems to be totally uncrossed. The course of the descending fibers is not yet known with certainty, but in longitudinal sections we have observed two areas containing fibers running in the rostro-caudal direction. The first area is layer I of the dorsal horn and the adjoining part of the reticular nucleus and the dorsolateral funiculus. The second

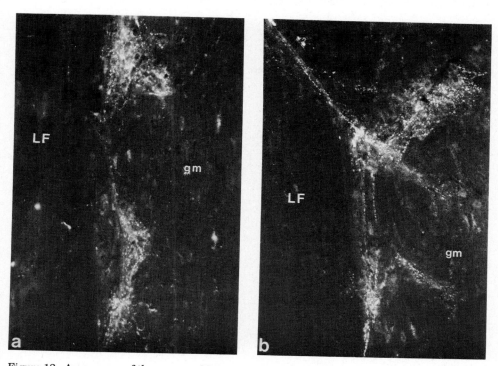

Figure 12. Appearance of the presumed DA innervation in the intermediolateral cell column in a rat pretreated with the combined 6-OHDA and 5,7-DHT injections. LF, lateral funiculus; gm, gray matter. (From Skagerberg et al., 1982, with permission.)

is the area surrounding the central canal. In view of the similarity of the distribution of DA fibers in the spinal cord with the distribution of the descending somatostatin system (Krisch, 1981) and neurophysin I system (Swanson, 1979), which also arises from the diencephalon, it is tempting to speculate that the DA system is organized in a similar way as that proposed for the former systems, namely with one descending component running along the central canal and giving rise to the terminals in the intermediate zone including the intermediolateral cell column, and with another bilateral system coursing down through the superficial parts of the dorsal horn and the adjacent part of the dorsolateral funiculus, giving rise to terminals in the dorsal horn.

In summary (Fig. 13), the spinal DA innervation originates primarily, and possibly exclusively, in the diencephalic A11 cell group. We propose that the axons descend partly along the superficial layers of the dorsal horn and within the adjacent part of the dorsolateral funiculus, to innervate relatively densely the intermediolateral column and associated parts of the intermediate zone; and more sparsely the dorsal horn.

THE DIENCEPHALO–SPINAL DA SYSTEM

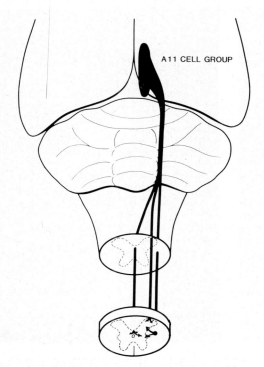

Figure 13. Proposed arrangement of the diencephalo-spinal DA system, as revealed after combined neurotoxin treatment in the rat. (From Skagerberg et al., 1982, with permission.)

Parent, A. (1979) Monoaminergic systems of the brain. In C. Gous et al. (Eds.), *Biology of the Reptilia*, Academic Press, London, p. 247.

Parent, A. (1981) Comparative anatomy of the serotoninergic systems, *J. Physiol. (Paris)*, 77: 147-156.

Persson, M. and Wiklund, L. (1981) Scattered catecholaminergic cells in the dorsolateral tegmentum caudal to locus coeruleus in cat, *Neurosci. Lett.*, 23: 275-280.

Reid, J.L., Zivin, J.A., Foppen, F.H. and Kopin, I.J. (1975) Catecholamine neurotransmitters and synthetic enzymes in the spinal cord of the rat, *Life Sci.*, 16: 975-984.

Room, P., Postema, F. and Korf, J. (1981) Divergent axon collaterals of rat locus coeruleus neurons: Demonstration by a fluorescent double labeling technique, *Brain Res.*, 221: 219-230.

Ross, R.A. and Reis, D.J. (1974) Effects of lesions of locus coeruleus on regional distribution of dopamine-beta-hydroxylase activity in rat brain, *Brain Res.*, 73: 161-166.

Ross, R.A., Joh, T.H. and Reis, D.J. (1975) Reversible changes in the accumulation and activities of tyrosine hydroxylase and dopamine-beta-hydroxylase in neurons of nucleus locus coeruleus during the retrograde reaction, *Brain Res.*, 92: 57-72.

Saavedra, J.M. and Axelrod, J. (1974) Brain Tryptamine and the effects of drugs. In E.Costa et al. (Eds.), *Advances in Biochemistry and Psychopharmacology, Vol. 10, Serotonin: New Vistas*, Raven Press, New York, pp. 135-139.

Satoh, K. (1979) The origin of reticulospinal fibers in the rat: A HRP study, *J. Hirnforsch.*, 20: 313-332.

Satoh, K., Tohyama, M., Yamamoto, K., Sakumoto, T. and Shimizu, N. (1977) Noradrenaline innervation of the spinal cord studied by the horseradish peroxidase method combined with monoamine oxidase staining, *Exp. Brain Res.*, 30: 175-186.

Seiger, A. and Olson, L. (1973) Late prenatal ontogeny of central monoamine neurons in the rat: Fluorescence histochemical observations, *Z. Anat. Entwickl.-Gesch.*, 140: 281-318.

Skagerberg, G. and Björklund, A. (1982) Organization of serotoninergic and non-serotoninergic projections from serotonin-containing cell-groups in the caudal brainstem of the rat, to be published.

Skagerberg, G., Björklund, A., Lindvall, O. and Schmidt, R.H. (1982) Origin and termination of the diencephalo-spinal dopamine system in the rat, *Brain Res. Bull.*, in press.

Slaon, J.W., Martin, W.R., Clements, T.H., Buchwald, W.F. and Bridges, S.R. (1975) Factors influencing brain and tissue levels of tryptamine: Species, drugs and lesions, *J. Neurochem.*, 24: 523-532.

Smolen, A.J., Glazer, E.J. and Ross, L.L. (1979) Horseradish peroxidase histochemistry combined with glyoxylic acid-induced fluorescence used to identify brain stem catecholaminergic neurons which project to the chick thoracic spinal cord, *Brain Res.*, 160: 353-357.

Snodgrass, S.R. and Horn, A.S. (1973) An assay procedure for tryptamine in brain and spinal cord using its (^{3}H)dansyl derivative, *J. Neurochem.*, 21: 687-696.

Steinbusch, H.W.M. (1981) Distribution of serotonin-immunoreactivity in the central nervous system of the rat – cell bodies and terminals, *Neuroscience*, 6: 557-618.

Swanson, L.W. (1976) The locus coeruleus: A cytoarchitectonic, golgi and immunohistochemical study in the albino rat, *Brain Res.*, 110: 39-56.

Swanson, L.W. and Hartman, B.K. (1975) The central adrenergic system. An immunofluorescence study of the location of cell bodies and their efferent connections in the rat utilizing dopamine-beta-hydroxylase as a marker, *J. comp. Neurol.*, 163: 467-506.

Swanson, L.W. and McKellar, S. (1979) The distribution of oxytocin- and neurophysin-stained fibers in the spinal cord of the rat and monkey, *J. comp. Neurol.*, 188: 87-106.

Versteeg, D.H.G., van der Gugten, J., De Jong, W. and Palkovits, M. (1976) Regional concentrations of noradrenaline and dopamine in rat brain, *Brain Res.*, 113: 563-574.

Vogt, M. (1954) The concentration of sympathin in different parts of the central nervous system under normal conditions and after the administration of drugs, *J. Physiol (Lond.)*, 123: 451-481.

Watkins, L.R., Griffin, G., Leichnetz, G.R. and Mayer, D.J. (1980) The somatotopic organization of the nucleus raphe magnus and surrounding brain stem structures as revealed by HRP slow-release gels, *Brain Res.*, 181: 1-15.

Watkins, L.R., Griffin, G., Leichnetz, G.R. and Mayer, D.J. (1981) Identification and somatotopic organization of nuclei projecting via the dorsolateral fasciculus in rat: A retrograde tracing study using HRP slow-release gels, *Brain Res.*, 223: 237-255.

Wiklund, L., Léger, L. and Persson, M. (1981) Monoamine cell distribution in the cat brain stem. A fluorescence histochemical study with quantification of indolaminergic and locus coeruleus cell groups, *J. comp. Neurol.*, 203: 613-647.

Zemlan, F.P., Kow, L.-M., Morell, J.I. and Pfaff, D.W. (1979) Descending tracts of the lateral columns of the rat spinal cord: A study using the horseradish peroxidase and silver impregnation techniques, *J. Anat. (Lond.)*, 128: 489-512.

Zivin, J.A., Reid, J.L., Saavedra, J.M. and Kopin. I.J. (1975) Quantitative localization of biogenic amines in the spinal cord, *Brain Res.*, 99: 293-301.

Brain Stem Control of Spinal Mechanisms
– B. Sjölund and A. Björklund, editors
© 1982 Elsevier Biomedical Press

4

Peptide Neurons in the Spinal Cord with Special Reference to Descending Systems

TOMAS HÖKFELT, LANA SKIRBOLL, CARL-JOHAN DALSGAARD, OLLE JOHANSSON, JAN M. LUNDBERG, GUN NORELL and GABOR JANCSO

Departments of Histology, Anatomy and Pharmacology, Karolinska Institutet, Stockholm, Sweden; Neuroendocrine Unit, Laboratory of Clinical Sciences, Fogarty International Center and Section of Biochemistry and Pharmacology, Biological Psychiatry Branch, National Institutes of Mental Health, Bethesda, MD, U.S.A. and Department of Anatomy, University of Szeged, Szeged, Hungary

I. Introduction

Interest in peptide-containing neurons in the spinal cord has been growing steadily during the past years. The first peptide focused on in the spinal cord was substance P, originally discovered by von Euler and Gaddum (1931). Subsequent biochemical studies revealed a marked regional distribution of this compound in the central nervous system and in peripheral tissues (Pernow, 1953). Its high content in spinal dorsal roots prompted Lembeck (1953) to suggest that substance P may act as a transmitter in primary sensory neurons. After the structural characterization of this peptide by Leeman and collaborators (Chang et al., 1971), the transmitter role of substance P was strengthened by the elegant biochemical and electrophysiological studies by Otsuka and collaborators (Konishi and Otsuka, 1974; Takahashi, et al., 1974; Takahashi and Otsuka, 1975), demonstrating a marked excitatory action of substance P on spinal motorneurons. Immunohistochemical studies directly demonstrated substance P-like immunoreactivity in some primary sensory neurons (Hökfelt et al., 1975d, e; 1976).

Subsequently, many other peptide systems have been described in the spinal cord, for example, somatostatin-containing primary sensory neurons (Hökfelt et al., 1976) and enkephalin-containing spinal neurons in the dorsal horn (Elde et al., 1976; Hökfelt et al., 1977a, c). The subsequent biochemical and histochemical analyses have revealed that the organization of peptide neurons at the spinal cord level is complex. Thus, peptides of different kinds are present not only in primary afferent fibers originating in dorsal root ganglia, but also in neurons in the spinal cord, as well as in supraspinal descending systems.

There are also peptide-containing preganglionic efferent neurons with cell bodies in the sympathetic lateral and parasympathetic intermediolateral columns. In some cases the peptide occurs with a classical transmitter in the same neurons and in other cases, more than one peptide can be seen in a neuron. In some cases, the same immunoreactive peptide may be present in one or a combination of the systems described above. This complexity makes it very difficult to understand and elucidate the functional significance of peptides at the spinal cord level. We would like to give a brief account of the current status of the peptide neurons present in the spinal cord and we will focus our attention primarily on results obtained with immunohistochemical techniques.

II. Aspects of Methodology

Immunohistochemistry was introduced about 40 years ago by Coons and collaborators (see Coons, 1958). The original technique included labeling of the specific antiserum with the fluorophore fluoresceinisothiocyanate (FITC). Subsequently an indirect method was developed. The specific antiserum was followed by a second antibody labeled with the fluorophore (see Coons, 1958). The indirect technique offers considerable advantages, because it is more sensitive and since the same labeled second antibody can be used for any number of primary antisera raised in the same species, i.e. each primary antiserum does not have to be individually labeled. More recent modifications employ horseradish peroxidase (HRP) as a marker, which can be used for studies both at the light and electron microscopic levels (Nakane and Pierce, 1967; Avrameas, 1969), as well as the peroxidase–antiperoxidase (PAP) technique of Sternberger and collaborators (1970; see Sternberger, 1979), which combines the advantages of the peroxidase technique with a very high sensitivity.

II.1. Immunohistochemistry

The main advantage of immunohistochemical techniques is their general applicability. Thus, successful immunohistochemical results have not only been obtained for tracing larger proteins such as enzymes, but also for smaller molecules such as peptides and even low molecular weight compounds such as 5-hydroxytryptamine (5-HT) and noradrenaline (Steinbusch et al., 1978; Steinbusch, 1981; Verhofstad et al., 1980). In principle, any compound with antigenic properties can be traced in tissue sections under the conditions that it will remain at its endogenous storage site during the histochemical procedure and that sufficient amounts of its antigenicity are retained. Whereas the former condition in most instances requires fixation of the tissue, such fixation causes damage, to a greater or lesser degree, to the antigens. Therefore, the processing and preparation of tissue for immunohistochemistry has to be balanced to obtain a good retention of the peptide as well as an acceptable morphology and a sufficient amount of remaining antigenicity. Therefore, it is often favorable to use a very sensitive immunohistochemical technique, such as the PAP method, since this allows a stronger fixation which results in a better morphology.

Several procedures have been developed which are useful for immunohistochemical studies on enzymes and peptides. The one used routinely in our laboratories includes perfusion with ice-cold formalin, made according to Pease (1962) from paraformaldehyde powder, rinsing in buffer with 5% sucrose and sectioning on a cryostat. Incubations are mostly carried out at 4°C overnight, followed by rinsing and incubation with a labeled second antibody for 30 min at 37°C. As markers for the second antibody, either FITC or rhodamine is used.

II.2. Analysis of multiple antigens in one cell

Of special interest are techniques to evaluate whether one and the same cell contains more than one antigen, e.g. a transmitter-synthesizing enzyme and a peptide. This can be achieved principally in two ways (Fig. 1). Firstly, thin adjacent sections may be incubated with two different antisera. Under fortunate circumstances one cell will be split into two halves, which can be identified as belonging to the same cell in the adjacent sections. These adjacent sections are then stained with different antisera and the presence of one or two of the investigated compounds in this cell can then be established. Secondly, an elution-restaining technique can be used (Nakane, 1968; Tramu et al., 1978). After photography of the staining patterns obtained with the first antibody, this antiserum is eluted with acid solutions, e.g. a mixture of sulfuric acid and potassium permaganate (Tramu et al., 1978), and subsequently restained with a new antibody. The second pattern is then compared with the first one and identity can be established.

Both approaches have advantages and disadvantages. With the "adjacent section method", it is essential to use very thin sections to establish beyond doubt the identity of cell profiles. With the second technique, the elution procedure often causes damage to the antigens in the section. Thus, it may often be difficult to obtain a reliable restaining with the second antibody. In fact, we have found it impossible to restain with certain antisera, for example, to 5-HT and glutamic acid decarboxylase (GAD). Such antigens are, in all probability, irreversibly destroyed even under very mild elution conditions. The use of this approach is also complicated by the fact that different antisera seem to bind to the antigens on the sections with a varying "strength". Thus, to elute certain antisera, "strong" elution conditions will have to be used, whereas others require only very mild treatment. Therefore, test series have to be carried out for each experiment and no standard protocol can be given (see Tramu et al., 1978; Schultzberg et al., 1980; Johansson et al., 1981).

92

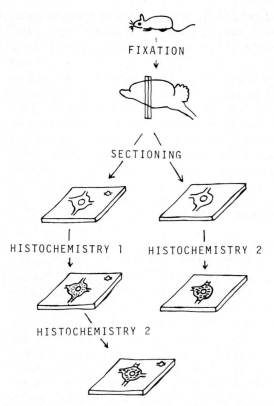

FIXATION

SECTIONING

HISTOCHEMISTRY 1   HISTOCHEMISTRY 2

HISTOCHEMISTRY 2

Figure 1. Schematic illustration of histochemical approaches for identifying two compounds in one cell. Firstly, thin adjacent sections are incubated with two different antibodies (or processed for two different histochemical techniques). Cells will be split into two halves, which under favorable conditions can be identified as belonging to the same cell. According to the second alternative, one and the same section will be processed first for visualization of one compound, and subsequently for a second one. If immunohistochemistry is the technique used, the processing may be carried out as follows: after photography of the staining pattern for the first compound, the section will be treated with acid permanganate which elutes the antibodies, and then reincubated with antiserum to the second compound. For further details, see text.

II.3. Combined retrograde tracing and immunohistochemistry

A major problem in neuroanatomical studies is to outline the projections of a neuronal system. This is due to the fact that, with most neuroanatomical and neurohistochemical techniques, the very thin axons are difficult to visualize in the microscope. Attempts to solve these problems rely on experiments in which selective staining of degenerating axons and nerve endings (see Heimer, 1970) or disappearance of transmitter specific terminal networks (see, e.g., Andén et al., 1966) is recorded after lesions in certain areas. More recently, ingenious techniques have been developed which allow outlining of neuronal pathways. These techniques are based on dynamic properties of neurons, which have the ability to take up, incorporate and transport exogenously administered compounds. Two principal approaches are used. One is based on uptake of tritiated amino acids into cell somata and subsequent incorporation into proteins and *anterograde* transport through the axon to the nerve endings. The labeled proteins can then be visualized by autoradiography (Lasek et al., 1968; see also Cowan and Cuenod, 1975). The second approach utilizes the *retrograde* transport in neurons. A marker, e.g. HRP or a fluorescent compound, is injected and taken up into nerve endings and subsequently retrogradely transported to the cell somata, where the compounds can be visualized by histochemical means at the light, fluorescence and/or electron microscopic levels (Kristensson, 1970; Kristensson and Olsson, 1971; LaVail and LaVail, 1972; Kuypers et al., 1977; see also Cowan and Cuenod, 1975). Neither of these two techniques allows concomitant identification of, for example, the transmitter used by the system outlined, since uptake processes of both types are considered unspecific and essentially occur in all types of neurons. To overcome this problem, attempts have been made to combine transmitter histochemical techniques with such tracing techniques. Initial attempts were based on combination of the HRP and indirect (immunofluorescence) techniques (Ljungdahl et al., 1975; Satoh et al., 1977; Berger et al., 1978; Blessing et al., 1978; Smolen et al., 1977, 1979). A major advance was made when a systematic investigation of various fluorescent dyes with regard to their ability to be transported retrogradely was undertaken by Kuypers and collaborators (Kuypers et al., 1977, 1979, 1980; Bentivoglio et al., 1979, 1980a, b). This allowed a convenient combination of the retrograde technique with immunofluorescence or formaldehyde-induced fluorescence for visualization of transmitters and/or transmitter-related compounds (Björklund and Skagerberg, 1979; Hökfelt et al., 1979a, b; Van der Kooy and Wise, 1980; Steinbusch et al., 1980; Sawchenko and Swanson, 1981; Skirboll and Hökfelt, 1982). This approach has successfully been used to label cell bodies after their retrograde transport of fluorescent dyes of various types and subsequently performing immunohistochemistry for visualization of transmitter-related enzymes and peptides. It has even been possible to identify more than one such compound in a retrogradely labeled cell. There are now also further techniques available, e.g. retrograde tracing of HRP combined with PAP immunohistochemistry (Bowker et al., 1981). Thus, several approaches and combinations can be used, but in the following we will give a brief protocol for the procedure used in our laboratories, as worked out in collaboration with Kuypers and his associates and as outlined by Skirboll and Hökfelt (1982) and Skirboll et al. (1982).

Three dyes have mainly been used: True Blue [*trans*-1,2-bis(5-amidino-2-benzofuranyl)ethylene-2HCl], Fast Blue (a diamidino compound related to True Blue) and propidium iodide, which exhibit blue and red fluorescence, respectively. The dyes are dissolved in saline or distilled water and injected by hand with a Hamilton syringe or by a glass micropipette. After two to four days the animals are treated with colchicine intraventicularly to improve the immunohistochemical visualization of peptides and other compounds within the cell bodies. Twenty-four hours later the rats are perfused with ice-cold formalin and, after rinsing, the brains are cut in a cryostat. The sections are then examined without prior mounting in the microscope, since True and Fast Blue but not propidium iodide tend to diffuse out of the sections in phosphate-buffered saline (PBS):glyerol mounting media. Mounting can, however, be done if xylene is used as medium. After photography of the labeled cells, the sections are processed for immunohistochemistry using various antisera. To be able to distinguish between retrogradely transported fluorescent dye and immunofluorescent marker, the choice of the second antibody is an important issue. Furthermore, this differentiation can only be achieved by selecting appropriate filter combinations for the microscope. The fluorescent dyes will remain in the sections during the immunohistochemical procedure to different degrees. For example, propidium iodide does not diffuse during incubation procedures and will not fade during exposure to ultraviolet light and will, therefore, be present in the section during the immunohistochemical examination. True and Fast Blue, on the other hand, disappear to some extent during the incubation procedure and are, in addition, sensitive to ultraviolet light. Fast Blue is somewhat more stable, but may disappear if initial labeling is weak.

Different systems retain the dye to a different degree and each system will therefore have to be analyzed individually with regard to retention of dye. Briefly, the following combinations are used. In experiments with True and Fast Blue, rhodamine-labeled second antibodies are used, since with appropriate combinations these dyes can be separated from the immunofluorescence. When propidium iodide is used as retrograde tracer, FITC-labeled second antibodies are used. (For more detailed information on excitation and emission spectra of retrogradely transported dyes, see Björklund and Skagerberg, 1979; and for details on the entire procedure see Skirboll and Hökfelt, 1982; Skirboll et al., 1982b.)

As mentioned briefly, experimental animals are often treated with colchicine or vinblastine, two miotic inhibitors, which interrupt intracellular and intraaxonal transport, but not protein synthesis, and thus cause accumulation of compounds in cell somata (Dahlström, 1971). The drugs are mostly administered intraventricularly, either into the lateral ventricle or into the fourth ventricle, but can also be given with the intrathecal technique of Yaksh et al. (1979). The latter is a convenient technique for analysis of the spinal system, since it causes less tissue damage than intraspinal injections.

Finally, it has to be emphasized that immunohistochemical techniques do not provide absolute specificity and often lack sufficient sensitivity. Proteins or peptides with similar amino acid sequences may cross-react with the antisera. It is a common experience that different antisera raised to the same peptide exhibit varying degrees of "potency", i.e. some give a "strong" staining,

scribed in lamina X in the area around the central canal at the level of the lumbar spinal cord of rat (to be published).

A further category of peptide-immunoreactive cell bodies have been observed in the spinal cord localized in the sympathetic lateral and in the parasympathetic intermediolateral columns. Their localization suggests that they may represent preganglionic neurons projecting to the periphery. This hypothesis has, however, to be verified by experimental data. In the case of enkephalin-immunoreactive neurons at the thoracic and lumbar levels, such experiments have, in fact, been carried out. Thus, combined retrograde tracing and immunohistochemistry have demonstrated that, in the guinea pig, enkephalin-immunoreactive neurons at the lumbar level project to prevertebral ganglia (the inferior mesenteric ganglion) (Dalsgaard et al., 1982). Experimental evidence is also present for preganglionic enkephalin immunoreactive neurons in the cat sacral cord (Glazer and Basbaum, 1980; Lundberg et al., 1980b). Indirect evidence further suggests that a population of preganglionic neurons in the cat may contain neurotensin-like immunoreactivity and that these fibers project, for example, to sympathetic ganglia in the sympathetic chain (Lundberg et al., 1981b). In the rat numerous somatostatin-immunoreactive neurons have been seen in the parasympathetic intermediolateral nucleus at the lumbar level (Dalsgaard et al., 1981). Finally, single substance P-positive neurons have been observed in the sympathetic lateral column of the rat (Ljungdahl et al., 1978).

In conclusion, numerous types of peptide-containing cell bodies can be found in the dorsal horn of rat and other species. In fact, so far, all peptides present in primary sensory neurons have, with immunohistochemical techniques, been demonstrated also in local neurons in the dorsal horn. An exception to this is VIP, which so far has only been demonstrated in fibers of the dorsal horn, in all probability belonging to primary sensory neurons. However, it may be noted that a few VIP-immunoreactive neurons have been seen in the ventromedial part of the spinal trigeminal nucleus (Hökfelt et al., 1981b).

III.3. Supraspinal descending neurons

Numerous systems originating in supraspinal areas project to the spinal cord (see papers by Walberg, Kuypers and Huisman, and Lundberg, this volume), and the present discussion will limit itself to peptide-containing projections. With regard to the transmitter substance of such systems, it is well known that some of these neurons contain a monoamine, e.g. 5-HT or noradrenaline (Dahlström and Fuxe, 1965). These systems will be discussed in this volume by Björklund and Skagerberg. Peptides are also present in descending systems and there is evidence that, at least in some cases, these peptides are present in neurons which also contain a classical transmitter such as 5-HT.

The first evidence for the existence of descending peptide-containing systems was obtained for substance P. Thus, after transection of the spinal cord a disappearance of almost all substance P-immunoreactive nerve endings in the ventral horn of the spinal cord was observed below the lesion (Hökfelt et al., 1977b), although at that time the exact origin of these fibers was unknown. Somewhat later it was observed that, in colchicine-treated rats, large numbers of substance P-immunoreactive cell bodies could be seen in the medullary raphe nuclei and in adjacent areas of the lower medulla oblongata (Ljungdahl et al., 1978). It was well known on the basis of neuroanatomical techniques (Taber et al., 1963) that the nucleus raphe magnus projects to the spinal cord, and it seemed likely that the substance P-immunoreactive cell bodies in these nuclei represented the origin of the spinal ventral horn substance P fibers disappearing after spinal transection. This hypothesis has recently been confirmed using the combined retrograde tracing–immunohistochemical technique (Skirboll et al., 1982b; Skirboll and Hökfelt, 1982), and this technique has also been used to analyze descending peptide systems in more detail. With this technique an enkephalin-reactive system which gives rise to descending axons was observed with cell bodies located dorso-lateral to the pyramidal tracts (approximately corresponding to the pars alpha of the paragigantocellular nucleus). The exact area of the terminations of these axons in the cord is, however, not known (Hökfelt et al., 1979b). However, in contrast to the substance P fibers in the ventral horn, enkephalin-immunoreactive fibers seemed unaffected by spinal transection. The descending enkephalin-immunoreative neurons may therefore give rise only to a small part of the nerve endings in the ventral horn and may perhaps also innervate mainly the dorsal horn, intermingling with the dense enkephalin innervation originating in this part of the cord. Here, a loss of a small proportion of enkephalin-immunoreactive fibers with a supraspinal origin would hardly be discovered with immunohistochemical techniques. The cell bodies of the above described descending enkephalin system are located at the level of the rostral part of the inferior olive, and represent only a small population of the enkephalin cells in the medulla oblongata, with about 5–10 cell profiles on each side in a 10 μm thick section. More recently we have observed also that other medullary enkephalin-immunoreactive cells have descending projections. Thus, after injection of Fast Blue into the spinal cord, enkephalin-immoreactive cells in the rostral nucleus raphe magnus are labeled (Skirboll et al., to be published).

A system containing thyrotropin releasing hormone (TRH), neuroanatomically related closely to the substance P system in the ventral medulla oblongata, has recently been observed (Hökfelt et al., 1980b; Johansson et al., 1981). The cell bodies are located in the medullary raphe nuclei and adjacent areas, and the projections terminate in the ventral horn of the spinal cord. Since TRH-immunoreactive fibers in the spinal cord are only found in the ventral horn (Hökfelt et al., 1975a, b), the exact projections of these cells seem fairly well established. As will be discussed below, it is likely that at least some of these TRH neurons are identical to 5-HT- and substance P-containing neurons.

Evidence has also been obtained for somatostatin immunoreactive descending systems (Skirboll et al., to be published). The cell bodies of these neurons are located in the nucleus intercommissuralis, but elution and restaining experiments have revealed that they are not identical to the catecholamine cells observed in this nucleus (the A2 cell group according to Dahlström and Fuxe, 1964). So far the projections have only been demonstrated to the cervical cord.

A population of the hypothalamic ACTH–β-endorphin system localized in the arcuate nucleus (Bloch et al., 1978; Bloom et al., 1978; Watson et al., 1978; Nilaver et al., 1979) has also been demonstrated to project to the spinal cord (Skirboll et al., to be published). So far, the combined retrograde tracing–immunohistochemical experiments have only demonstrated spinally projecting cells mainly slightly lateral to be rostral part of the arcuate nucleus.

A group of neurons in the midline of the rostral periaqueductal central gray projects to the spinal cord (Skirboll et al., 1982b). This group contains both CCK (Fig. 3A and B) and substance P (Fig. 3C and D) immunoreactive cells, and there is evidence that at least a proportion of these cells contains both peptides (Fig. 4A and B) (Skirboll et al., 1982b).

Finally, APP-immunoreactive nerve endings have been observed in the sympathetic lateral column and these fibers disappear below a spinal transection, suggesting a supraspinal origin (Hökfelt et al., 1981a). This AAP-like immunoreactivity is probably present in adrenaline neurons (Lundberg et al., 1980a; Hunt et al., 1981a, see below) and originates in the A1/C1 adrenaline cell group (Hökfelt et al., 1974) and project to the spinal cord (Skirboll et al., to be published).

In conclusion, several peptide-containing neurons located in supraspinal structures have been shown to project to the spinal cord using the combined retrograde tracing–immunohistochemical technique. Since no attempts have been made to inject the retrograde transported dye into a specific part of the spinal cord, the exact termination areas for these systems are mostly not exactly defined. The systems include hypothalamic ACTH–β-endorphin neurons, mesencephalic substance P and CCK neurons and medullary substance P, TRH, enkephalin, APP and somatostatin neurons. In two cases the descending systems may contain two peptides, substance P and CCK in the mesencephalon and TRH and substance P in the lower medulla oblongata.

IV. Coexistence of Classical Transmitters and Peptides and of Peptides

IV.1. Occurrence and distribution

It has become evident that some neurons may contain a classical transmitter and a peptide. This appears to be a widespread phenomenon, and examples can

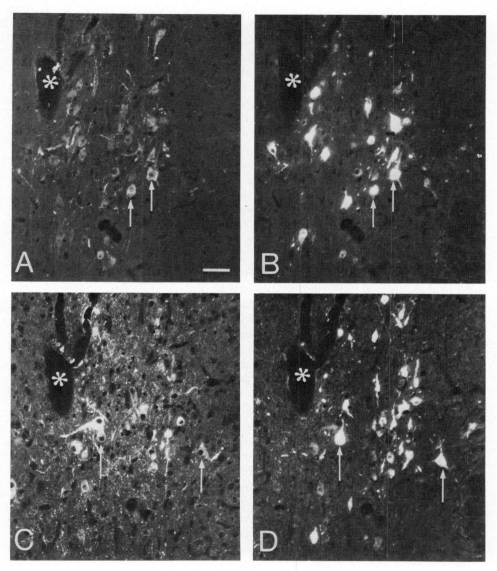

Figure 3. Immunofluorescence (A and C) and fluorescence (B and D) micrographs of the mesencephalic central gray of colchicine-treated rat after incubation with antiserum to cholecystokinin
(CCK) (A) and substance P (C). Four days before sacrifice, the fluorescent dye Fast Blue was injected into the spinal cord. The colchicine was given 24 h before sacrifice. A and B, show the same
section, as do C and D. These two sections are semi-adjacent, as indicated by the similarity of the
form of the blood vessels (asterisks indicate the same blood vessel). The fluorescent cells in B and D
contain Fast Blue which has been retrogradely transported from the spinal cord, indicating that
these cells project to the spinal cord. Many of these cells are immunoreactive to CCK (compare arrows in A and B) and substance P (compare arrows in C and D), indicating that these projections
contain CCK- and substance P-like peptides. Although the two sections (A and B and C and D) are
very close to each other, it is difficult to point to cell-profiles which belong, with certainty, to the
same cell, i.e. to demonstrate that the same cells contain both CCK- and substance P-like immunoreactivity. This is probably due to the fact that the sections are slightly too thick. The coexistence of the two peptides is, however, demonstrated in Fig. 4. Bar = 50 μm.

The origin, distribution and synaptic relationships of substance P axons in rat spinal cord, *J. comp. Neurol.*, 184: 331-352.

Baumgarten, H.G., Björklund, A., Lachenmayer, L., Nobin, A. and Stenevi, U. (1971) Long-lasting selective depletion of brain serotonin by 5,6-dihydroxytryptamine, *Acta physiol. scand.*, Suppl. 373: 1-15.

Baumgarten, H.G., Björklund, A., Lachenmayer, L. and Nobin, A. (1973) Evaluation of the effect of 5,7-dihydroxytryptamine on serotonin and catecholamine neurons in the rat CNS, *Acta physiol. scand.*, Suppl. 391: 1-19.

Bentivoglio, M., Kuypers, H.G.J.M., Catsman-Berrevoets, C. and Dann, O. (1979) Fluorescent retrograde neuronal labeling in rat by means of substances binding specifically to adenine-thymine rich DNA, *Neurosci. Lett.*, 12: 235-240.

Bentivoglio, M., Kuypers, H.G.J.M. and Catsman-Berrevoets, C. (1980a) Retrograde neuronal labeling by means of bisbenzimide and nuclear yellow (Hoechst S 769121). Measures to prevent diffusion of the tracers out of retrogradely labelled cells, *Neurosci. Lett.*, 18: 19-24.

Bentivoglio, M., Kuypers, H.G.J.M., Catsman-Berrevoets, C. and Dann, O. (1980b) Two new fluorescent retrograde neuronal tracers which are transported over long distances, *Neurosci. Lett.*, 18: 25-30.

Berger, B., Nguyen-Legros, J. and Thierry, A. (1978) Demonstration of horseradish peroxidase and fluorescent catecholamines in the same neuron, *Neurosci. Lett.*, 9: 297-302.

Björklund, A. and Skagerberg, G. (1979) Simultaneous use of retrograde fluorescence tracers and fluorescence histochemistry for convenient and precise mapping of monoaminergic projections and collateral arrangements in the CNS, *J. Neurosci. Meth.*, 1: 261-277.

Björklund, A., Emson, P.C., Gilbert, R.F.T. and Skagerberg, G. (1979) Further evidence for the possible coexistence of 5-hydroxytryptamine and substance P in medullary raphe neurones of rat brain, *Brit. J. Pharmacol.*, 66: 112-113.

Blessing, W.W., Furness, J.B., Costa, M. and Chalmers, J.P. (1978) Localization of catecholamine fluorescence and retrogradely transported horseradish peroxidase within the same nerve cell, *Neurosci. Lett.*, 9: 311-315.

Bloch, B., Bugnon, C., Fellman, D. and Lenys, D. (1978) Immunocytochemical evidence that the same neurons in the human infundibular nucleus are stained with anti-endorphins and anti-sera of other related peptides, *Neurosci. Lett.*, 10: 147-152.

Bloom, F.E., Rossier, J., Battenberg, E.G., Bayon, A., French, E., Hendricksen, S., Siggins, G., Segal, D., Browne, R., Ling, N., and Guillemin, R. (1978) Beta endorphin: cellular localization, electrophysiological and behavioral effects. In E. Costa and M. Trabucci (Eds.), *Advanc. Biochem. Psychopharmacol.*, Raven Press, New York, pp. 89-109.

Bowker, R.M., Westlund, K.N. and Coulter, J.D. (1981) Serotoninergic projections to the spinal cord from the midbrain in the rat: an immunocytochemical and retrograde transport study, *Neurosci. Lett.*, 24: 221-226.

Burnweit, C. and Forssmann, W.G. (1979) Somatostatinergic nerves in the cervical spinal cord of the monkey, *Cell Tiss. Res.*, 200: 83-90.

Chang, M.M., Leeman, S.E. and Niall, H.D. (1971) Amino acid sequence of substance P, *Nature New Biol.*, 232: 86-87.

Chan-Palay, V. (1979) Combined immunocytochemistry and autoradiography after in vivo injections of monoclonal antibody to substance P and ^{3}H-serotonin: coexistence of two putative transmitters in single raphe cells and fiber plexuses, *Anat. Embryol.*, 156: 241-254.

Chan-Palay, V., Jonsson, G. and Palay, S.L. (1978) Serotonin and substance P coexist in neurons of the rat's central nervous system, *Proc. nat. Acad. Sci. U.S.A.*, 75: 1582-1586.

Coons, A.H. (1958) Fluorescent antibody methods. In J.F. Danielli (Ed.), *General Cytochemical Methods*, Academic Press, New York, pp. 399-422.

Cowan, W.W. and Cuenod, M. (Eds.) (1975) *The use of Axonal Transport for Studies of Neuronal Connectivity*, Elsevier, Amsterdam.

Cuello, A.C., Del Fiacco, M. and Paxinos, G. (1978) The central and peripheral ends of the substance P-containing sensory neurons in the rat trigeminal system, *Brain Res.*, 152: 499-509.

Dahlström, A. (1971) Effects of vinblastine and colchicine on monoamine containing neurons of the rat with special regard to the axoplasmic transport of amine granules, *Acta neuropath.*, Suppl. 5: 226-237.

Dahlström, A. and Fuxe, K. (1964) Evidence for the existence of monoamine-containing neurons in the central nervous system. I. Demonstration of monoamines in the cell bodies of brain stem neurons, *Acta physiol. scand.*, 62, Suppl. 232: 1-55.

Dahlström, A. and Fuxe, K. (1965) Evidence for the existence of monoamine-containing neurons in the central nervous system. II. Experimentally induced changed in the intra-neuronal amine levels, *Acta physiol. scand.*, 64, Suppl. 274: 1-36.

Dalsgaard, C.-J., Hökfelt, T., Johansson, O. and Elde, R. (1981) Somatostatin immunoreactive cell bodies in the dorsal horn and the parasympathetic intermediolateral nucleus of the rat spinal cord, *Neurosci. Lett.*, 27: 335-339.

Dalsgaard, C.-J., Hökfelt, T., Elfvin, L.-G. and Terenius, L. (1982) Enkephalin-containing sympathetic preganglionic neurons projecting to the inferior mesenteric ganglion: evidence from combined retrograde tracing and immunohistochemistry, *Neuroscience*, in press.

Daly, J., Fuxe, K. and Jonsson, G. (1971) Effects of intracerebral injections of 5,6-dihydroxytryptamine on central monoamine neurons: evidence for selective degeneration of central 5-hydroxytryptamine neurons, *Brain Res.*, 49: 476-482.

Daly, J., Fuxe, K. and Jonsson, G. (1974) 5,7-Dihydroxytryptamine as a tool for the morphological and functional analysis of central 5-hydroxytryptamine neurons. *Res. Commun. Chem. Pathol. Pharmacol.*, 7: 175-187.

Del Fiacco, M. and Cuello, A.C. (1980) Substance P- and enkephalin-containing neurones in the rat trigeminal system, *Neuroscience*, 5: 803-815.

Elde, R., Hökfelt, T., Johansson, O. and Terenius, L. (1976) Immunohistochemical studies using antibodies to leucine-enkephalin; Initial observations on the nervous system of the rat, *Neuroscience*, 1: 349-351.

Forssmann, W.G. (1978) A new somatostatinergic system in the mammalian spinal cord, *Neurosci. Lett.*, 10: 293-297.

Forssmann, W.G., Burnett, C., Shehab, T. and Triepel, J. (1979) Somatostatin-immunoreactive nerve cell bodies and fibers in the medulla oblongata et spinacis, *J. Histochem. Cytochem.*, 27: 1391-1393.

Fuxe, K., Andersson, K., Locatelli, V., Agnati, L.F., Hökfelt, T., Skirboll, L. and Mutt, V. (1980) Cholecystokinin peptides produce marked reduction of dopamine turnover in discrete areas in the rat brain following intraventricular injection, *Europ J. Pharmacol.*, 67: 329-332.

Fuxe, K., Agnati, L.F., Köhler, C., Kuonen, D., Ögren, S.-O., Andersson, K. and Hökfelt, T. (1981) Characterization of normal and supersensitive dopamine receptors: Effects of ergot drugs and neuropeptides, *J. Neural Transm.*, 51: 3-37.

Gamse, R., Leeman, S.E., Holzer, P. and Lembeck, F. (1981) Differential effects of capsaicin on the content of somatostatin, substance P, and neurotensin in the nervous system of the rat, *Arch. Pharmacol*, 317: 140-148.

Gibson, S.J., Polak, J.A., Bloom, S.R. and Wall, P.D. (1981) The distribution of nine peptides in rat spinal cord with special emphasis on the substantia gelatinosa and on the area around the central canal (lamina X), *J. comp. Neurol.*, 281: 65-80.

Gilbert, R. (1981) *Descending 5-hydroxytryptamine, substance P and TRH neurons*, M.D. Thesis, Cambridge.

Glazer, E.J. and Basbaum, A.I. (1980) Leucine enkephalin: Localization in and axoplasmic transport by sacral parasympathetic preganglionic neurons, *Science*, 208: 1479-1481.

Glazer, E.J. and Basbaum, A.I. (1981) Immunohistochemical localization of leucine-enkephalin in the spinal cord of the cat: Enkephalin-containing marginal neurons and pain modulation, *J. comp. Neurol.*, 196: 377-389.

Heimer, L. (1970) Selective silver impregnation of degenerating axoplasm. In J.H. Nauta and S.O.E. Ebbesson (Eds.), *Contemporary Research Methods in Neuronanatomy*, Springer-Verlag, Berlin, pp. 106-131.

Hökfelt, T., Fuxe, K., Goldstein, M. and Johansson, O. (1974) Immunohistochemical evidence for the existence of adrenalin neurons in the rat brain, *Brain Res.*, 66: 235-251.

Hökfelt, T., Fuxe, K., Johansson, O., Jeffcoate, S. and White, N. (1975a) Distribution of thyrotropin-releasing hormone (TRH) in the central nervous system as revealed with immunohistochemistry, *Europ. J. Pharmacol.*, 34: 389-392.

Hökfelt, T., Fuxe, K., Johansson, O., Jeffcoate, S. and White, N. (1975b) Thyrotropin releasing hormone (TRH)-containing nerve terminals in certain brain stem nuclei and in the spinal cord, *Neurosci. Lett.*, 1: 133-139.

Hökfelt, T., Johansson, O., Luft, R. and Arimura, A. (1975c) Immunohistochemical evidence for the presence of somatostatin, a powerful inhibitory peptide in some primary sensory neurons, *Neurosci. Lett.*, 1: 231-235.

Hökfelt, T., Kellerth, J.-O., Nilsson, G. and Pernow, B. (1975d) Substance P: Localization in the central nervous system and in some primary sensory neurons, *Science*, 190: 889-890.

Hökfelt, T., Kellerth, J.-O., Nilsson, G. and Pernow, B. (1975e) Experimental immunohistochemical studies on the localization and distribution of substance P in cat primary sensory neurons, *Brain Res.*, 100: 235-252.

Hökfelt, T., Elde, R., Johansson, O., Luft, R., Nilsson, G. and Arimura, A. (1976) Immunohistochemical evidence for separate populations of somatostatin-containing and substance P-containing primary afferent neurons in the rat, *Neuroscience*, 1: 131-136.

Hökfelt, T., Elde, R., Johansson, O., Terenius, L. and Stein, L. (1977a) The distribution of enkephalin-immunoreactive cell bodies in the rat central nervous system, *Neurosci. Lett.*, 5: 25-31.

Hökfelt, T., Johansson, O., Kellerth, J.O., Ljungdahl, A., Nilsson, G., Nygårds, A. and Pernow, B. (1977b) Immunohistochemical distribution of Substance P. In U.S. Von Euler and B. Pernow (Eds.), *Substance P*, Raven Press, New-York, pp. 117-145.

Hökfelt, T., Ljungdahl, Å., Terenius, L., Elde, R.P. and Nilsson, G. (1977c) Immunohistochemical analysis of peptide pathways possibly related to pain and analgesia: Enkephalin and substance P, *Proc. nat. Acad. Sci. U.S.A.*, 74: 3081-3085.

Hökfelt, T., Ljungdahl, Å., Steinbusch, H., Verhofstad, A., Nilsson, G., Brodin, E., Pernow, B. and Goldstein, M. (1978) Immunohistochemical evidence of substance P-like immunoreactivity in some 5-hydroxytryptamine-containing neurons in the rat central nervous system, *Neuroscience*, 3: 517-538.

Hökfelt, T., Phillipson, O., Kuypers, H.G.J.M., Bentivoglio, M., Catsman-Berrevoets, C. and Dann, O. (1979a) Tracing of transmitter histochemically identified neuron projections: immunohistochemistry combined with fluorescent retrograde labeling, *Neurosci. Lett.*, Suppl. 3: S342.

Hökfelt, T., Terenius, L., Kuypers, H.G.J.M. and Dann, O. (1979b) Evidence for enkephalin immunoreactive neurons in the medulla oblongata projecting to the spinal cord, *Neurosci. Lett.*, 14: 55-60.

Hökfelt, T., Johansson, O., Ljungdahl, Å., Lundberg, J.M. and Schultzberg, M. (1980a) Peptidergic neurones, *Nature (Lond.)*, 284: 515-521.

Hökfelt, T., Lundberg, J.M., Schultzberg, M., Johansson, O., Ljungdahl, Å. and Rehfelt, J. (1980b) Coexistence of peptides and putative transmitters in neurons. In E. Costa and M. Trabucci (Eds.), *Neural Peptides and Neuronal Communication*, Raven Press, New York, pp. 1-23.

Hökfelt, T., Lundberg, J.M., Terenius, L., Jancsó, G. and Kimmel, J. (1981a) Avian pancreatic polypeptide (APP) immunoreactive neurons in the spinal cord and spinal trigeminal nucleus, *Peptides*, 2: 81-87.

Hökfelt, T., Schultzberg, M., Lundberg, J.M., Fuxe, K., Mutt, V., Fahrenkrug, I. and Said, S. (1981b). Distribution of vasoactive intestinal polypeptide in the central and peripheral nervous system as revealed by immunocytochemistry. In S. Said (Ed.), *Vasoactive Intestinal Peptide, Advances in Peptide Hormone Research Series*, Raven Press, New York, pp. 65-90.

Hunt, S.P., Emson, P.C., Gilbert, R., Goldstein, M. and Kimmel, J.R. (1981a) Presence of avian pancreatic polypeptide-like immunoreactivity in catecholamine and methionine-enkephalin-containing neurons within the central nervous system, *Neurosci. Lett.*, 21: 125-130.

114

Hunt, S.P., Kelly, J. and Emson, P.C. (1981b) The electron microscopic localization of methionine enkephalin within the superficial layers (I and II) of the spinal cord, *Neuroscience*, 5: 1871-1890.

Jancsó, G., Kiraly, E. and Jancsó-Gabor, A. (1977) Pharmacologically induced selective degeneration of chemosensitive primary sensory neurons, *Nature (Lond.)*, 270: 741-743.

Jancsó, G., Hökfelt, T., Lundberg, J.M., Kiraly, E., Halasz, N., Nilsson, G., Terenius, L., Rehfeld, J., Steinbusch, H., Verhofstad, A., Elde, R., Said, S. and Brown, M. (1981) Immunohistochemical studies on the effect of capsaicin on peptide and monoamine neurons using antisera to substance P, gastrin/CCK, somatostatin, VIP, enkephalin, neurotensin and 5-hydroxytryptamine, *J. Neurocytol.*, in press.

Jessell, T.M., Iversen, L.L. and Cuello, C. (1978) Capsaicin-induced depletion of substance P from primary sensory neurones, *Brain Res.*, 152: 183-188.

Johansson, O., Hökfelt, T., Pernow, B., Jeffcoate, S.L., White, N., Steinbusch, H.W.M., Verhofstad, A.A.J., Emson, P.C. and Spindel, E. (1981) Immunohistochemical support for three putative transmitters in one neuron: Coexistence of 5-hydroxytryptamine, substance P- and thyrotropin releasing hormone-like immunoreactivity in medullary neurons projecting to the spinal cord, *Neuroscience*, 6: 1857-1881.

Konishi, S. and Otsuka, M. (1974) Excitatory action of hypothalamic substance P on spinal motoneurones of newborn rats, *Nature (Lond.)*, 252: 734-735.

Kristensson, K. (1970) Transport of fluorescent protein tracer in peripheral nerves, *Acta neuropath.*, 16: 293-300.

Kristensson, K. and Olsson, Y. (1971) Retrograde axonal transport of protein, *Brain Res.*, 29: 363-365.

Kuypers, H.G.J.M., Catsman-Berrevoets, C. and Padt, R.E. (1977) Retrograde axonal transport of fluorescent substances in rats forebrain, *Neurosci. Lett.*, 6: 127-135.

Kuypers, H.G.J.M., Bentivoglio, M., Van der Kooy, D. and Catsman-Berrevoets, C.E. (1979) Retrograde transport of bisbenzimide and propidium iodide through axons to their parent cell bodies, *Neurosci. Lett.*, 12: 1-7.

Kuypers, H.G.J.M., Bentivoglio, M., Catsman-Berrevoets, C. and Baros, A.T. (1980) Double retrograde neuronal labeling through divergent collaterals, using two fluorescent tracers with the same excitation wavelength which label different features of the cell, *Exp. Brain Res.*, 40: 383-392.

Larsson, L.-I. and Rehfeld, J.F. (1979) Localization and molecular heterogeneity of cholecystokinin in the central and peripheral nervous system, *Brain Res.*, 165: 201-218.

Larsson, L.-I., Sundler, F. and Håkanson, R. (1975) Fluorescence histochemistry of polypeptide hormone-secreting cells in the gastrointestinal mucosa. In J.D. Thompson (Ed.). *Gastrointestinal Hormones*, University of Texas Press, Austin, pp. 169-195.

Lasek, R.J., Joseph, B.S. and Withlok, D.G. (1968) Evaluation of a radioautographic neuroanatomical tracing method, *Brain Res.*, 8: 319-336.

LaVail, J.H. and LaVail, M. (1972) Retrograde axonal transport in the central nervous system, *Science*, 176: 1416-1417.

Lembeck, F. (1953) Zur Frage der zentralen Übertragung afferenter Impulse. III. Mitteilung. Das Vorkommen und die Bedeutung der Substanz P in den dorsalen Wurzeln des Rückenmarks. *Naunyn-Schmiedeberg's Arch. Pharmcol.*, 219: 197-213.

Ljungdahl, Å., Hökfelt, T., Goldstein, M. and Park, D. (1975) Retrograde peroxidase tracing of neurons combined with transmitter histochemistry, *Brain Res.*, 84: 313-319.

Ljungdahl, Å., Hökfelt, T. and Nilsson, G. (1978) Distribution of substance P-like immunoreactivity in the central nervous system of the rat. I. Cell bodies and nerve terminals, *Neuroscience*, 3: 861-943.

Lundberg, J.M. (1981) Evidence for coexistence of vasoactive intestinal polypeptide (VIP) and acetylcholine in neurons of cat exocrine glands. Morphological, biochemical and functional aspects, *Acta physiol. scand.*, 112, Suppl. 496: 1-57.

Brain Stem Control of Spinal Mechanisms
– B. Sjölund and A. Björklund, editors
© 1982 Elsevier Biomedical Press

5

Anatomical Substrates for the Descending Control of Nociception

ALLAN I. BASBAUM

Departments of Anatomy and Physiology, School of Medicine, University of California, San Francisco, San Francisco, CA 94143, U.S.A.

I. Introduction

It is appropriate that this symposium be held in Sweden, for it is here that some of the most fundamental observations on brain stem control systems were made. Following on the early studies of Sherrington and Magoun, Lundberg and his colleagues (Engberg et al., 1968a–c) detailed many of the complex medullary and pontine inhibitory and excitatory controls that are exerted on spinal cord neurons. Since many studies of pain and pain modulation use reflex measures, e.g. the tail-flick reflex, to assess pain behavior, their analysis of descending control systems which modulate the central effects of flexor reflex afferents stimulation was of particular interest to our own studies of pain modulatory systems. It appears, in fact, that the descending control of second order nociceptive neurons involved in withdrawal reflexes and pain generation is very similar.

Lundberg and his colleagues provided evidence for at least two major descending inhibitory systems in the rostral medulla of the cat. One was presumed to originate in the midline serotonin-containing nucleus raphe magnus (NRM); the second derives from the adjacent reticular formation. Electrical stimulation of both regions inhibited the central effects of high threshold, flexor reflex afferent stimulation via a pathway in the spinal dorsolateral funiculus (DLF). Serotonin-containing raphe spinal fibers were presumed to mediate descending monoaminergic control. On the other hand, since anatomical studies at that time had only demonstrated indirect raphe-spinal connections via the DLF (Brodal et al., 1960), it was concluded that the anatomical substrate for the inhibition from the reticular formation was a polysynaptic system, albeit a relatively rapidly conducting one. Since the reticular effects were abolished by DLF lesions it was named the dorsal reticulospinal system.

119

Our subsequent anatomical studies of this region established that, in fact, both the raphe and the adjacent reticular formation project via the DLF to the spinal dorsal horn (Basbaum et al., 1976, 1978; Basbaum and Fields, 1979). Clearly retrograde chromatolytic studies were not sensitive enough to detect the direct reticulospinal fibers in the DLF. More importantly, we determined that the ventromedial medulla projects heavily to laminae I, II and V of the spinal dorsal horn. Since nociceptors are found in high concentrations in these regions (Christensen and Perl, 1970; Wall, 1967), it was hypothesized that inhibition of these neurons is an important element in the control of pain, both the perception of it and its accompanying reflexes. The demonstration that DLF lesions antagonize the analgesic action of periaqueductal grey (PAG) electrical brain stimulation and of systemic opiates provided additional evidence for the importance of descending pathways in the DLF to the control of pain (Barton et al., 1980; Basbaum et al., 1977). Subsequent electrophysiological studies established that nociceptors, including a population of spinothalamic tract neurons are, indeed, profoundly inhibited by raphe and reticular stimulation via a pathway in the DLF (Fields et al., 1977; Willis et al., 1977). In agreement with Lundberg's original studies, therefore, we concluded that there are at least two medullospinal inhibitory systems that control spinal nociceptors, via a pathway in the DLF. In keeping with the nomenclature of Brodal, and taking into account observations of Taber (1961) and Berman (1968) we referred to the origin of the dorsal reticulospinal system as the nucleus reticularis magnocellularis (Rmc) (see Fig. 1).

We have repeated these autoradiographic studies in the primate and demonstrated comparable results; a dense projection to laminae I and II from the raphe and adjacent reticular formation was seen (Basbaum and Ralston, 1978). In one sense, the projection in the monkey is more readily demonstrated. The larger size of the medulla makes it easier to confine amino acid injections to one region. Thus, more caudal, midline injections into the raphe obscurus and/ or raphe pallidius revealed descending pathways only in the ventral and ventrolateral funiculi. These generate dense projections to motorneuron pools. No projection to the superficial dorsal horn was found. Only rostral injections resulted in projections via the DLF.

Mayer and his colleagues (Watkins et al., 1981) questioned whether the raphe and adjacent reticular formation are at the origin of two separate bulbospinal modulatory systems. Based on studies in the rat, they concluded that the dorsal reticulospinal system (i.e. Rmc) is a lateral extension of the raphe. Their arguments are based, in part, on early fluorescent histochemical studies of Dahlström and Fuxe (1964, 1965) which demonstrated that the B-3 serotonin cell group of the rat has lateral extensions over the medullary pyramids. They concluded that the reticular component corresponds, in fact, to the lateral extensions of B-3.

NRM and B-3, however, are not synonymous. First, the large, multipolar serotonin (5-HT)-containing cells, which give NRM its name, are restricted to the midline. The large multipolar cells of the reticular formation, from which inhibition is generated, do not contain 5-HT. While the NRM, indeed, contains many neurons which are not 5-HT-containing, it differs significantly from the Rmc in that the latter contains *no* 5-HT neurons. There is, however, a thin band of neurons that lies just over the pyramids. Some of these are 5-HT-containing neurons; however, they are cytoarchitecturally distinct from the magnocellular reticular neurons, in that they are small fusiform cells. It is not clear what the homologue of Rmc in the rat is, or whether there is one. It may correspond to the nucleus reticularis paragigantocellularis (Rpg) of the Fifkova and Marsala (1967) atlas. Johannessen et al. (1981) recently discovered a source of non-5-HT axons in the DLF of the rat that lie just off the midline, dorsal to the wings of B-3. This region probably corresponds to what we have defined as Rmc of the cat.

That the Rmc/Rpg is functionally distinct from the NRM is strongly indicated from the studies of Satoh and Takagi and their colleagues. They demonstrated that electrical stimulation of, or opiate microinjection into, the Rpg produces a profound analgesia (Akaike et al., 1978; Kuraishi et al., 1979; Satoh et al., 1980). The analgesia could be reversed by administering the adrenergic receptor blockers phentolamine or phenoxybenzamine, but not by the 5-HT blocker methysergide. Stimulation-produced analgesia from NRM, consistent with its 5-HT-containing neurons, was reversed by methysergide. Most importantly, they reported that analgesia from Rpg stimulation was antagonized by naloxone, the specific opiate antagonist; the analgesia from NRM was not. The latter results directly contradict those of Rivot et al. (1979) who reported complete antagonism of NRM-produced analgesia by naloxone. Underscoring the lack of agreement between the two groups, the French laboratory finds almost no analgesic effect of electrical stimulation or of opiate microinjection off the middline, i.e. in Rpg (Dickenson et al., 1979). Zorman et al. (1981, 1982) however, demonstrated that naloxone is equally effective in reversing Rpg and NRM electrically produced suppression of the heat-evoked tail-flick reflex. The explanation for the differences may depend on stimulation current parameters or the pain test used.

The complexity of these control systems is perhaps best illustrated by studies of Azami et al. (1981) who, in agreement with Takagi's group, found that analgesia produced by Rpg stimulation is reversed by naloxone. However, they further demonstrated that a lesion of the raphe abolishes the Rpg-induced analgesia. Since they found naloxone sensitivity from Rpg, but not from NRM, one could postulate that the link between Rpg and NRM involves an endogenous opiate-containing interneuron originating in or coursing through Rpg. The effects of Rpg stimulation would thus be naloxone sensitive. In contrast, electrical stimulation produced analgesia from NRM might be refractory to naloxone. This would arise because the NRM output neuron (e.g. 5-HT-containing) would be stimulated, as well as the afferent opioid axons. This anatomical arrangement connecting Rpg and NRM, via an enkephalin link, might also explain the reversal of analgesia by local injection of naloxone into the ventral medulla. It is conceivable that naloxone disrupts the link between Rpg and NRM.

Unfortunately, the most recent data from Azami et al. argue against an Rpg–NRM connection. They have provided evidence that the pharmacology of Rpg- and NRM-produced analgesia is different. In agreement with Takagi et al. (Kuraishi et al., 1979; Satoh et al., 1980) they found a 5-HT-sensitive NRM inhibition and a norepinephrine-mediated Rpg inhibition. Thus, two separate systems are indicated.

The complexity of the medullary bulbospinal systems is further increased by the presence of another group of cells located just lateral to Rpg, in the nucleus reticularis paragigantocellularis lateralis (Pgl). For a detailed anatomical analysis of this region the reader is referred to Andrezik et al. (1981). The Pgl is most prominent just medial to the facial nucleus (Fig. 1). Many of its component cells project via the DLF, but its precise spinal terminal field has not been established. It is likely, however, that many of the effects generated by electrical stimulation of Rpg/Rmc reflect current spread laterally to the Pgl.

Immunohistochemical analysis of the rostral medulla underscores how important Pgl may be. Its pharmacology is remarkably complex. First, 5-HT-containing neurons are found not only in NRM, but also in the Pgl. In addition, a variety of peptide-containing neurons are present, including substance, P, enkephalin, TRH, etc. (Hökfelt et al., 1978; and see Hökfelt, this volume). It is of interest that, while enkephalin-containing neurons are found in Pgl, there are few terminals. This suggest that Pgl enkephalin neurons are, in fact, projection neurons. They may be a source of opioid axons to the NRM, via the Rmc/Rpg. It is also significant that in many neurons of the Pgl of the cat, 5-HT and enkephalin coexist (Glazer and Basbaum, 1981b). Thus the naloxone and methysergide sensitivity of medullary stimulation-produced analgesia, could

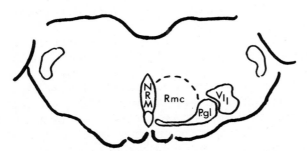

Figure 1. Schematic drawing of a section through the ventral medulla of the cat illustrating the organization of three nuclear regions which contribute axons to the DLF. The nucleus raphe magnus (NRM) and nucleus reticularis paragigantocellularis lateralis (Pgl) contain 5-HT neurons, peptide neurons and neurons in which 5-HT and a variety of peptides coexist. Neurons of the nucleus reticularis magnocellularis (Rmc) have not been pharmacologically characterized.

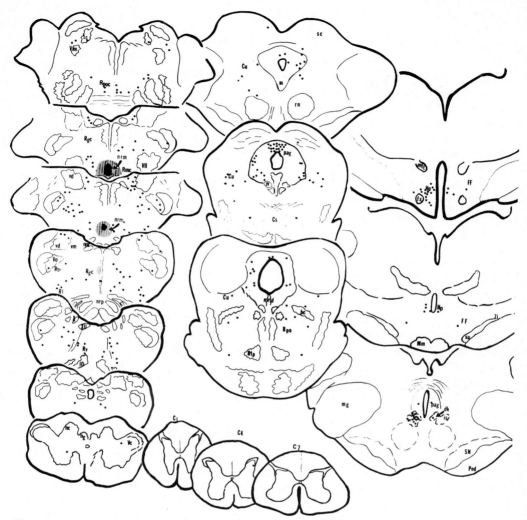

Figure 3. Schematic drawing illustrating distribution of retrogradely labeled neurons (dots) recorded in a cat with an HRP injection in the nucleus raphe magnus (nrm). Note dense cell cluster in dorsal periaqueductal gray (pag). Abbreviations: bc, brachium conjunctivum; Cs, centralis superior; Cu, nucleus cuneiformis; dk, nucleus of Darkschewitsch; ff, fields of Forel; fx, fornix; Hp, posterior hypothalamus; Io, inferior olive; is, interstitial nucleus of Cajal; lc, locus coeruleus; mg, medial geniculate body; Mm, mammilary bodies; mtt, mammillothalamic tract; nc, cuneate nucleus; ng, gracile nucleus; npr, nucleus prepositus hypoglossi; nra, retroambiguus nucleus; nrd, nucleus raphe dorsalis; nrp, nucleus raphe pallidus; Ped, cerebral peduncle; Rgc, nucleus reticularis gigantocellularis; Rl, nucleus reticularis lateralis; Rmc, nucleus reticularis magnocellularis; rn, red nucleus; Rpc, nucleus reticularis parvocellularis; Rpo, nucleus reticularis pontis oralis; Rpoc, nucleus reticularis pontis caudalis; Rtp, nucleus reticularis tegmenti pontis; Rv, nucleus reticularis ventralis; sc, superior colliculus; SN, substantia nigra; su, subthalamic nucleus; vd, inferior vestibular nucleus; vm, medial vestibular nucleus; Zi, zona incerta; III, oculomotor nuclei; IV, trochlear nucleus; Vc, trigeminal nucleus, pars caudalis; Vm, trigeminal nucleus (motor division); Vo, trigeminal nucleus, pars oralis; VII, facial nucleus; X, dorsal motor nucleus of vagus; XII, hypoglossal nucleus. (Reproduced from Abols and Basbaum, 1981, with permission.)

dominant projection to the NRM derives from the PAG, an observation that was consistent with earlier studies in the rat (Gallagher and Pert, 1978). Although most studies emphasize the importance of the ventrolateral PAG and dorsal raphe in opiate and stimulation-produced analgesia (Gebhart and Toleikas, 1978; Oliveras et al., 1979), the majority of labeled neurons were, in fact, found in the dorsal PAG. A second cluster of retrogradely labeled neurons was located in the midlateral PAG. The two cell groups were cytoarchitecturally distinguishable; those located dorsally included a population of small round cells, those located laterally were fusiform.

While we emphasize the pharmacological differences between the NRM and Rmc, it is of interest that few differences characterize the afferent connections of the raphe magnus or the adjacent Rmc. One exception is that, while some spinal cord neurons project to Rmc, a direct spinal projection to the raphe could not be demonstrated. In contrast to Rmc and the raphe, the more dorsally located Rgc, a region from which Jankowska et al. (1968) demonstrated descending inhibition via ventral spinal pathways, receives few afferent connections from the PAG. On the other hand, Rgc receives the majority of spinal afferents.

The results of this study indicated that those regions of rostral medulla which project via the DLF to the spinal cord — and stimulation of which inhibits spinal nociceptors, i.e. NRM and Rmc (and probably Pgl) — receive a significant projection from the PAG. Those regions which project via the ventral cord do not. Thus, the morphological substrate for midbrain–medullary interactions in the control of spinal nociceptors by opiates and/or electrical brain stimulation was clearly demonstrated.

The fact that different PAG regions project to the rostral medulla, coupled with the pharmacological diversity of the medullospinal pathways, raises questions concerning the selectivity and/or redundancy of the descending control generated from the PAG–medullary interactions. While our laboratory emphasizes the control of nociception, other groups have focused on the control of sleep, sexual behavior (e.g. lordosis), etc. Does the emphasis on a particular behavioral modulation merely reflect an individual laboratory's bias? Is there, in fact, an "endogenous pain control system" or is it a component of a more general, non-specific descending control system?

There is some evidence that, for generating analgesia, the PAG is relatively specific, at least pharmacologically. For example, Cannon et al. (1980) demonstrated that whether or not naloxone will reverse the analgesia produced by PAG stimulation critically depends on the particular stimulation locus. Stimulation dorsally (in the region which, in cat, projects directly to the NRM) produces a naloxone-insensitive analgesia. In contrast, stimulation of the ventral PAG, including the raphe dorsalis (RD) (which does not project directly to NRM), produces a naloxone-reversible analgesia. Moreover, raphe magnus lesions only antagonize the analgesia generated from ventral electrode placements, including the RD. Apparently, different regions of PAG generate pharmacologically different forms of pain control.

These differences may reflect the anatomical heterogeneity of the PAG itself. Cytoarchitecturally, the PAG has been subdivided into three distinct zones (Hamilton, 1973); however, on the basis of afferent and efferent connections, the PAG (not including the raphe dorsalis) appears to be relatively homogeneous, i.e. different PAG regions receive afferents from and project to the same brain areas (Mantyh, 1982). In terms of peptide content, however, the PAG is far from homogeneous (see Fig. 4). For example, in the caudal PAG, enkephalin-immunoreactive cells are concentrated ventrally (Moss et al., 1982). Of particular interest are the large numbers of enkephalin cells in the RD (Moss et al., 1981). In fact, many 5-HT-containing RD neurons also contain enkephalin (Glazer et al., 1981). More rostrally, the enkephalin cells are clustered dorsally and laterally; at the level of the third nucleus there are few enkephalin neurons located in the ventral or ventrolateral PAG. Substance P-immunoreactive cells have a similar distribution, although clustering of cells is less evident. Our preliminary analysis of vasoactive intestinal polypeptide (VIP)-immunoreactive neurons revealed only a small population of cells clustered under the rostrocaudal extent of the ventral aspect of the aqueduct. This light microscopic analysis is only a first step in analyzing the mechanisms that operate within the PAG. Detailed EM analyses are necessary.

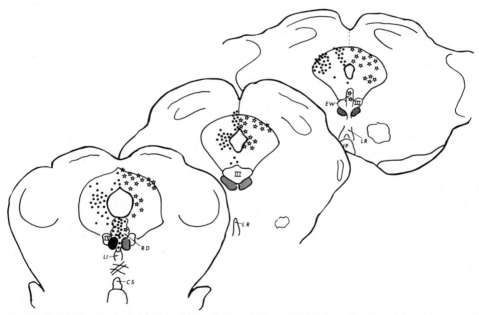

Figure 4. Schematic diagram illustrating distribution of peptide-containing neurons in the midbrain PAG of the cat. Immunoreactive-enkephalin cells (dots) and substance P neurons (stars) have overlapping, but not identical, distribution. Note dense enkephalin cell clusters in the 5-HT-containing nucleus raphe dorsalis (RD). EW, Edinger–Westphal nucleus; LI, nucleus linearis caudalis; LR, nucleus linearis rostralis.

Clearly, the regional variation in peptide content may influence the pharmacology of PAG-induced analgesia. For example, the susceptibility to naloxone may reflect the numbers of PAG enkephalin-containing neurons stimulated; this would certainly vary with stimulation locus. Alternatively, the variability of naloxone reversibility may depend on the specific PAG connections made in the medulla. Some PAG regions may interact more strongly with medullary peptide-containing neurons, other with aminergic systems; still others may interact with combinations of the two. The multiplicity of bulbospinal control systems is thus magnified by the combinations of PAG neurons with which they may interact. A detailed analysis of the pharmacology of PAG–medullary connections is obviously required.

IV. Conclusions

As is unfortunately often true, our initial view of the components of descending control was highly oversimplified. This is not unexpected and should be viewed as a challenge to future studies. Numerous questions await an answer. How many distinct descending control systems are yet to be discovered? What is the significance of coexistence of putative neurotransmitters within the elements of descending control systems? Do different peptides exert temporally different control mechanisms? The fact that norepinephrine and serotonin make such a significant contribution to descending control leads one to consider whether their profound potential for sprouting after damage is, in fact, manifested continuously. For example, does the development of descending control reflect ongoing changes in the arborization of descending monoaminergic fibers? How plastic is the anatomy of these descending control systems? A question raised earlier concerns the selectivity of particular descending systems for the varieties of spinal circuits that have been demonstrated. Given modern morphological tools, the latter question may be the most easily answerable.

Finally, and perhaps most importantly, what is the significance of descending control to the animal? What factors initiate descending control? To how many behavioral patterns does it contribute? While we dissect the components of descending control, an ultimate goal is to understand the "why" of its existence. I believe this symposium is an important step in that direction.

Acknowledgements

I thank Ms. Michelle Moss for permission to use Fig. 4, Mr. Dave Akers for excellent photograph assistance and Ms. Alana Schilling for typing the manuscript. This work was supported by NIH-NS14627, and NSF-BNS-78-24762. The author is the recipient of an NIH Research Career Development Award and is a Sloan Foundation Fellow.

References

Abols, I.A. and Basbaum, A.I. (1981) Afferent connections of the rostral medulla of the cat: A neural substrate for midbrain-medullary interactions in the modulation of pain, *J. comp. Neurol.*, 201: 285-297.

Akaike, A., Shibata, T., Satoh, M. and Takagi, H. (1978) Analgesia induced by microinjection of morphine into and electrical stimulation of the nucleus reticularis paragigantocellularis of rat medulla oblongata, *Neuropharmacology*, 17: 775-778.

Akil, H., Mayer, D.J. and Liebeskind, J.C. (1976) Antagonism of stimulation-produced analgesia by naloxone, a narcotic antagonist, *Science*, 191: 961-962.

Andrezik, J.A., Chan-Palay, V. and Palay, S.L. (1981) The nucleus paragigantocellularis lateralis in the rat, *Anat. Embryol.*, 161: 35-371.

Aronin, N., Difiglia, M., Liotta, A.S. and Martin, J.B. (1981) Ultrastructural localization and biochemical features of immunoreactive Leu-enkephalin in monkey dorsal horn, *J. Neurosci.*, 1: 561-578.

Atweh, S.F. and Kuhar, M.J. (1977) Autoradiographic localization of opiate-receptors in rat brain. II. The brainstem, *Brain Res.*, 129: 1-12.

Azami, J., Lewlyn, M.B. and Roberts, M.H.T. (1981) The contribution of nucleus reticularis paragigantocellularis and nucleus raphe magnus to the analgesia produced by systemically administered morphine, investigated with the microinjection technique, *Pain*, in press.

Barber, R.P., Vaughn, J.E., Saito, K., McLaughlin, B.J. and Roberts, E. (1979) GABAergic terminals in the substantia gelatinosa of the rat spinal cord, *Brain Res.*, 141: 35-55.

Barton, C., Basbaum, A.I. and Fiels, H.L. (1980) Dissociation of supraspinal and spinal actions of morphine: a quantitative evaluation, *Brain Res.*, 188: 487-498.

Basbaum, A.I. and Fields, H.L. (1978) Endogenous pain control mechanisms: review and hypothesis, *Ann. Neurol.*, 4: 451-462.

Basbaum, A.I. and Fields, H.L. (1979) The origin of descending pathways in the dorsolateral funiculus of the spinal cord of the cat and rat: further studies on the anatomy of pain modulation, *J. comp. Neurol.*, 187: 513-522.

Basbaum, A.I. and Ralston, H.J. (1978) Projections from nucleus raphe magnus in the primate, *Pain Abstr.*, 1: 259.

Basbaum, A.I., Clanton, C.H. and Fields, H.L. (1976) Opiate and stimulus-produced analgesia: Functional anatomy of a medullospinal pathway, *Proc. nat. Acad. Sci. U.S.A.*, 73: 4685-4688.

Basbaum, A.I., Marley, N.J.E., O'Keefe, J. and Clanton, C.H. (1977) Reversal of morphine and stimulus-produced analgesia by subtotal spinal cord lesions, *Pain*, 3: 43-56.

Basbaum, A.I., Clanton, C.H. and Fields, H.L. (1978) Three bulbospinal pathways from the rostral medulla of the cat: an autoradiographic study of pain modulating systems, *J. comp. Neurol.*, 178: 209-224,

Basbaum, A.I., Glazer, E.J. and Oertel, W. (1981) A light and EM analysis of immunoreactive glutamic acid decarboxylase (GAD) in the spinal and trigeminal dorsal horn of the cat, *Soc. Neurosci. Abstr.*, 7: 528.

Bennett, G.J., Abdelmoumene, M., Hayashi, H. and Dubner, R. (1980) Physiology and morphology of substantia gelatinosa neurons intracellularly stained with horseradish peroxidase, *J. comp. Neurol.*, 194: 809-828.

Bennet, G.J., Abdelmoumene, M., Hayashi, H., Hoffert, M.J. and Dubner, R. (1981) Spinal cord layer I neurons with axon collaterals that generate local arbors, *Brain Res.*, 209: 421-426.

Berman, A.L. (1968) *The Brainstem of the Cat*, University of Wisconsin, Press, Madison, 1975.

Brodal, A., Taber, E. and Walberg, F. (1960) The raphe nuclei of the brainstem of the cat. II. Efferent connections, *J. comp. Neurol.*, 114: 239-259.

Cannon, J.T., Prieto, G.J., Lee, A. and Liebeskind, J.C. (1980) Antagonism of stimulation-produced analgesia by naloxone: effects of stimulation, dose and time, *Fed. Proc.*, 39: 603.

Christensen, B.N. and Perl, E.R. (1970) Spinal neurons specifically excited by noxious or thermal stimuli: marginal zone of the dorsal horn, *J. Neurophysiol.*, 33: 293-307.

Dahlström, A. and Fuxe, K. (1964) Evidence for the existence of monoamine containing neurons in the central nervous system: I. Demonstration of monoamines in the cell bodies of brainstem neurons, *Acta physiol. scand.*, 62, Suppl. 232: 1-55.

Dahlström, A. and Fuxe, K. (1965) Evidence for the existence of monoamine neurons in the central nervous system, *Acta, physiol. scand.*, 64, Suppl. 247: 1-30.

Descarries, L., Beaudet, A. and Watkins, K.C. (1975) Serotonin nerve terminals in adult rat neocortex, *Brain Res..*, 100: 563-588.

Dickenson, A.H., Oliveras, J.L. and Besson, J.M. (1979) Role of the nucleus raphe magnus in opiate analgesia as studied by the microinjection technique in the rat, *Brain Res.*, 170: 95-112.

Elde, R., Hökfelt, T., Johanssen, O. and Terenius, L. (1976) Immunohistochemical studies using antibodies to leu-enkephalin: initial observations on the nervous system of the rat, *Neurosci. Lett.*, 1: 349-351.

Engberg, I., Lundberg, A. and Ryall, R.W. (1968a) The effect of reserpine on transmission in the spinal cord, *Acta physiol. scand.*, 72: 115-122.

Engberg, I., Lundberg, A. and Ryall, R.W. (1968b) Is the tonic decerebrate inhibition of reflex paths mediated by monoaminergic pathways? *Acta physiol. scand.*, 72: 123-133.

Engberg, I., Lundberg, A. and Ryall, R.W. (1968c) Reticulospinal inhibition of interneurones, *J. Physiol. (Lond.)*, 194: 226-236.

Fields, H.L. and Basbaum, A.I. (1978) Brainstem control of spinal pain transmission neurons, *Ann. Rev. Physiol.*, 40: 193-221.

Fields, H.L., Basbaum, A.I., Clanton, C.H. and Anderson, S.D. (1977) Nucleus raphe magnus inhibition of spinal cord dorsal horn neurons, *Brain Res..*, 126: 441-453.

Fifkova, E. and Marsala,, J. (1967) Stereotaxic atlas for the cat. In J. Bureš, M. Petran and J. Zacher (Eds.), *Electrophysiological Methods in Biological Research*, Academic Press, New York, pp. 653-731.

Gallagher, D.W. and Pert, A. (1978) Afferents to brainstem nuclei (brainstem raphe, nucleus reticularis pontis caudalis and nucleus gigantocellularis) in the rat as demonstrated by microiontophoretically applied HRP, *Brain Res.*, 144: 257-276.

Gebhart, G. and Toleikas, J. (1978) An evaluation of stimulation-produced analgesia in the cat, *Exp. Neurol.*, 62: 570-579.

Glazer, E.J. and Basbaum, A.I. (1981a) Immunohistochemical localization of leucine-enkephalin in the spinal cord of the cat: enkephalin-containing marginal neurons and pain modulation, *J. comp. Neurol.*, 196: 377-390.

Glazer, E.J. and Basbaum A.I. (1981b) Ultrastructural localization of leucine-enkephalin in the superficial dorsal horn of the cat, *Soc. Neurosci. Abstr.*, 6: 523.

Glazer, E.J., Steinbusch, H., Verhofstad, A. and Basbaum, A.I. (1981) Serotonin and enkephalin coexist in neurons of the nucleus raphe dorsalis and paragigantocellularis of the cat, *J. Physiol. (Paris)*, 77: 241-245.

Hamilton, B.L. (1973) Cytoarchitecture subdivisions of the periaqueductal grey matter in the cat, *J. comp. Neurol.*, 149: 1-28.

Hiller, J.M., Simon, E.J., Crain, S.M. and Peterson, E.R. (1978) Opiate receptors in cultures of fetal mouse dorsal root ganglia (DRG) and spinal cord: predominance in DRG neurites, *Brain Res.*, 145: 396-400.

Hökfelt, T., Ljungdahl, A., Terenius, L., Elde, R. and Nilsson, G. (1977) Immunohistochemical analysis of peptide pathways possibly related to pain and analgesia: enkephalin and substance P, *Proc. nat. Acad. Sci. U.S.A..*, 74: 3081-3085.

Hökfelt, T., Ljungdahl, A., Steinbusch, H., Verhofstad, A., Nilssen, G., Brodin, E., Pernow, B. and Goldstein, M. (1978) Immunohistochemical evidence of substance P-like immunoreactivity in some 5HT-containing neurons in the rat central nervous system, *Neuroscience*, 3: 517-538.

Hunt, S.O., Kelly, J.S. and Emson, P.C. (1980) The electron microscopic localization of methionine-enkephalin within the superficial layers (I and II) of the spinal cord, *Neuroscience*, 5: 1871-1890.

Jankowska, E., Lund, S., Lundberg, A. and Pompeiano, O. (1968) Inhibitory effects evoked through ventral reticulospinal pathways, *Arch. ital. Biol.*, 106: 124-140.

Johannessen, Y.N., Watkins, L.R. and Mayer, D.J. (1981) Non-serotonergic cells at the origin of the dorsolateral funiculus (DLF) in rat medulla, *Soc. Neurosci. Abstr.*, 7: 532.

Kuraishi, Y., Harada, Y., Satoh, M. and Takagi, H. (1979) Antagonism by phenoxybenzamine of the analgesic effect of morphine injected into the nucleus reticularis gigantocellularis of the rat, *Neuropharmacology*, 18: 107-110.

Kuypers, H.G.J.M. and Maisky, V.A. (1975) Retrograde axonal transport of horseradish peroxidase from spinal cord to brain stem cell groups in the cat, *Neurosci. Lett.*, 1: 9-14.

LaMotte, C., Pert, C.B. and Snyder, S.H. (1976) Opiate receptor binding in primate spinal cord: distribution and changes after dorsal root section, *Brain Res.*, 112: 407-412.

Light, A.R., Trevino, D.L. and Perl, E.R. (1979) Morphological features of functionally defined neurons in the marginal zone and substantia gelatinosa of the spinal dorsal horn, *J. comp. Neurol.*, 186: 151-172.

Mantyh, P. (1982) The midbrain periaqueductal grey in the rat, cat and monkey: A Nissl, Weil and Golgi analysis, *J. comp. Neurol.*, in press.

Moss, M.S., Glazer, E.J. and Basbaum, A.I. (1981) Enkephalin-imunoreactive perikarya in the cat raphe dorsalis, *Neurosci. Lett.*, 21: 33-37.

Moss, M.S., Glazer, E.J. and Basbaum, A.I. (1982) Light and electron microscopic observations of leucine enkephalin in the cat periaqueductal grey, *Advanc. Pain Res. Ther.*, in press.

Oliveras, J.L., Guilbaud, G. and Besson, J.M. (1979) A map of serotoninergic structures involved in stimulation producing analgesia in unrestrained freely moving cats, *Brain Res.*, 164: 317-322.

Rivot, J.P., Chaouch, A. and Besson, J.M. (1979) The influence of naloxone on the C fiber response of dorsal horn neurons and their inhibitory control by raphe magnus stimulation, *Brain Res.*, 176: 355-364.

Sar, M., Stumpf, W.E., Miller, R.J., Chang, K.J. and Cuatrecasas, P. (1978) Immunohistochemical localization of enkephalin in rat brain and spinal cord, *J. comp. Neurol.*, 182: 17-38.

Satoh, M., Akaike, A., Takahiro, N. and Takagi, H. (1980) Evidence for involvement of separate mechanisms in the production of analgesia by electrical stimulation of the nucleus reticularis paragigantocellularis and nucleus raphe magnus in the rat, *Brain Res.*, 194: 525-529.

Sjölund, B.H. and Eriksson, M.B.E. (1979) The influence of naloxone on analgesia produced by peripheral conditioning stimulation, *Brain Res.*, 178: 295-302.

Taber, E. (1961) The cytoarchitecture of the brainstem of the cat, *J. comp. Neurol.*, 116: 27-69.

Tohyama, M., Sakai, K., Touret, M., Salvert, D. and Jouvet, M. (1979) Spinal projections from the lower brainstem in the cat as demonstrated by the HRP technique: I. Origins of the reticulospinal tracts and their funicular trajections, *Brain Res.*, 173: 383-404.

Wall, P.D. (1967) The laminar organization of dorsal horn and effects of descending impulses, *J. Physiol. (Lond.)*, 188: 403-423.

Watkins, L.R., Griffin, G., Liechnetz, C.R. and Mayer, D.J. (1980) The somatotopic organization of the nucleus raphe magnus and surrounding brain stem structures as revealed by HRP slow release gels, *Brain Res.*, 187: 1-15.

Willis, W.D., Haber, L.H. and Martin, R.F. (1977) Inhibition of spinothalamic tract cells and interneurons by brainstem stimulation in the monkey, *J. Neurophysiol.*, 40: 968-981.

Yaksh, T.L. (1979) Direct evidence that spinal serotonin and noradrenaline terminals mediate the spinal antinociceptive effects of morphine in the periaqueductal grey, *Brain Res.*, 160: 180-185.

Yaksh, T.L. and Rudy, T.A. (1978) Narcotic analgesics: CNS sites and mechanisms of action as revealed by intracerebral injection techniques, *Pain*, 4: 299-360.

Zorman, G., Hentall, I.D. Adams, J.E. and Fields, H.L. (1981) Naloxone-reversible analgesia produced by microstimulation in the rat medulla, *Brain Res.*, 219: 137-148.

Zorman, G., Belcher, G., Adams, J.E. and Fields, H.L. (1982) Lumbar intrathecal naloxone blocks analgesia produced by microstimulation of the ventromedial medulla in the rat, *Brain Res.*, in press.

Brain Stem Control of Spinal Mechanisms
– B. Sjölund and A. Björklund, editors
© 1982 Elsevier Biomedical Press

6

Synaptic Connectivity of Substantia Gelatinosa Neurons With Reference to Potential Termination Sites of Descending Axons

STEPHEN GOBEL, GARY J. BENNETT, BARBARA ALLEN, EMMA HUMPHREY, ZEEV SELTZER, MOHAMMED ABDELMOUMENE, HARUHIDE HAYASHI and MARVIN J. HOFFERT

Neurobiology and Anesthesiology Branch, National Institute of Dental Research, National Institutes of Health, 9000 Rockville Pike, Bethesda, MD 20205, U.S.A.

I. Introduction

The neurons of the substantia gelatinosa of Rolando (Rexed's laminae I and II) receive synaptic inputs from two kinds of axonal endings, elongated scalloped endings and small dome-shaped endings. The major source of the scalloped endings is the terminal axonal arborizations of primary neurons. The parent branches of small caliber primary axons enter the spinal cord through Lissauer's tract and then give rise to ending-bearing collaterals in laminae I and II. These collaterals extend for appreciable distances in the rostrocaudal axis of these laminae and generate numerous axonal endings (Beal and Fox, 1976; Gobel and Falls, 1979; Light and Perl, 1979; Gobel et al., 1981a). The morphology and synaptic connections of primary endings in these laminae have been studied using a variety of approaches. These include: degeneration studies following either trigeminal root section (Gobel, 1974) or dorsal root section (e.g. Ralston and Ralston, 1979); the use of EM-autoradiography following the injection of tritiated amino acids into dorsal root ganglia (Ralston and Ralston, 1979); and, most recently, intra-axonal filling of primary axons with horseradish peroxidase (HRP) by applying HRP to the cut central ends of dorsal roots (Gobel et al., 1981a) and iontophoretic injection of HRP into individual axons (Light et al., 1980). These studies have yielded a fairly comprehensive picture of the synaptic connections of primary axons in laminae I and II. Primary endings are elongated endings with scalloped outlines which transfer their inputs largely to dendritic spines and also to small caliber dendritic shafts of

136

the neurons of laminae I and II at asymmetrical Gray type I synapses. Each primary ending generally synapses on two or more dendritic processes which are impressed into scalloped depressions in the primary ending. Some of these dendrites contain synaptic vesicles and form dendrodendritic synapses on adjacent dendrites that do not contain synaptic vesicles and dendroaxonic synapses back on the primary endings. In addition, small axonal endings also surround the primary ending and some of these form axodendritic synapses on some of the dendrites that do not contain synaptic vesicles and axoaxonic synapses on the primary endings. All of these processes make up structures called glomeruli in which the primary ending lies in the center. Non-primary serotonergic scalloped endings have also been found in laminae I and II (Ruda and Gobel, 1980; Ruda et al., 1981a) but these are relatively rare compared to the number of scalloped primary endings.

The second source of synaptic input to the neurons of laminae I and II is the many small dome-shaped axonal endings which typically form single synapses with the structures with which they come in contact. The vast majority of these dome-shaped endings could be categorized into one of two morphologically distinct types on the basis of the morphology of their agranular synaptic vesicles (Fig. 1). One kind, the D1 ending, contains a mixture of small, highly flattened and oval vesicles. Their highly flattened vesicles are quite distinctive; they have extremely narrow lumina and their long diameters can be up to four or five times as long as their short diameters. These highly flattened vesicles constitute the most conspicuous feature of the D1 ending. The D2 endings (Fig. 1)

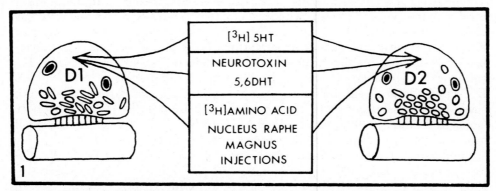

Figure 1. Schematic diagram illustrating the two kinds of dome-shaped serotonergic endings identified in laminae I and II of the dorsal horn. The D1 ending contains many highly flattened, agranular synaptic vesicles together with different sized, small oval ones. The D2 ending contains more uniformly sized oval synaptic vesicles with only a rare flattened one. Both contain occasional dense core vesicles and are most commonly found forming symmetrical synapses on small dendritic shafts. These endings were labeled using three different experimental approaches. Tritiated serotonin and the serotonin neurotoxin 5,6-dihydroxytryptamine, were taken up by these endings following topical applications (Ruda and Gobel, 1980). They were also labeled following the injection of tritiated amino acids in nucleus raphe magnus and the adjacent reticular formation (Ruda et al., 1981a).

contain small, oval agranular synaptic vesicles whose long diameters are generally less than twice their short diameters. Flattened vesicles, while occasionally seen in D2 endings, are relatively rare. Both of these dome-shaped endings contain occasional dense core vesicles and show considerable variation in the packing density of their agranular synaptic vesicles which can be either evenly distributed throughout the ending or tightly clustered at the presynaptic membrane. These dome-shaped endings have multiple sources which include descending axons of neurons in the brain stem and intrinsic axon collaterals of dorsal horn neurons. We have recently shown that descending serotonergic axons constitute a major source of the dome-shaped endings in laminae I and II (Ruda and Gobel, 1980; Ruda et al., 1981a).

Three experimental approaches have been utilized to identify serotonergic axonal endings in laminae I and II of adult cats. The major findings of these experiments are summarized in Figure 1. First, tritiated serotonin was topically applied to the surface of the tuberculum cinerium where it percolated into the upper laminae of the medullary dorsal horn (trigeminal subnucleus caudalis) and was specifically taken up by serotonergic axons (Ruda and Gobel, 1980). Second, the serotonin neurotoxin, 5,6-dihydroxytryptamine, was topically applied in the same manner in the same location and, following a 3 h survival time, blackened degenerating serotonergic axons were identified in laminae I and II (Ruda and Gobel, 1980). Third, tritiated amino acids were injected in nucleus raphe magnus and the immediately adjacent reticular formation. Following a 7 day survival time, autoradiographically labeled axonal endings similar to those identified in the two previous uptake experiments were identified in laminae I and II (Ruda et al., 1981a).

In each of these three experiments, numerous dome-shaped endings were found in laminae I and II. In contrast to the scalloped primary endings, these dome-shaped endings typically formed single symmetrical synapses in which the synaptic cleft was only slightly wider than the adjacent intercellular space. These synapses were most commonly found on small caliber dendritic shafts but were also occasionally seen on dendritic spines and cell bodies. D1 serotonergic endings were the most commonly observed serotonergic endings in each of the above-mentioned experiments. They were most common in lamina I but were also present in the superficial and deep parts of lamina II, i.e. IIa and IIb, respectively (Ruda and Gobel, 1980; Ruda et al., 1981b). D2 serotonergic endings were found within laminae I, IIa and IIb with about equal frequency (Ruda and Gobel, 1980).

These serotonergic axons, as well as the primary axons which arborize in laminae I and II, can potentially establish synaptic connections with four major neuronal cell types which in large part comprise the neuropil of these laminae (Fig. 2). These neurons are the projection neurons of lamina I; two kinds of interneurons in lamina II – the stalked cells (Fig. 2, dark cell body) and the islet cells of laminae IIa and IIb (Fig. 2, clear cell bodies); and neurons in the deeper laminae of the dorsal horn which send their dendrites dorsally

138

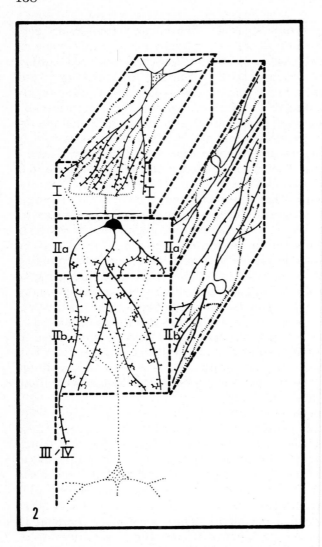

Figure 2. This summary diagram illustrates the morphological characteristics and laminar distribution of the dendrites of the major neuronal cell types which contribute to the neuropil of laminae I and II. Lamina I neurons have their dendrites confined in lamina I. The dendrites of stalked cells (dark cell body) are distributed throughout laminae IIa and IIb, with some occasionally entering lamina III. Stalked cell axons (striped) arborize in lamina I, where they are in position to synapse on the dendrites of lamina I neurons. Islet cells (clear cell bodies) are found in laminae IIa and IIb and their dendrites and axons (striped) arborize largely within the same lamina in which their cell body is found. Some neurons in laminae III and IV send some of their dendrites (dotted) dorsally into laminae I and II, where they branch extensively.

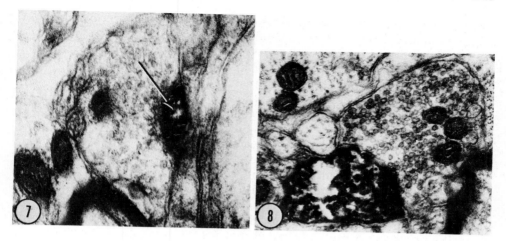

Figure 7. This D1 ending synapses (arrow) on a small dendritic spine head of the lamina I neuron. × 52,000.

Figure 8. This D2 ending, with its fairly uniformly sized, oval synaptic vesicles, abuts on a small caliber dendritic shaft of the lamina I neuron. D2 endings were encountered less frequently than D1 endings along the surface of the lamina I neuron. × 39,000.

D1 synaptic connections on this HRP-filled lamina I neuron was on fine caliber dendritic shafts less than 2 μm in diameter, such as the one in Figure 6. This observation is consistent with the observations from the tritiated serotonin and 5,6-dihydroxytryptamine experiments in which autoradiographically labeled and blackened degenerating D1 endings in lamina I were most commonly found on similar sized, small caliber dendritic shafts (Ruda and Gobel, 1980). D2 endings (Fig. 8) were also occasionally observed synapsing on small caliber dendritic shafts of the lamina I cell but were much less common than the D1 endings.

III. Stalked Cells

Stalked cells are small interneurons whose cell bodies are found in lamina IIa close to the I/IIa border (Fig. 2, black cell body). They give rise to fan-shaped dendritic arbors which descend through lamina II. The dendrites of some stalked cells arborize only in lamina IIa, while others course through the full thickness of lamina IIb. Still others send some branches into lamina III (Gobel, 1978b). A consistent morphological feature of stalked cells is that they have fine unmyelinated axons which, after arising either from the cell body or a basal dendrite, ascend into lamina I where they generate extensive axonal arbors in umbrella-like fashion (Gobel, 1978b; Bennett et al., 1980). Stalked cells which had been intracellularly impaled and subsequently filled with HRP were found to be either nociceptive specific neurons, which received primary input exclusively from Aδ or Aδ and C nociceptive primary axons, or wide dynamic range neurons, which received primary input from low threshold mechanoreceptive and nociceptive primary axons (Bennett et al., 1979, 1980). One possible function of stalked cells is that they serve as excitatory inter-neurons, receiving primary inputs on their dendrites in laminae II and III and then transferring these inputs to the dendrites of lamina I neurons via their axons. For example, stalked cells could convey low threshold primary inputs from hair follicle primary axons, which terminate across laminae III and IV (Brown et al., 1977; Light and Perl, 1979), to wide dynamic range projection neurons in lamina I. Another possibility is that some stalked cells which exhibit enkephalin-like immunoreactivity (Glazer and Basbaum, 1981; Bennett et al., in press) may function as inhibitory interneurons.

An EM analysis of one intracellularly filled stalked cell in which the entire dendritic arbor was sampled revealed that it sent many dendritic spines into glomeruli throughout lamina II, where it received axodendritic synapses from centrally situated scalloped endings which are thought to be of primary affe-rent origin (Gobel et al., 1980). The distribution of D1 and D2 endings on this

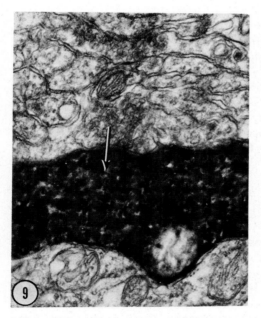

Figures 9–11. EM sections through different parts of an HRP-filled stalked cell.

Figure 9. A small dome-shaped ending synapses (arrow) on a small caliber dendritic shaft of an HRP-filled stalked cell. The extremely tight packing of the vesicles makes classification of this ending difficult, although a number of flattened vesicles can be discerned suggesting that it is a D1 ending. × 47,000. (From Gobel et al., 1980, with permission.)

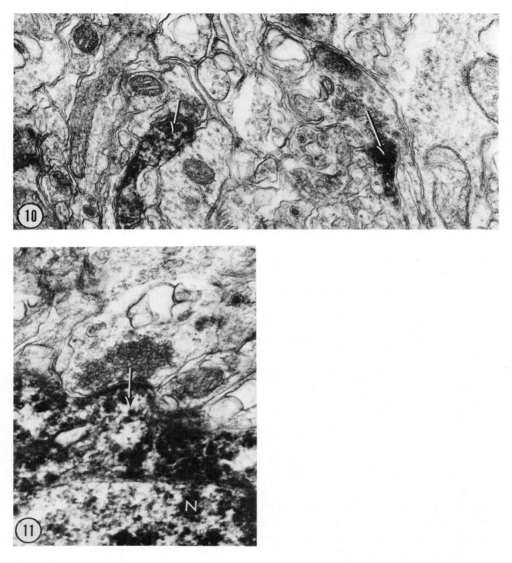

Figure 10. Two small D1 endings synapse (arrows) on two small dendritic spine heads of the HRP-filled stalked cell. × 44,000.

Figure 11. A small dome-shaped ending synapses (arrow) on a mound-shaped elevation on the surface of the HRP-filled stalked cell body. Some flattened vesicles can be discerned among the extremely tightly packed vesicles suggesting that it is probably a D1 ending. A portion of the nucleus (N) is visible beneath a thin rim of the cytoplasm of the cell body. × 47,000. (From Gobel et al., 1980, with permission.)

stalked cell was generally similar to that of the HRP-filled lamina I neuron. Many D1 and a few D2 endings were widely distributed on all parts of the dendritic arbor, especially on fine caliber dendritic shafts (Fig. 9) and on some of the stalked cell's fine dendritic spines (Fig. 10), where they established single short axodendritic synapses. The general impression gleaned from the EM analysis was that D1 endings were present on every dendritic branch that was sectioned but that they were fairly widely spaced along these branches and interspersed between the primary axonal endings in the glomeruli. Clusters of D1 or D2 endings were not found on any of the dendritic shafts. D1 endings were also found synapsing on the stalked cell body (Fig. 11).

IV. The IIa and IIb Islet Cells

Islet cell bodies are found in small clusters in laminae IIa and IIb (Fig. 2, clear cell bodies). Each islet cell body gives rise to extensive rostral and caudal dendritic arbors which are largely confined in either lamina IIa or lamina IIb (Gobel, 1978b; Bennett et al., 1980). Fine unmyelinated axons arise either from the cell body or a primary dendrite and, in typical Golgi type II fashion, branch repeatedly within the confines of the cell's dendritic arbor. Islet cell axonal arbors are also largely confined within the same lamina as their cell body and dendritic arbor, i.e. either in laminae IIa and IIb, and extend for several hundred μm beyond the rostrocaudal extent of their dendritic arbors (Gobel, 1975, 1978b; Bennett et al., 1980). The primary inputs of four lamina IIa islet cells were analyzed and each received nociceptive primary inputs; two were classified as nociceptive specific neurons and two were classified as wide dynamic range neurons (Bennett et al., 1980).

An EM analysis of two lamina IIa islet cells revealed that the dendritic arbors of these cells contained numerous clusters of synaptic vesicles (Gobel et al., 1980). These were found in large and small caliber dendritic shafts as well as in dendritic spine heads (Fig. 12). These small caliber dendritic shafts and spines entered many glomeruli in lamina IIa, where they were found impressed in scalloped depressions in the central scalloped endings of the glomeruli. In each instance they received a single asymmetrical axodendritic synapse from the scalloped central ending (Fig. 12). These synapses are considered to be the sites of transfer of primary inputs to the lamina IIa islet cells. They are the most common synapses received by the lamina IIa islet cell dendritic arbor. No other axons synapsed on those vesicle-containing portions of the islet cell dendritic arbors, either within the glomeruli or outside of the glomeruli. For example, most of the surface of the vesicle-containing spine head in the glomerulus in Figure 12 is covered by a thin astrocytic process. Transmitter release from these islet cell dendrites can occur through dendro-dendritic synapses both inside the glomeruli (Fig. 12) and outside of glomeruli (Gobel et al., 1980) on small dendritic shafts and spines as well as through den-

laminae have remained unknown. Figure 18 illustrates one such neuron with smooth aspiny dendrites that was intracellularly filled with HRP. Its cell body lies in lamina IV close to the IV/V border. In addition to sending a few dendrites ventrally through the neck of the dorsal horn into the ventral horn, it gives rise to three dorsally directed dendrites. These dorsal dendrites begin to branch in the dorsal part of lamina III and generate many fine branches in laminae I and II, as well as in Lissauer's tract. They also send a few branches into the dorsal columns. The axon arises from the cell body and gives rise to

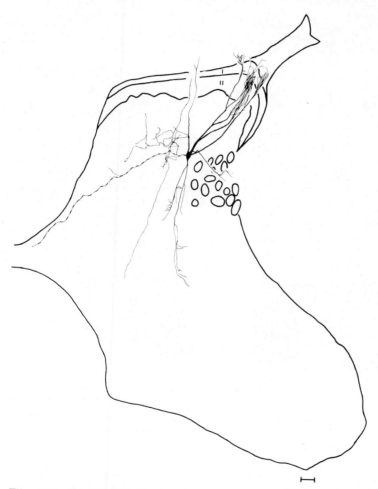

Figure 18. This HRP-filled lamina IV neuron has its cell body near the IV/V border. In addition to sending some dendrites ventrally, it also sends dendrites dorsally into laminae I and II and into Lissauer's tract. The axon of the cell (striped) courses toward the midline after generating several collaterals (dotted) in the vicinity of its dendrites. The large circles show the outlines of the coarse axon bundles in the lateral half of laminae V and VI. Scale = 100 μm.

152

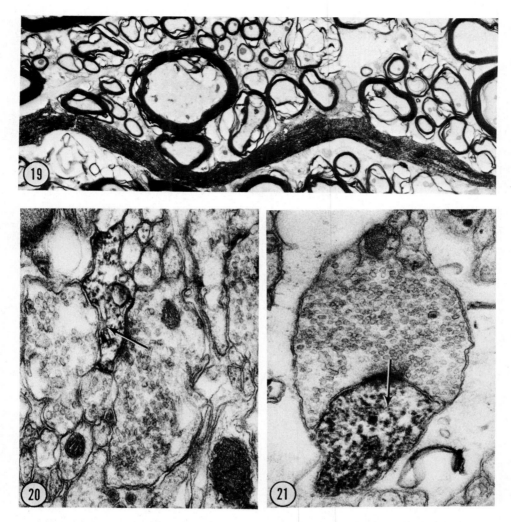

Figures 19–23. EM sections through a portion of some of the dorsally directed dendrites of the HRP-filled lamina IV neuron in Figure 18 as they course through lamina I and Lissauer's tract.

Figure 19. A fine caliber dendrite of the HRP-filled lamina IV neuron extends well into Lissauer's tract, where it courses among the numerous small myelinated and unmyelinated axons. × 7,600.

Figure 20. A D1 ending synapses (arrow) on a small caliber dendritic shaft of the HRP-filled lamina IV neuron. × 51,000.

Figure 21. This fine caliber dendritic shaft of the HRP-filled lamina IV neuron receives a synapse (arrow) from a D2 ending. × 51,000.

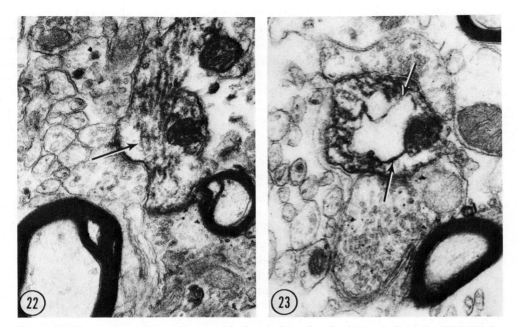

Figure 22. Two adjacent D1 endings reach the surface of a dendritic shaft of the HRP-filled lamina IV neuron in lamina I. The axodendritic synapse of the upper one (arrow) is clearly visible while the lower one has been sectioned obliquely. × 36,000.

Figure 23. Two dome-shaped endings synapse (arrows) on this fine dendritic shaft of the HRP-filled lamina IV neuron in Lissauer's tract. The bottom ending is a D1 ending and the top ending has too few clearly visible vesicles to permit definitive classification. × 36,000.

many collaterals in laminae III and IV before coursing toward the midline.

An EM analysis confirmed that some of these fine dorsal dendrites pass through the entire thickness of laminae I and II and extend well into Lissauer's tract, where they traveled among the numerous, tightly packed, small myelinated and unmyelinated axons (Fig. 19). The small shafts typically contained numerous neurotubules (Figs. 20–22) but did not contain aggregates of synaptic vesicles. These dendrites received synaptic connections from numerous D1 (Fig. 20) and D2 (Fig. 21) endings in lamina I and in Lissauer's tract. They were found with far greater frequency on these dendrites than on the dendrites of any of the other cell types examined. In several instances two or three adjacent dome-shaped endings were found on a single dendritic shaft in both lamina I (Fig. 22) and in Lissauer's tract (Fig. 23).

The fine dendritic shafts in their passage through laminae I and II and Lissauer's tract did not emit any spines and were not found entering any glomeruli where they might come in contact with the axonal endings of C and Aδ primary axons, which are known to terminate in these locations (see Gobel et al., 1981b for review). Electrophysiological characterizations of the primary input to this lamina IV neuron revealed that it received only low threshold Aβ input. It did not respond to noxious pinch or the application of noxious heat. It had no C response to electrical stimulation. These anatomical and physiological findings together suggest that this lamina IV neuron is not receiving primary inputs from those primary axons which arborize in laminae I and II. It probably receives its Aβ input on that portion of its dendritic arbor which courses through laminae III and IV, since Aβ primary axons are known to generate most of their axonal endings in these laminae (e.g. Brown et al., 1980).

VI. Conclusions

The descending axonal projection of the serotonergic neurons in nucleus raphe magnus and the immediately adjacent reticular formation has been intensively investigated in recent years. The results of experiments exploring the inhibitory effects of this projection have shown that it is capable of diminishing or inhibiting the response of dorsal horn neurons including spinothalamic and trigeminothalamic projection neurons to nociceptive primary inputs (e.g. Fields et al., 1977; Fields and Basbaum, 1978; Gerhart et al., 1981; Sessle et al., 1981; Willis et al., 1977; see also Basbaum, this volume and Willis, this volume). There are also some suggestions that some descending serotonergic axons may excite neurons in lamina I and II (Dubisson and Wall, 1979; Ruda and Gobel, 1980).

Figure 24 summarizes the distribution of non-primary, dome-shaped endings on the surface of examples of the four kinds of neurons which comprise the neuropil of laminae I and II. We think that most of these endings are probably serotonergic for the following two reasons. First, we already know that descending serotonergic axons constitute a major source of these dome-shaped endings. Second, the distribution of D1 and D2 endings in this study parallels the distribution of the same kinds of endings which were labeled in the tritiated serotonin and 5,6-dihydroxytryptamine uptake study (Ruda and Gobel, 1980) in several respects: these dome-shaped endings, especially the D1 endings, synapse outside of glomeruli largely on small caliber dendritic shafts; they are found less commonly synapsing on cell bodies, thick basal dendrites and dendritic spines; and they are much more prevalent along dendrites in laminae I and IIa than along dendrites in lamina IIb.

On the basis of the distribution of the dome-shaped axonal endings on the HRP-filled neurons, three mechanisms are suggested as to how descending serotonergic axons could inhibit the response of neurons in laminae I and II to primary axonal inputs. First, in the case of the lamina I neuron (Fig. 24, upper panel) and the stalked cell (Fig. 24, middle left panel), widely separated dome-shaped serotonergic endings (Fig. 24, clear endings) synapse along all parts of the dendritic arbors of these neurons, mostly on fine caliber shafts but also occasionally on spines. They lie interspersed among the scalloped primary

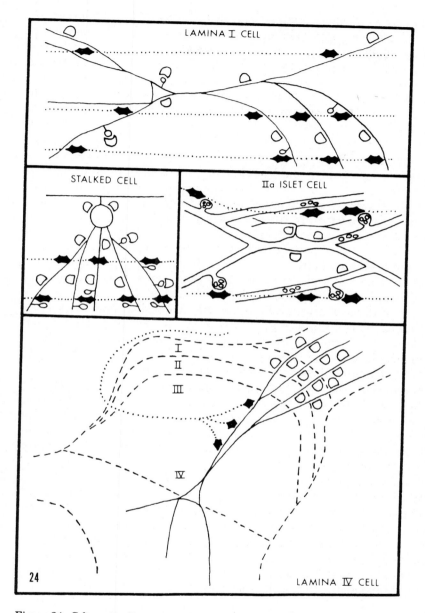

Figure 24. Schematic diagram depicting how the scalloped axonal endings of primary axons (filled) and the dome-shaped endings of descending serotonergic axons (clear) are thought to be distributed along the surface of the four major neuronal cell types which comprise the neuropil of laminae I and II. See Conclusion section for a discussion of how descending serotonergic axons might affect the response of these neurons to their primary inputs.

axonal endings (Fig. 24, dark endings) which are also widely dispersed and synapse on fine dendrites, although more commonly on spines than on shafts. The dome-shaped endings are in an ideal strategic position to prevent the spatial summation of primary inputs by generating inhibitory postsynaptic potentials. In this schema, it can be seen that, if the activity of the dome-shaped endings were synchronous, they could be very effective in blocking or inhibiting the response of a lamina I neuron or a stalked cell to its primary inputs (Ruda and Gobel, 1980).

In contrast, in the case of the lamina IIa islet cell (Fig. 24, middle right panel), the occurrence of dome-shaped endings on fine caliber dendrites was so infrequent that they probably would not be very effective in preventing summation of primary inputs. The same holds true in the case of the lamina IIb islet cell (not illustrated), where dome-shaped endings were encountered only rarely along its fine dendrites. In this same context, it is highly unlikely that descending serotonergic inputs could effectively block transmitter release from the synaptic vesicle-containing dendrites of the islet cells, since dome-shaped endings have not been found either on vesicle-filled islet cell spines and shafts in the glomeruli (Figs. 13 and 17) or on those portions of vesicle-containing islet cell dendritic shafts lying outside of glomeruli (Fig. 18).

The presence of dome-shaped endings on the cell bodies and thick basal dendrites of the above cell types (Figs. 4, 10, 15, 16 and 24) suggests a second mechanism through which descending serotonergic axons could act. Dome-shaped endings could generate IPSPs in the region of the cell body around the initial axonal segment and thereby prevent these cells from responding to even adequately summated primary inputs. This mechanism may be especially important in the case of one of the two lamina IIa islet cells examined because, first, two dome-shaped endings were found on its initial axonal segment (Fig. 16; and Gobel et al., 1980), and second, the very sparse distribution of dome-shaped endings along its dendritic arbor seems insufficient to block spatial summation of primary inputs.

The third mechanism relates to the lamina IV neuron, whose dorsal dendrites enter laminae I and II and Lissauer's tract where they receive an intense focus of synaptic input from D1 and D2 dome-shaped axonal endings but do not enter any glomeruli (Fig. 24, bottom panel). In this instance dome-shaped serotonergic endings could function by generating a sufficiently intense inhibitory focus on the dorsal dendritic arbor of this cell. In so doing, the cell may be rendered unresponsive to its Aβ primary input which it probably receives along its dendrites in laminae III and IV.

References

Barber, R.P., Vaughn, J.E., Saito, K., McLaughlin, B.J. and Roberts, E. (1978) GABAergic terminals are presynaptic to primary afferent terminals in the substantia gelatinosa of the rat spinal cord, *Brain Res.*, 141: 35-55.

Beal, J.A. and Fox, C.A. (1976) Afferent fibers in the substantia gelatinosa of the adult monkey (*Macaca mulatta*): A Golgi study, *J. comp. Neurol.*, 168: 113-144.

Bennett, G.J., Hayashi, H., Abdelmoumene, M. and Dubner, R. (1979) Physiological properties of stalked cells of the substantia gelatinosa intracellularly stained with horseradish peroxidase, *Brain Res.*, 164: 285-289.

Bennett, G.J., Abdelmoumene, M., Hayashi, H. and Dubner, R. (1980) Physiology and morphology of substantia gelatinosa neurons intracellularly stained with horseradish peroxidase, *J. comp. Neurol.*, 194: 809-828.

Bennett, G.J., Abdelmoumene, M., Hayashi, H., Hoffert, M.J. and Dubner, R. (1981) Spinal cord layer I neurons with axon collaterals that generate local arbors, *Brain Res.*, 209: 421-426.

Bennett, G.J., Ruda, M.A., Gobel, S. and Dubner, R. Enkephalin immunoreactive stalked cells and lamina IIb islet cells in cat substantia gelatinosa, *Brain Res.*, in press.

Brown, A.G., Rose, P.K. and Snow, P.J. (1977) The morphology of hair follicle afferent collaterals in the spinal cord of the cat, *J. Physiol. (Lond.)*, 272: 779-797.

Brown, A.G., Fyffe, R.E.W. and Noble, R. (1980) Projections from Pacinian corpuscles and rapidly adapting mechanoreceptors of glabrous skin to the cat's spinal cord, *J. Physiol. (Lond.)*, 307: 385-400.

Burton, H. and Loewy, A. (1976) Descending projections from the marginal cell layer and other regions of monkey spinal cord, *Brain Res.*, 116: 485-491.

Dubisson, D. and Wall, P.D. (1979) Medullary raphe influences on units in laminae 1 and 2 of cat spinal cord. *J. Physiol. (Lond.)*, 41: 41P.

Fields, H.L. and Basbaum, A.I. (1978) Brainstem control of spinal transmission neurons, *Ann. Rev. Physiol.*, 40: 193-221.

Fields, H.L., Basbaum, A.I., Clanton, C.H. and Anderson, S.D. (1977) Nucleus raphe magnus inhibition of spinal cord dorsal horn neurons, *Brain Res.*, 126: 441-454.

Gerhart, K.D., Wilcox, T.K., Chung, J.M. and Willis, W.D. (1981) Inhibition of nociceptive and nonnociceptive responses of primate spinothalamic cells by stimulation in medial brain stem, *J. Neurophysiol.*, 45: 121-136.

Glazer, E.J. and Basbaum, A.I. (1981) Immunocytochemical localization of leucine-enkephalin in the spinal cord of the cat: Enkephalin-containing marginal neurons and pain modulation, *J. comp. Neurol.*, 196: 377-389.

Gobel, S. (1974) Synaptic organization of the substantia gelatinosa glomeruli in the spinal trigeminal nucleus of the adult cat, *J. Neurocytol.*, 3: 219-243.

Gobel, S. (1975) Golgi studies of the substantia gelatinosa neurons in the spinal trigeminal nucleus, *J. comp. Neurol.*, 162: 397-415.

Gobel, S. (1978a) Golgi studies of the neurons in layer I of the dorsal horn of the medulla (trigeminal nucleus caudalis), *J. comp. Neurol.*, 180: 375-394,

Gobel, S. (1978b) Golgi studies of the neurons in layer II of the dorsal horn of the medulla (trigeminal nucleus caudalis), *J. comp. Neurol.*, 180: 395-414.

Gobel, S. and Falls, W.M. (1979) Anatomical observations of horseradish peroxidase filled terminal primary axonal arborizations in layer II of the substantia gelatinosa of Rolando, *Brain Res.*, 175: 335-340.

Gobel, S., Falls, W.M., Bennett, G.J., Abdelmoumene, M., Hayashi, H. and Humphrey, E. (1980) An EM analysis of the synaptic connections of horseradish peroxidase-filled stalked cells and islet cells in the substantia gelatinosa of adult cat spinal cord, *J. comp. Neurol.*, 194: 781-808.

Gobel, S., Bennett, G.J., Seltzer, Z., Hoffert, M.J. and Humphrey, E. (1981a) Synaptic inputs on the dorsally directed dendrites of an HRP-filled lamina IV dorsal horn neuron in the substantia gelatinosa of Rolando, *Soc. Neurosci. Abstr.*, 7: 529.

Gobel, S., Falls, W.M. and Humphrey, E. (1981b) Morphology and synaptic connections of ultrafine primary axons in lamina I of the spinal dorsal horn: Candidates for the terminal axonal arbors of primary neurons with unmyelinated (C) axons, *J. Neurosci.*, 1: 1163-1179.

Hockfield, S. and Gobel, S. (1978) Neurons in and near nucleus caudalis with long ascending projection axons demonstrated by retrograde labeling with horseradish peroxidase, *Brain Res.*, 139: 333-339.

Light, A.R. and Perl, E.R. (1979) Spinal termination of functionally identified primary afferent neurons with slowly conducting myelinated fibers, *J. comp. Neurol.*, 186: 117-132.

Light, A.R., Trevino, D.L. and Perl, E.R. (1979) Morphological features of functionally defined neurons in the marginal zone and substantia gelatinosa of the spinal dorsal horn, *J. comp. Neurol.*, 186: 133-155.

Light, A.R., Rethelyi, M. and Perl, E.R. (1980) Synaptology of physiologically identified, HRP-stained, neurons in the superficial dorsal horn of cats, *Soc. Neurosci. Abstr.*, 6: 38.

McLaughlin, B.J., Barber, R., Saito, K. and Roberts, E. (1975) Immunocytochemical localization of glutamate decarboxylase in rat spinal cord, *J. comp. Neurol.*, 164: 305-322.

Price, D.D. and Dubner, R. (1977) Neurons that subserve the sensory-discriminative aspects of pain, *Pain*, 3: 307-338.

Ralston, H.J., III and Ralston, D.D. (1979) The distribution of dorsal root axons in laminae I, II and III of the Macaque spinal cord: A quantitative electron microscope study, *J. comp. Neurol.*, 184: 643-684.

Ramón y Cajal, S. (1895) La fine anatomie de la moelle epiniere. In *Atlas der pathologischen Histologie des Nervensystems, Vol. 4*, Hirschwald, Berlin, pp. 1-35.

Ramón y Cajal, S. (1911) *Histologie du Système Nerveux de l'Homme et des Vertébrés, Vols. I and II* (1952 reprint), Instituto Ramón y Cajal, Madrid.

Ruda, M.A. and Gobel, S. (1980) Ultrastructural characterization of axonal endings in the substantia gelatinosa which take up [^{3}H]serotonin, *Brain Res.*, 184: 57-83.

Ruda, M.A., Allen, B. and Gobel, S. (1981a) Ultrastructural analysis of serotonergic medial brainstem afferents to the superficial dorsal horn, *Brain Res.*, 205: 175-180.

Ruda, M.A., Allen, B. and Gobel, S. (1981b) Ultrastructure of descending serotoninergic axonal endings in layers I and II of the dorsal horn, *J. Physiol. (Paris)*, 77: 205-209.

Sessle, B.J., Hu, J.W., Dubner, R. and Lucier, G.E. (1981) Functional properties of neurons in cat trigeminal subnucleus caudalis (medullary dorsal horn). II. Modulation of responses to noxious and nonnoxious stimuli by periaqueductal gray, nucleus raphe magnus, cerebral cortex and afferent influences, and effect of naloxone, *J. Neurophysiol.*, 45: 193-207.

Snyder, R.L., Faull, R.L.M. and Mehler, W.R. (1978) A comparative study of the neurons of origin of the spinocerebellar afferents in the rat, cat and squirrel monkey based on the retrograde transport of horseradish peroxidase, *J. comp. Neurol.*, 181: 883-852.

Willis, W.D., Haber, L.H. and Martin, R.F. (1977) Inhibition of spinothalamic tract cells and interneurons by brainstem stimulation in the monkey, *J. Neurophysiol.*, 40: 968-981.

Willis, W.D., Kenshalo, D.R., Jr. and Leonard, R.B. (1979) The cells of origin of the primate spinothalamic tract, *J. comp. Neurol.*, 188: 543-574.

Willis, W.D. and Coggeshall, R.E. (1978) *Sensory mechanisms of the Spinal Cord*, Plenum Press, New York, pp. 387-407.

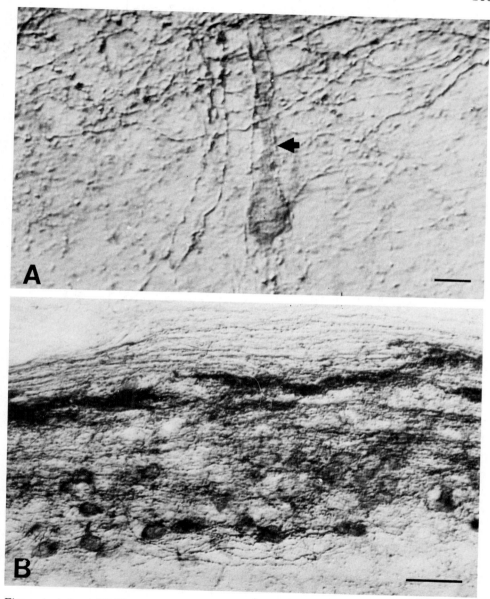

Figure 4. A, layer III SP-containing neuron invested with SP-positive fibers. Scale bar = 10 μm. B, SP-immunoreactivity in perikarya within layers I and II of the spinal cord. Parasagittal section. Most neurons are seen within layer II inner. Scale bar = 30 μm. (All immunohistochemistry prepared by Sternberger's (1979) method.)

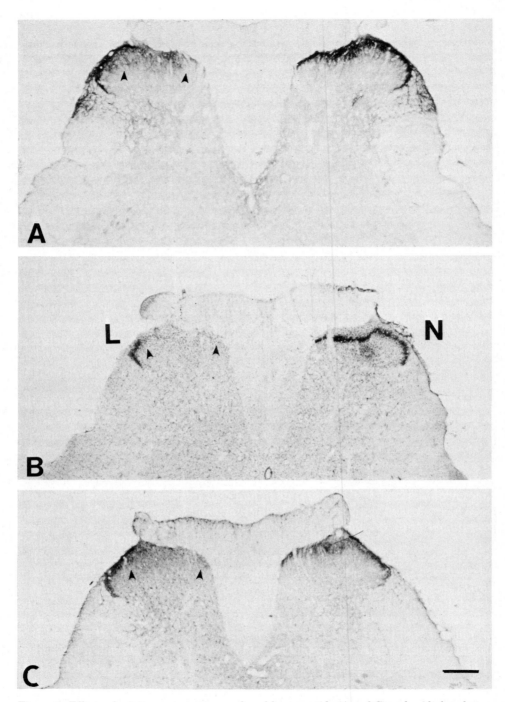

Figure 5. Effects of sciatic nerve section on dorsal horn peptide (A and C) and acid phosphatase levels at 35 days survival. A, SP; B, acid phosphatase; C, cholecystokinin-like immunoreactivity. N, normal side; L, lesioned side; arrowheads indicate region of depletion. Scale bar = 250 μm.

glutamic acid decarboxylase (GAD) content (Fig. 6). Correlation of histochemically defined cell types with those described from Golgi preparations has been particularly difficult, because of the poor dendritic labeling of cells in histochemical studies and the failure of workers to agree on an acceptable classification of gelatinosa neurons. Most published studies would support the presence of at least two distinct cell types as named by Gobel (1978) – the stalked cell (the limitotrophe neurons of Cajal, 1909) and the islet cell. The perikaryon of the stalked cell lies on the I/II_o border with spiny dendrites which pass diagonally into more ventral laminae. The axon ramifies within layer I. Islet cells are found throughout layer II and have long rostrocaudally directed dendrites with restricted spread in the medio-lateral plane, and an axon which ramifies within the vicinity of the neuron's dendritic tree. Both cell types have been described and characterized following intracellular injections of HRP with, in some cases, electron microscopic analysis (Gobel et al., 1980; Bennett et al., 1980; Light and Perl, 1979b). Two points of particular importance emerged. The receptive field properties of neurons could not be predicted on the basis of their morphology, although islet cells within II_i tended to be nonnociceptive, and islet cell dendrites are packed with synaptic vesicles and presynaptic to other dendrites and in some cases primary afferent axon terminals (Gobel et al., 1980).

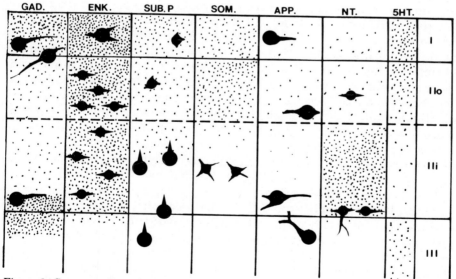

Figure 6. Summary diagram of terminal and perikaryal immunoreactivity of glutamate decarboxylase (GAD) and peptide-containing interneurons described in the text. ENK, enkephalin; SUB. P, substance P; SOM, somatostatin; APP, avian pancreatic polypeptide; NT, neurotensin; 5-HT, serotonin. Perikarya with proximal dendritic segments illustrated against a background of fine stipple which indicates the distribution of intrinsic peptide or GAD + "terminals". (From Hunt et al., 1981b, with permission.)

In an immunohistochemical study of the rat spinal cord using local injections of colchicine to build up perikaryal levels of peptides (Hunt et al., 1981b), we suggested that certain islet cells may contain enkephalin (Fig. 7), but that the only cell type which looked at all like a stalked cell was that containing GAD. This would suggest an inhibitory link between layers II and I. In the cat, however, a similar study suggested that most enkephalin-containing neurons were found within layer I (Glazer and Basbaum, 1981). While we were able to confirm the presence of enkephalin-positive perikarya within layer I in the rat, re-examination of the cat spinal cord following colchicine treatment (Hunt and Lovick, unpublished observations) revealed a number of enkephalin-positive neurons within layer II which would seem to be of the islet cell type (Fig. 7). The reasons for the discrepancies between the two studies are unknown but antibody specificity and methods of tissue preparation doubtless play a large part.

However, a further difficulty arises if it is accepted that islet cells are at least in part the enkephalinergic neurons of the substantia gelatinosa. Within gelatinosa opiate receptors are found both on intrinsic elements and on primary afferent fibers (LaMotte et al., 1976; Ninkovic et al., 1981b) (Fig. 8). This finding led to the suggestion that the direct inhibitory action of enkephalin upon primary afferents was responsible for the analgesia caused by opiates (Jessell and Iversen, 1977). However, investigation of the relationship between enkephalinergic terminals and primary afferents at the electron microscopic level in the rat (Hunt et al., 1980), cat (Glazer and Basbaum, 1981) and monkey (Aronin et al., 1981) has failed to find evidence for more than the occasional axo-axonic interaction. While methodological difficulties may in part be responsible for this negative finding the results as they stand are not completely compatible with the suggestion that islet cells are the enkephalinergic interneuron as these cells do seem to have direct interactions with primary afferents (Gobel et al., 1980). Perhaps the most parsimonious explanation is that there are several biochemical subclasses of islet cell, and that not all subclasses of islet cells are in synaptic relationship with primary afferents.

Other cell types distinct from islet and stalked cells have been described. Perhaps the most recognizable cell type, but not one which has been commented on in Golgi studies, is that containing neurotensin-like immunoreactivity. This cell type straddles the II/III border zone, with axon terminals forming a dense band within layer II_i, and matches the distribution of neurotensin receptors mapped autoradiographically (Ninkovic et al., 1981a). SP-containing cell bodies within layers II–IV of the spinal cord have predominantly bipolar dendritic trees and are enveloped in SP-positive primary afferents (Fig. 4) (Hunt et al., 1981b; Nagy et al., 1981b). Somatostatin-containing cell bodies are also found in layer II_i.

Avian pancreatic polypeptide (APP) is a relatively recent addition to the list of peptides found within the spinal cord (Lundberg et al., 1980; Hunt et al., 1981a) and is of particular interest as it has been shown to coexist with nor-

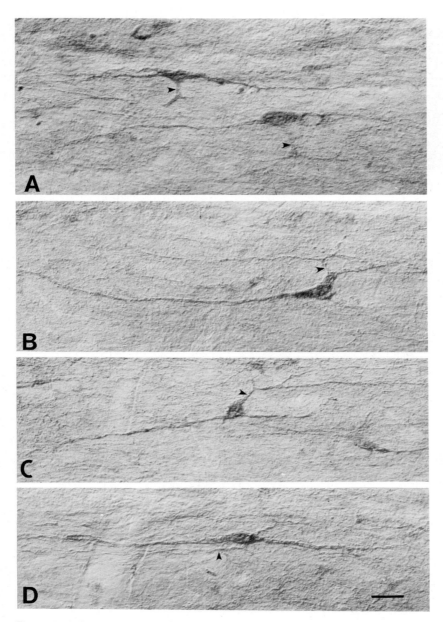

Figure 7. A–D, neurons stained for enkephalin-like immunoreactivity within layers I and II of the cat lumbar dorsal horn, 24 h after injection of 3 µl of colchicine (10 mg/ml). Neurons in A within layer II_o; B, C and D in II_i. The predominant orientation of the dendrites in these parasagittal sections is rostrocaudal, and neurons B, C and D are probably islet cells. The neurons in A, however, do have one large, ventrally directed dendritic process (arrowhead). These may therefore be stalked cells or more likely a form of neuron not easily classified into either class. Scale bar = 20 µm. (From Hunt and Lovick, unpublished observations.)

170

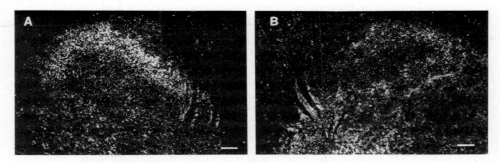

Effect of dorsal root section on the distribution of
specific ^{3}H-Etorphine binding sites in the rat
spinal cord dorsal horn.

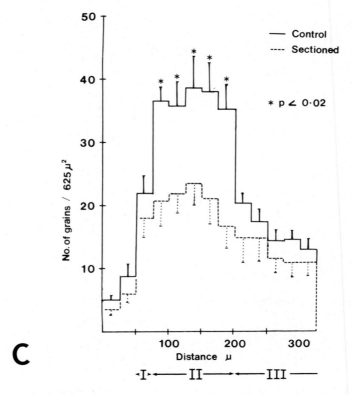

Figure 8. Distribution of opiate receptors within the superficial layers of the dorsal horn (A) and effect of dorsal root section (B). Opiate binding sites are reduced by approximately 40% within the superficial layers of the dorsal horn, and binding sites present on dorsal root fibers are concurrently lost (B) arrow. Scale bar = 100 μm. (From Ninkovic et al., 1981a.) C, grain counts across the superficial dorsal horn before (solid line) and 10 days after dorsal root section (hatched line).

adrenaline in certain medullary cell groups (A1–A3) and within the locus coeruleus (A6). However, injection of fluorescent dyes into the hypothalamus or spinal cord (Van der Kooy and Hunt, unpublished observation) demonstrated that APP neurons projected rostrally and not to the spinal cord. APP is present in large neurons scattered throughout the dorsal horn, with concentrations of terminal immunoreactivity in layers I and II_o. High concentrations of APP also occur in relation to the sacral parasympathetic system (Fig. 9). In the sacral cord, enkephalin coexists with APP (Hunt et al., 1981a). It has also been shown that enkephalin immunoreactivity is found within parasympathetic motor neurons (Glazer and Basbaum, 1980) but whether these are the neurons that also contain APP has not been directly demonstrated.

V. Local Interactions

The peptides neurotensin and enkephalin and the biogenic amines serotonin (5-HT) and noradrenaline produce a powerful analgesia when perfused intrathecally over the spinal cord (Yaksh and Rudy, 1976; Yaksh, 1980; Yaksh and Wilson, 1979; Yaksh, personal communication). The analgesic action of these compounds seems to be mediated through independent pharmacological channels. For example, only enkephalin-produced analgesia is naloxone reversible, while 5-HT and α_2 adrenoreceptors mediate the effects of 5-HT and noradrenaline, respectively (Yaksh and Rudy, 1976; Yaksh et al., 1976). Neurotensin and enkephalin may be released from spinal cord interneurons, while the amines originate from brain stem cell groups.

Local interactions were suggested as a possible means of mediating the analgesia caused by large fiber stimulation in man and rat (Melzack and Wall, 1965; Sjölund and Eriksson, 1979; Cervero and Iggo, 1978, 1980; Woolf et al., 1980). This inhibition may be mediated by enkephalin and/or neurotensin-releasing interneurons which are in a position deep within layer II and in layer III to receive input from large diameter non-nociceptive primary afferents, and influence the activity of overlying layers I and II neurons which receive much of the Aδ and C fiber input. However, the clinical significance of these findings is less clear. The effects of acupuncture, but not transcutaneous stimulation, are naloxone reversible (Sjölund and Eriksson, 1979), but in animals acupuncture analgesia is thought to be mediated by the midbrain and descending aminergic pathways (Cheng and Pomeranz, 1981). The work of Willer and Bussel (1980) would, however, suggest that certain nociceptive reflexes remaining in paraplegic humans are morphine sensitive.

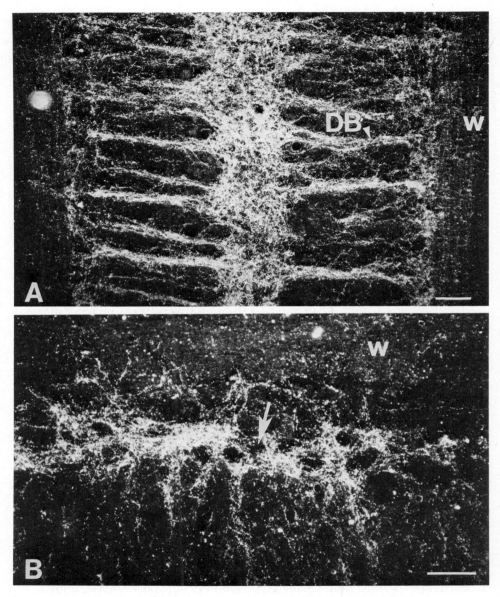

Figure 9. APP-like immunoreactivity within the lumbar and sacral spinal cord of the rat. A, horizontal section of sacral cord showing the strands of immunoreactive material within the dorsal bands (DB, arrow) and forming a continuous plexus of immunoreactive fibers and cells over the central canal. Dark-field illumination of immunoperoxidase staining. W, white matter. B, horizontal section of Onuf's nucleus within rat lumbar cord showing immunoreactivity densely packed around the motor neurons (arrow). Scale bar in A = 100 μm, in B = 50 μm. (From Gilbert and Hunt, unpublished observations.)

VI. Descending Control

A major source of control of dorsal horn output is thought to be through descending pathways originating from the hindbrain and pons (Kuypers and Maisky, 1975; Fields and Basbaum, 1978; Watkins et al., 1980).

Noradrenergic innervation of the dorsal horn originates from pontine cell groups (Nygren and Olson, 1977; Westlund et al., 1981) while 5-HT-containing neurons are found extensively within the nuclei of the raphe (Dahlström and Fuxe, 1964; Steinbusch, 1981).

The biochemical specificity of descending inhibition is far from clear. Within the raphe nuclei there are also perikarya which contain SP and thyrotropin-releasing hormone (TRH) as well as 5-HT, and there are numbers of neurons with various combinations of these substances (Johansson et al., 1981). The analysis of the system is further confused by the presence of an independent, descending enkephalin-containing pathway in the rat (Hökfelt et al., 1979; Finley et al., 1981).

Powerful analgesia can be produced by electrical stimulation of the central gray substance of the midbrain or of the nucleus raphe magnus. At certain sites within these areas the effects of stimulation are naloxone reversible, implying an enkephalinergic link in the descending pathway to the hindbrain or spinal cord (Akil et al., 1976; Oliveras et al., 1977; Zorman et al., 1981). Presumably the non-naloxone reversible sites implicate non-opiate systems in the development of analgesia. However, the system is made rather more complex by the finding that, in the cat, many 5-HT-containing neurons of the nucleus raphe magnus also contain enkephalin-like immunoreactivity (Hunt and Lovick, unpublished observations). Serotonin immunoreactivity is found within layers I and II_o and in deeper layers but is noticeably weak in the deeper portions of the substantia gelatinosa (II_i). This may imply that descending serotonergic axons in parallel or coexisting with a variety of peptidergic descending projections terminate in the region of the spinal projection neurons. For example, the spino-thalamic tract originates from neurons within layers I and V and these may well be the targets for descending influences (Giesler et al., 1978; Trevino and Carstens, 1975).

VII. Summary

The primary afferent input can be divided into two major groups of neurons on the basis of cell size. Large neurons give rise to large myelinated axons which terminate in layer III and more ventral layers of the spinal cord. Small diameter and unmyelinated axons with smaller perikarya terminate within layers I and II but in a differential manner. C fiber terminals are found throughout layers I and II but with concentrations of terminals within layers I_o and II_{int}. Aδ fibers terminate largely within layers I and II_o and on the II/III border zone.

Histochemically C fibers can be broken down into at least three discrete groups. SP-containing axons terminate within layers I and II_o and SOM-positive fibers within layer II_{int}. FRAP-positive terminals are found only in layer II_{int}. Destruction of C fibers with the drug capsaicin results in the loss of these peptides and FRAP from the dorsal roots and dorsal horn.

Within the substantia gelatinosa and adjacent layers it is possible to recognize a number of biochemically specific interneuronal populations containing SP-, enkephalin-, neurotensin-, APP- and SOM-like immunoreactivity. In rat, cat and monkey a number of neurons stained for enkephalin-like immunoreactivity were identified as islet cells. While there was a significant loss of opiate receptor from primary afferents after dorsal root section, electron microscopic investigation failed to demonstrate axo-axonic interactions between enkephalin interneurons and primary afferents.

Descending control of the dorsal horn is mediated by a biochemically heterogeneous population of neurons lying within pons and hindbrain. Serotonergic neurons may also contain one or a combination of peptides including SP, SOM, thyrotropin-releasing hormone and enkephalin or these peptide-containing neurons may exist independently of one another.

The substantia gelatinosa has been regarded as a "closed" neuronal system, i.e. without long projection systems. It receives a large portion of the primary afferent input and directs the information to adjacent and deeper layers containing projection neurons. Descending pathways seem to terminate most extensively within layers which contain projection neurons.

References

Akil, H., Mayer, D.J. and Liebeskind, T.C. (1976) Reduction of stimulation-produced analgesia by the narcotic antagonist, naloxone, *Science*, 191: 961-962.

Aronin, N., Di Figlia, M., M. Liotta, A.S. and Martin, J.B. (1981) Ultrastructural localization and biochemical features of immunoreactive Leu-enkephalin in monkey dorsal horn, *J. Neurosci.*, 1: 561-577.

Arvidsson, J. and Gobel, S. (1981) An HRP study of the central projections of primary trigeminal neurons which innervate tooth pulps in the cat, *Brain Res.*, 210: 1-16.

Barber, R.P., Vaughn, J.E., Randall Slemmon, J., Salvaterra, M., Roberts, E. and Leeman, S. (1979) The origin, distribution and synaptic relationships of substance P axons in rat spinal cord, *J. comp. Neurol.*, 184: 309-330.

Barbut, D., Polak, J.M. and Wall, P.D. (1981) Substance P in spinal cord dorsal horn decreases following peripheral nerve injury, *Brain Res.*, 205: 289-298.

Bennett, G.J., Abdelmoumene, M., Hayashi, H. and Dubner, R. (1980) Physiology and morphology of substantia gelatinosa neurons intracellularly stained with horseradish peroxidase, *J. comp. Neurol.*, 194: 781-808.

Bessou, P. and Perl, E.R. (1969) Response of cutaneous sensory units with unmyelinated fibers to noxious stimuli, *J. Neurophysiol.*, 32: 1025-1043.

Brown, A.G., Rose, P.K. and Snow, P.J. (1977) The morphology of hair follicle afferent fibre collaterals in the spinal cord of the cat, *J. Physiol. (Lond.)*, 272: 779-797.

Brown, A.G., Rose, P.K. and Snow, P.J. (1978) Morphology and organization of axon collaterals

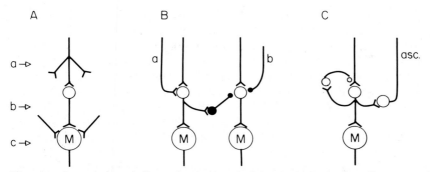

Figure 1. A, arrows a–c indicate the sites at which transmission in the reflex arc can be inhibited. In B, part a shows indirect inhibition of interneurons by excitation of other interneurons giving inhibition; part b shows primary inhibition which can be evoked either by descending inhibitory fibers, as shown in the diagram, or by excitation of interneurons not influenced from primary afferents. C, schematic diagram of interneuronal connections to motoneurons (M), primary afferent terminals and ascending (asc.) pathways. The effects to the former two target neurons are possibly mediated by separate interneuronal pathways.

facilitation is due to disinhibition. The primary inhibition of one reflex pathway removes an interactive inhibition of another pathway and thus releases transmission in it (diagram, Fig. 10). It should be mentioned that the classification of the dorsal reticulospinal system as primary inhibitory has been questioned by Jeneskog and Johansson (1977), not from findings with direct stimulation of the system, but from results obtained with mesencephalic stimulation *assumed* to induce synaptic activation of the dorsal reticulospinal system. Reasons for the assumption that the two monoaminergic systems act at an interneuronal level and not by evoking PAD have been given previously (Lundberg, 1966).

All the investigations reviewed below regarding the descending inhibitory control of interneurons were performed with the indirect technique of recording their effects on target neurons shown in Figure 1C (cf. Lundberg, 1975). For the vast majority of interneuronal pathways this is still the only technique available if we wish to investigate effects on interneuronal pathways with a known function.

III. The Flexor Reflex Afferents (FRA)

To a large extent this review deals with the inhibitory control from the brain stem of transmission from the flexor reflex afferents (FRA). They include group II and III muscle afferents, joint afferents and low and high threshold cutaneous afferents, which act together by virtue of convergence on common interneurons (cf. Lundberg, 1979; Kniffki et al., 1981b). They were called the FRA because they all may evoke flexor reflex actions in the acute spinal preparation (Eccles and Lundberg, 1959a), but they also supply a number of alternative reflex paths, e.g. excitatory to extensors, inhibitory to flexors (cf. Lundberg, 1979). In all cases, the reflex actions are drawn from a wide receptive field which, for muscle afferents, includes both flexors and extensors. There are two classes of reflexes from the FRA: the short-latency reflexes found in the acute spinal cat, and the late, long-latency reflexes (Fig. 10) which appear in acute spinal cats after DOPA or 5-HTP (Sections V and VI). In this review "reflex actions from the FRA" denotes the former actions when not otherwise stated. It should be admitted that the term FRA has been somewhat unfortunate because of the association it has with a fixed reflex pattern of flexor activation and extensor inhibition activated by nociceptors. Experiments with adequate stimulation of muscles suggest that strong FRA effects are evoked by group III afferents from mechanoreceptors (Holmqvist and Lundberg, 1961). There is also evidence that afferents belonging to the FRA are activated during active limb movements (cf. Lundberg, 1979), and our hypothesis presupposes that mechanoreceptive group III muscle afferents (Bessou and Laporte, 1961; Paintal, 1960; Kniffki et al., 1981a) are responsible – about 70% of the group III afferents are mechanoreceptors (Mense, personal communication). A contribution from nociceptive afferents to the interneuronal reflex paths from the FRA to motoneurons has not yet been proven. The critical experiment would be spatial facilitation of actions from the other afferents from a pure nociceptive input. Kniffki et al. (1981a) have demonstrated convergence on common interneurons in reflex pathways to motoneurons between group II afferents (cutaneous and muscular) and group III and/or IV muscle afferents activated by algesic substances. However, they point out that the chemical stimuli do not differentiate between muscular nociceptors and muscular receptors not having a nociceptive function. Similar experiments should be performed with pure nociceptive stimulation of the skin. I think it is likely that nociceptive afferents contribute to the interneuronal reflex pathways from the FRA, but my only support for this view comes from the observation that, when the reflex activation of flexor motoneurons from the FRA reverses to inhibition, there is also reversal of the effect of noxious stimulation of the skin (Fig. 4). *It is not known if there is a special spinal reflex pathway from nociceptors.* Interneurons belonging to reflex pathways from the FRA relay effects to motoneurons from descending motor tracts such as the corticospinal, rubrospinal, vestibulospinal and long propriospinal fibers, and it is assumed that afferents belonging to the FRA are activated by the ensuing movement and, by their action on common interneurons, give a reinforcing feedback of movements commanded from higher motor centers (cf. Baldissera et al., 1981; Lundberg, 1979).

Volleys in the FRA also activate interneuronal pathways which produce PAD. They evoke some depolarization in Ib terminals and in terminals of low threshold cutaneous afferents which may not belong to the FRA, but the main effect appears to be in the terminals of the FRA (Eccles et al., 1962; cf. Schmidt, 1971), so that the FRA can presynaptically inhibit transmission from their own terminals (Fig. 1C). This negative feedback may serve to regulate the reinforcing action from the FRA onto the interneuronal paths to motoneurons. The investigations of supraspinal control of FRA paths to primary afferent terminals have aimed at testing the hypothesis that the presynaptic inhibition has a functional relationship to the actions from the FRA onto motoneurons.

The FRA also have powerful actions on many ascending pathways which are described by others as having "wide dynamic range" (Mendell, 1966; Willis, this volume). This was first noted for neurons with axons in the dorsal half of the lateral funiculus (DLF) which were activated from both skin and muscle afferents with very large receptive fields (Laporte et al., 1956). Subsequently, some of them were shown to belong to the dorsal spinocerebellar tract (DSCT) and others to the spinocervical tract (SCT) (Lundberg and Oscarsson, 1960, 1961; Lundberg, 1964b). In addition to the FRA input, they receive modality-specific monosynaptic excitation from small, receptive skin fields. The FRA-evoked discharge in these neurons gives a substantial contribution to the mass discharge in the DLF (Fig. 6C and D). However, the main excitatory ascending FRA pathways are ventrally located, as shown by the large mass discharge evoked in the dissected ventral quadrants (Fig. 7C and D). Lundberg and Oscarsson (1962) distinguished two main groups: the bilateral ventral flexor reflex tract (bVFRT) and the crossed ventral flexor reflex tract (coVFRT). Oscarsson and his colleagues have investigated the VFRT extensively and found that these tracts are part of the spino-olivo-cerebellar and spino-reticulo-cerebellar pathways (Oscarsson, 1973). Numerous subdivisions of these pathways exist, and the disclosure of longitudinal zones and microzones in cerebellum is based largely on the results of the projection of the different FRA-activated pathways (Oscarsson, 1973; Andersoon and Oscarsson, 1978; cf. also Sjölund, this volume). It is possible that some VFRT neurons are spinoreticular without cerebellar projection, and some axons may be spinothalamic (Trevino et al., 1972). It has recently been shown that there is an FRA-activated ("wide dynamic range") subdivision of the spinothalamic tract in primates (Foreman et al., 1977, 1979; Willis, 1979).

Volleys in the FRA also inhibit many ascending pathways, notably the VSCT, where it occurs in the subgroups of neurons monosynaptically activated from Ib afferents, from Ia afferents, and in those without monosynaptic projections from primary afferents (Oscarsson, 1957; Lundberg and Weight, 1971).

It was a surprising finding that so many ascending neurons were influenced from such large receptive fields and by such diverse receptor systems. Since the muscle, joint and skin afferents which influenced the ascending pathways also evoked flexion reflex actions in spinal cats and from correspondingly large receptive fields, I suggested that these ascending FRA pathways monitor the activity of interneurons in spinal reflex pathways and thus are not primarily concerned with signalling peripheral events (Lundberg, 1959). The discovery of descending excitation of interneurons belonging to these reflex pathways (cf. Baldissera et al., 1981; Lundberg, 1979) made it more understandable why the higher centers required information regarding this interneuronal activity. It is particularly noteworthy that the great majority of neurons belonging to spinocerebellar pathways are FRA influenced and appear to carry information regarding "the internal state of lower motor centers" (Oscarsson, 1973; Ekerot et al., 1979; Sjölund, this volume).

Such ascending "internal" information has been demonstrated for other interneuronal systems (Alstermark et al., 1981; Illert and Lundberg, 1978; Lindström, 1973). For the ascending FRA pathways, the evidence is more circumstantial and rests partly on the parallelism in supraspinal control of interneuronal transmission to motoneurons and ascending pathways, not only for the inhibitory systems discussed in this review but also for different excitatory systems (Baldissera and Bruggencate, 1976; Baldissera and Roberts, 1976; Hongo and Okada, 1967; Lundberg et al., 1963; Magni and Oscarsson, 1961). A lacking parallelism in control was found only for FRA-activated neurons of the SCT, and it was pointed out that the information in these neurons may be more directly sensory (Lundberg et al., 1963). These neurons are viewed by other investigators as carrying traditional, although composite, sensory information (Mendell, 1966; Brown, 1973; Cervero et al., 1977; Kniffki et al., 1977). Also, the FRA-activated subdivision of the primate spinothalamic tract is discussed as providing receptor information (Willis, 1979).

Experiments with the effect of adequate receptor activation on the FRA influenced pathway revealed effects by muscle stretch and contraction (Holmqvist et al., 1956; Oscarsson, 1960). Effects from skin are evoked by touch (hair), pressure and pinching (Holmqvist et al., 1956; Lundberg and Oscarsson, 1960; Oscarsson, 1957). In case of the FRA subdivision of DSCT and SCT, strong touch activation may be evoked monosynaptically from small receptive fields, but touch stimuli also influence the VSCT and the bVFRT, which have no monosynaptic projection from skin. The SCT neurons, which have C-fiber input (Mendell, 1966), respond to noxious heat (Brown, 1973; Cervero et al., 1977) and are discussed as a putative "pain pathway" (cf. also Kniffki et al., 1977). It is possible that further experiments may show that all the numerous FRA pathways have C-fiber input and respond to noxious heat.

IV. The Tonic Decerebrate Inhibition

The experiments were made mainly with the technique of conditioning monosynaptic reflexes (Figs. 2B, 3 and 4), by which synaptic actions in motoneurons can be measured. For those who prefer to see the synaptic potentials, Figure 2A–F shows that volleys in high threshold muscle afferents did not evoke synaptic actions before, but produced the characteristic polysynaptic EPSPs after, transection of the spinal cord (Eccles and Lundberg, 1959b). In the decerebrate state, there was often complete suppression of transmission in the excitatory pathway to flexor, and in the inhibitory pathway to extensor, motoneurons from single volleys in high threshold muscle afferents and joint afferents (Figs. 2 and 3). Volleys in cutaneous afferents usually gave some synaptic effect also in the decerebrate state, but the spinal transection invariably gave a large increase. These results revealed a very effective tonic inhibition of transmission in the reflex pathways from the FRA, but there has been some discussion on whether or not more specific reflex pathways from cutaneous afferents are tonically inhibited. Engberg (1964) demonstrated that this is the case for the pathway mediating the toe extensor reflex, which is evoked by gentle pressure on a very specific skin region, the plantar cushion. Investigation of reflex pathways from group I muscle afferents revealed tonic decerebrate inhibition of transmission in inhibitory and excitatory reflex pathways from Ib afferents but *not* in the reciprocal Ia inhibitory pathway.

Tests with adequate skin stimulation (Holmqvist and Lundberg, 1961) revealed very effective decerebrate tonic inhibition of the nociceptor flexor responses; sometimes even *extremely strong* noxious stimuli failed to influence flexor monosynaptic tests reflexes, while strong flexor facilitation invariably was evoked after spinalization (Fig. 4). Thus, it can be inferred that there is a very effective tonic decerebrate inhibition not only of the contribution that nociceptors may give to the reflex pathways from the FRA, but also of transmission in a putative private reflex path from nociceptors (cf. above).

Lesion experiments were performed to locate the brain stem centers responsible for the inhibition and the location of the descending pathways in the spinal cord (Holmqvist and Lundberg, 1959). Lesions of the vestibular nuclei, which are the main source of decerebrate rigidity, did not result in any release, but a medial medullary brain stem lesion which did not decrease decerebrate rigidity gave release of FRA transmission from the tonic inhibition. These results showed that the tonic inhibition was maintained by centers in the medial reticular formation. It was known that decerebrate rigidity depended on ventral spinal pathways (Fulton et al., 1930), but there was some evidence that ipsilateral dorsal pathways contributed to the tonic of reflexes (Liddell et al., 1932; Downman and Hussein, 1958). Our experiments with spinal cord lesions revealed that the tonic inhibition of ipsilateral reflex pathways was retained after spinal hemisection of either side. In either hemicord the tonic inhibition was maintained after a ventral transection (Figs. 2 and 3). On the other hand, when the DLF was sectioned in the hemisected preparation there was a *full release* to the spinal state (Fig. 3). It should be noted that these measurements of synaptic action allowed quantitative measurements of the degree of tonic inhibition. The lack of contribution to it from ventrally located pathways (except for some release of inhibition to flexors) was confirmed in experiments in which there was a partial release from the onset, which remained unchanged by transection of the ventral quadrant (Fig. 7 in Holmqvist and Lundberg, 1959). It was also shown that there is some tonic inhibition in the intact anesthetized cat, and that it increases after decerebration (Fig. 4).

Experiments in decerebrate cats with midline brain stem lesions at different

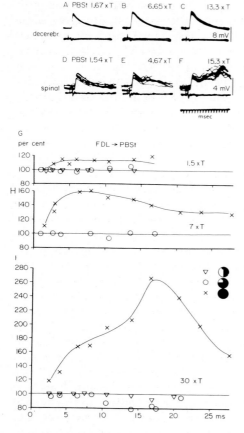

Figure 2. Decerebrate tonic control of transmission from high threshold muscle afferents to motoneurones and the effect of spinal cord lesions. A–F, intracellular recording from posterior biceps-semitendinosus (PBSt) motoneurons in a decerebrate cat before and after spinal transection as indicated. Stimulation of the PBSt nerve was graded. The strength of stimulation in these records and in all other figures is given in multiples of threshold for the nerve. Note the lack of effects from high threshold muscle afferents in B and C. G–I, effect of conditioning volleys in the flexor digitorum and hallucis longus (FDL) nerve on the flexor monosynaptic reflex from the nerve to PBSt. In each curve 100% on the ordinate represents the unconditioned amplitude of the test monosynaptic reflex. Conditioning amplitude of monosynaptic test reflexes, expressed as percentage of control amplitude, is plotted as a function of time interval between incoming conditioning and testing volleys. The experiment was made on a decerebrate cat and the synaptic effects after the different lesions indicated in I are given by different symbols (key in I). Note that release occurred only after transection of the ipsilateral dorsal part of the lateral funicle (DLF). Graph G, action by group I afferents; graph H, by group I and II afferents; and graph I , by group I, II and III afferents. (A–F from Eccles and Lundberg, 1959b; G–I from Holmqvist and Lundberg, 1959, with permission.)

Lundberg and Oscarsson, 1961), it is clear that the decerebrate inhibition effectively suppresses transmission from the FRA both to the DSCT and the SCT. The same holds true for the three systems described in Sections V, VI and VII of this paper. Figure 6E illustrates that the inhibition of the VSCT from the FRA is effectively suppressed in the decerebrate state, while in the spinal state the same conditioning volley gave complete inhibition of the monosynaptic test discharge in VSCT. Lesion experiments such as those described above revealed that the tonic decerebrate inhibition is, also in this case, maintained exclusively by pathways descending in the DLF (Fig. 6F–K), and that a bilateral effect is exerted from each side. For the study of the tonic control of transmission to the ventrally located bVFRT, it was possible to record from the dissected ventral quadrants while maintaining the DLF intact on both sides. Under these conditions volleys in high threshold muscle afferents did not evoke any ventral discharge, but during a cold block of conduction in the intact dorsal part of the spinal cord the characteristic polysynaptic discharge appeared (Fig. 7D and E). After rewarming, the tonic inhibition of transmission reappeared (Fig. 7G and H). The marked increase of baseline noise during the cold block (Fig. 7F) is due to the appearance of resting activity in the VFRT,

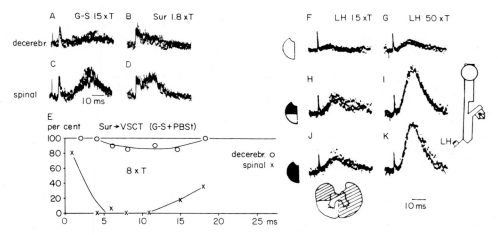

Figure 6. Decerebrate tonic control of transmission to ascending pathways. The discharges were recorded bipolarly from dissected fasciculi of the spinal cord: in A–D, from the ipsilateral DLF; and in F–K, from the contralateral spinal half on stimulation of the left hamstring (LH) nerve. The graph in E shows the conditioning effect from the cutaneous sural (Sur) nerve on the monosynaptic VSCT discharge evoked from group Ib afferents, G-S and PBSt in the contralateral spinal half. By this technique the synaptic effects in the VSCT neurons are measured by the same method as the synaptic actions in motoneurons in Figures 2–4. The reversible cold block method shown in Figure 7 was used to obtain the curves in E; spinal ×, cold block; decerebr. o, rewarming. Note in the spinal state the release of inhibition to VSCT (E) and of polysynaptic discharges in the ipsilateral (ipsi) DLF (C and D) and the contralateral (co) spinal half (J and K). Records F–K show that the tonic inhibition mediated by the intact ipsilateral hemicord is completely abolished by a DLF transection. (From Holmqvist et al., 1960, with permission.)

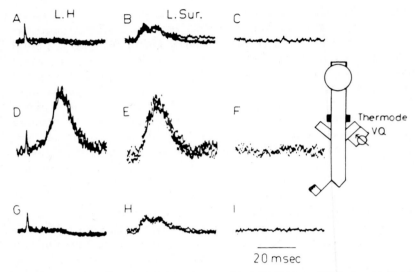

Figure 7. Reversible release of ascending transmission by cold block spinalization. The ventral fasciculi were dissected for recording as shown in the diagram and the thermode was placed under the intact dorsal cord. Strong stimuli were given to the left hamstring (L.H) and the left sural (L.Sur) nerves. A–C, control records obtained before cold block. D–F, during cold block. G–H, after rewarming the cord. Note the complete decerebrate suppression of polysynaptic discharge from high threshold muscle afferents before (A) and after (G) the cold block, and the release of transmission from both muscle and cutaneous afferents during cold block (D and F). The resting activity increases considerably during the block (F). Similar findings were made by recording from the ipsilateral ventral quadrant (VQ). (From Holmqvist et al., 1960, with permission.)

showing that the depression is not an occlusive phenomenon but due to genuine inhibition.

Oscarsson (1960) found that the inhibitory effect on VSCT neurons by muscle contraction was completely suppressed in the decerebrate state. Adequate stimulation of skin, tested on unit activity in the VSCT, revealed complete decerebrate tonic suppression of the inhibition exerted by touch and pressure and only slight action by strong pinching; the usual inhibitory effects were found after spinal transection. Similar, more extensive studies of the spinocervical tract (Brown, 1973; Cervero et al., 1977) with reversible cold block revealed effective decerebrate suppression of the effect of noxious heat, pinching and pressure and partly from touch, with remaining specific activation from hair follicle mechanoreceptors presumably due to their monosynaptic connections.

Since monosynaptic transmission to all three of the pathways tested (DSCT, SCT and VSCT) was not suppressed in the decerebrate state, it was postulated that the suppression was due to inhibition of interneuronal transmission to the ascending tract cells. The finding that interneuronal transmission to these ascending tracts was subject to a similar tonic control as interneuronal transmission to motoneurons clearly accorded with the hypothesis that these ascending pathways monitored activity in the interneuronal pathways to motoneurons. Further strong support for this view was provided by the finding that differential release of inhibitory and excitatory actions from the FRA with brain stem lesions at different rostrocaudal levels (cf. above) was also found for transmission to ascending pathways (Carpenter et al., 1965).

V. The Noradrenergic System

Soon after our analysis of the tonic decerebrate inhibition came the demonstration of monoaminergic nerve terminals in the spinal cord, which were shown to belong exclusively to descending pathways (Carlsson et al., 1964; Dahlström and Fuxe, 1965). A variety of findings indicated that the monoamines were transmitters, and it was shown that electrical stimulation of the spinal cord induced monoamine liberation to the surrounding fluid (Andén et al., 1964a). These results opened up the possibility of investigating the effect of the monoaminergic fibers by chemical activation, initially by giving transmitter precursors, which pass the blood–brain barrier, and then analysing, by pharmacological methods, whether the effects produced were due to transmitter liberation and action on specific receptors. It was an obvious advantage that these experiments could be performed with transected monoaminergic axons (acute spinal cats), so that effects exerted on their cell bodies could be excluded.

Magnusson and Rosengren (1963) reported that DOPA increased the flexor reflex in acute spinal rats, but our analysis revealed that an intravenous injection of DOPA in acute spinal cats very effectively inhibited transmission of single volleys from the FRA (Andén et al., 1964b, 1966b). This is illustrated in Figure 8 for transmission to motoneurons and in Figure 9 for transmission to primary afferent terminals and ascending pathways. There was also inhibition of Ib but not of reciprocal Ia inhibitory pathways to motoneurons. The group I DRP and component I of the cutaneous DRP were not depressed, and monosynaptic transmission to ascending pathways likewise was not affected (Fig. 9). The inhibitory effects were thus selective and identical with those exerted in the decerebrate state. A difference showed up, however, when a short train of stimuli was given to the FRA. After DOPA, but rarely in the decerebrate state, such a train evoked a massive, late, long-lasting reflex discharge in flexor motoneurons, together with a late long-lasting DRP (Fig. 10). The late discharge explains why Magnusson and Rosengren (1963) found an increased flexor reflex after DOPA. There is considerable evidence favoring the view that the pathways mediating the late effects from the FRA are inhibited by activity in the pathways mediating the short-latency effects from the FRA (diagram, Fig. 10), and that transmission in the late pathway is released when the short latency pathway is inhibited after DOPA (Jankowska et al., 1967). Results regarding the organization of the reflex pathways mediating

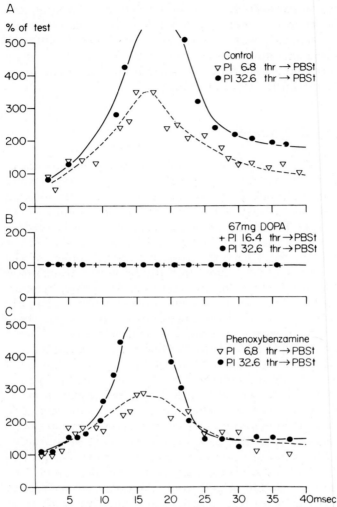

Figure 8. The effect of DOPA on synaptic actions from high threshold muscle afferents in motoneurons. The experiment was made on an unanesthetized, decorticated acute spinal cat. The synaptic actions from high threshold muscle afferents from Pl were measured by the conditioning effect on monosynaptic test reflexes to flexors (A–C) and extensors (D–F). An intravenous injection of DOPA resulted in complete inhibition, both of the excitatory pathway to flexors (B) and the inhibitory one to extensors (E). The curves in B and F were obtained 10 min after the DOPA injection, and an intravenous injection of phenoxybenzamine (20 mg/kg) 15 min later removed the inhibitory effect. (From Andén et al., 1966b, with permission.)

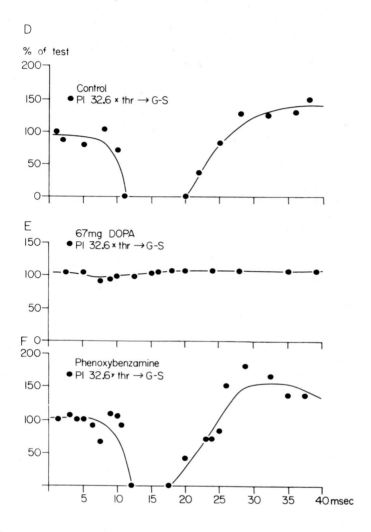

the late effects have been reviewed elsewhere (Baldissera et al., 1981; Lundberg, 1966, 1979, 1981), and I will only consider here the further analysis of the inhibitory effect of DOPA.

The effect of DOPA was prevented by inhibition of DOPA-decarboxylase, while inhibition of monoamine oxidase (MAO) gave a 10-fold potentiation (Andén et al., 1966a). The effect of DOPA was reversed by the adrenergic α-receptor blockers phenoxybenzamine and chlorpromazine, but not by the β-receptor blocker nethelide. DOPA was without effect after pretreatment with reserpine. Since there is normal formation of dopamine (DA), but not of noradrenaline (NA), after such pretreatment, this finding was taken to indicate that DOPA acts by liberation of NA and not of DA. The effect of DOPA was also investigated (Jurna and Lundberg, 1968) after inhibition by DTC (diethyl-dithiocarbamate) of DA-β-hydroxylase, the enzyme necessary for the formation of NA from DA. It was somewhat surprising that DOPA exerted its normal effect after inhibition of this enzyme (Fig. 11). However, a second DOPA injection given four hours later, after recovery from the first injection, was completely ineffective, whereas it exerted normal effects in cats without inhibition of DA-β-hydroxylase (Fig. 11). The results showed that DOPA acts by liberation of pre-existing stores of NA. After enzyme inhibition DA is still formed from DOPA, which in turn displaces NA from its stores and liberates NA from its terminals. DA cannot be hydroxylated into NA and the stores of NA are depleted. A second injection of DOPA will therefore be ineffective despite the formation of new DA from DOPA. These results provided further strong evidence for the view that DOPA acts by liberation of NA and not via DA, a finding which is relevant because DA fibers are now known to project to

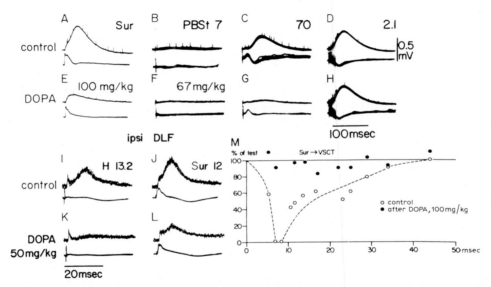

Figure 9. The effect of DOPA on transmission to primary afferent terminals and to ascending pathways. Same preparation as in Figure 8 A–H; the DRPs were recorded as in Figure 5 from the most caudal rootlet in L6. Note depression of transmission from high threshold muscle afferents (C and G) and of the second component of the cutaneous DRP (A and E) after DOPA, but no change in the DRPs evoked by a train of group I volleys from PBSt in record H or in the first component of the cutaneous DRP in record E. I–M, the records in I–L are mass discharges recorded from the ipsilateral DLF, and the curves in M show the effect of conditioning volleys in the cutaneous Sur. nerve on VSCT obtained as described in Figure 6. Note the virtually complete suppression of the polysynaptic discharge from high threshold muscle afferents (I and K), the marked depression of the discharge evoked from cutaneous afferents (J and L) and the complete removal of inhibition to VSCT (M). All the effects reversed quickly when phenoxybenzamine was administered. (From Andén et al., 1966b, with permission.)

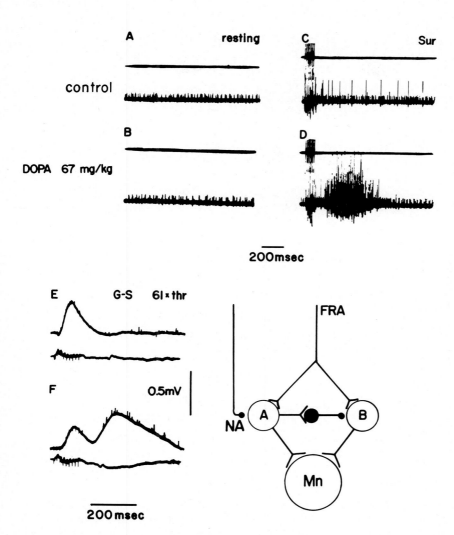

Figure 10. Late effects evoked after DOPA by a train of volleys in the FRA in motoneurons and primary afferent terminals. Same preparation as in Figure 8, but the lower traces in A–D were obtained from the tenuissimus nerve; the upper traces are triphasic recordings from the sciatic nerve. The upper traces in E and F are DRPs recorded as in Figure 5. A short train of volleys in the cutaneous Sur nerve before DOPA evoked an early reflex discharge followed by an after discharge. After DOPA (and also after 5-HTP) the same volleys evoke a massive late discharge in both α- and γ-afferents. Note the slow time base. The late DRP in F was evoked from high threshold muscle afferents and is due to PAD in Ia afferent terminals. Flaxedil was given in doses three times that required to produce a neuromuscular block, so the delayed effects are not secondary to reflex activation of peripheral receptors. In the diagram each interneuron represents a chain. A is the pathway for the short latency action found in the acute spinal state, and B is the pathway transmitting the late activation. (From Andén et al., 1964c, 1966b; diagram from Jankowska et al., 1967, with permission.)

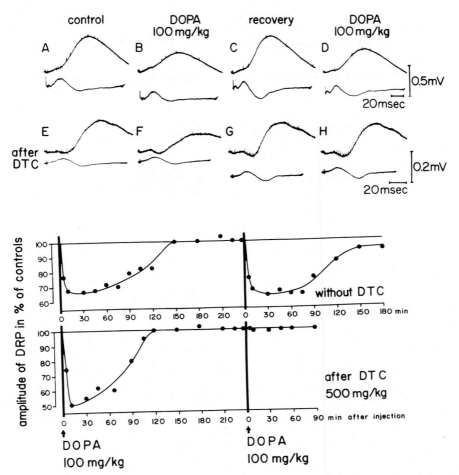

Figure 11. The effect of DOPA after inhibition of dopamine-β-hydroxylase. The effect of DOPA on the DRP was evoked by stimulation of the G-S nerve with a strength 70 times threshold. The two rows of records (A–D and E–H) were taken from two different experiments. The upper row is from an experiment without pretreatment, the lower row from an experiment after pretreatment with diethyldithiocarbamate (DTC, 500 mg/kg). The upper traces are recordings of DRPs. A and E are control records, E being taken 60 min after the injection of DTC. B and F were obtained 30 min after the first injection of DOPA. C and G were recorded 240 min after the first injection, shortly before the second injection of DOPA (recovery). D and H were taken 30 min after the second injection of DOPA, showing the difference in the action of DOPA without and with pretreatment with DTC. The time course of the effect of DOPA on the amplitude of the DRP is plotted for both experiments in the graph. Ordinates, amplitude of the DRP in % of control; abscissae, time in minutes after the injections, which are indicated by arrows and vertical bars. (From Jurna and Lundberg, 1968, with permission.)

with chemical activation of the individual descending systems, allow investigations of the extent to which each of them is fractionated into subsystems. It is my guess that there might be considerable fractionation within the dorsal reticulospinal system, and that higher motor centers, as a part of their commands and movement control, can differentially activate or inhibit subsystems which control different segmental feedback loops regulating movements. Such speculations raise the question as to how the dorsal reticulospinal system is controlled from the cerebral cortex, a problem which is amenable to analysis with the experimental arrangement shown in Fig. 16. It has generally been assumed that the NA and 5-HT systems have very diffuse general functions (for the NA system, cf. Moore and Bloom, 1979), but I believe that the number of descending monoaminergic neurons is sufficient to allow for specialization with each system (cf., Björklund and Skagerberg, this volume). For example, I would be surprised if the control of reflex pathways from the FRA and from Ib afferents turns out to be exerted by the same NA neurons. The same holds true with respect to the two effects exerted by the descending 5-HT fibers, excitation of motoneurons and inhibition of transmission from the FRA.

The problem of subsystems among the four descending inhibitory systems is also relevant with respect to pain control. The tonic decerebrate inhibition may completely suppress transmission to motoneurons of even extremely strong noxious stimuli (Section IV), but our analysis of the four descending systems does not include effects from nociceptors. It is possible that special subsystems of descending neurons inhibit interneurons activated exclusively from nociceptive afferents (cf. Fields and Basbaum, 1977; Cervero and Iggo, 1980). I have pointed out that we have insufficient knowledge regarding the input from nociceptors to the reflex pathways from the FRA, and we do not even know if there is a special reflex pathway from nociceptors (Section III). If nociceptive afferents contribute to the reflex pathway from the FRA, they might do so via special interneurons with exclusively nociceptive input subject to their own descending control. These interneurons might converge on interneurons belonging to reflex pathways from the FRA which might be under inhibitory control from other subsystems of descending neurons whose primary function, perhaps, is to assist in regulation of normal movements. If so, motor responses to noxious stimuli might be inhibited at an interneuronal level by descending subsystems with very different function. Accordingly, I feel that caution is required with regard to the significance of motor responses or different unidentified interneurons to noxious stimuli as indicators of "pain control". With regard to the problem of pain control, I would give special emphasis to the studies of interneurons with exclusive nociceptor input (for references, see Fields and Basbaum, 1977; Cervero and Iggo, 1980) and, in particular, to the studies of spinothalamic neurons activated from nociceptive afferents (Chung et al., 1979; Kenshalo et al., 1979, 1980; Willis, 1976). It has been shown that the effect of noxious stimuli on spinothalamic neurons is effectively inhibited by weak stimulation of raphe magnus (Willis et al., 1977) and of more lateral nearby regions in the medullary reticular formation (Gerhardt et al., 1981). The former effect remained after ventral spinal transection, and the authors ascribe it to raphespinal neurons, but they do not commit themselves as to whether or not these neurons are serotonergic. Gerhardt et al. (1981) discuss the possibility that the effect evoked from the reticular formation may be via the dorsal reticulospinal system in addition to the inhibition previously shown to be mediated by ventral reticulospinal neurons (Haber et al., 1980).

I believe that much more attention should be given to the role of ventral reticulospinal neurons in the control of segmental mechanisms. Ito et al. (1970) have shown that a considerable portion of the ventral reticulospinal neurons are inhibitory. It is not known if the ventral reticulospinal neurons discussed in Section VII act directly on the interneurons. Stimulation of ventral fibers in the spinal cord evokes monosynaptic IPSPs in many VSCT neurons (Lundberg and Weight, 1971) and in some bVFRT neurons (Baldissera, Hultborn and Lundberg, unpublished observations). The fibers may be of supraspinal origin, but this has only been demonstrated in the case of VSCT (Baldissera and Roberts, 1975). Monosynaptic IPSPs are evoked from different regions in the reticular formation in cervical propriospinal neurons (Illert et al., 1981). It seems likely that the inhibitory reticular neurons projecting to motoneurons (cf. Peterson, this volume) account only for minor parts of the inhibitory reticulospinal neurons, and that different subsystems exist which project to interneurons and propriospinal neurons.

References

Alstermark, B., Lindström, S., Lundberg, A. and Sybirska, E. (1981) Integration in descending motor pathways controlling the forelimb in the cat. Ascending projection to the lateral reticular nucleus from C3–C4 propriospinal neurones also projecting to forelimb motoneurones, *Exp. Brain Res.*, 42: 282-298.

Andén, N.-E., Carlsson, A., Hillarp, N.-Å. and Magnusson, T. (1964a) 5-Hydroxytryptamine release by nerve stimulation of the spinal cord, *Life Sci.*, 3: 473-478.

Andén, N.-E., Jukes, M.G.M. and Lundberg, A. (1964b) Spinal reflexes and monoamine liberation, *Nature (Lond.)*, 202: 1222-1223.

Andén, N.-E., Jukes, M.G.M., Lundberg, A. and Vyklický, L. (1964c) A new spinal flexor reflex, *Nature (Lond.)*, 202: 1344-1345.

Andén, N.-E., Jukes, M.G.M. and Lundberg, A. (1966a) The effect of DOPA on the spinal cord. 2. A pharmacological analysis, *Acta physiol. scand.*, 67: 387-397.

Andén, N.-E., Jukes, M.G.M., Lundberg, A. and Vyklický, L. (1966b) The effect of DOPA on the spinal cord. 1. Influence of transmission from primary afferents, *Acta physiol. scand.*, 67: 373-386.

Anderson, E.G. (1972) Bulbospinal serotonin-containing neurons and motor control. *Fed. Proc.*, 31: 107-112.

Andersson, G. and Oscarsson, O. (1978) Climbing fibre microzones in cerebellar vermis and their projection to different groups of cells in the lateral vestibular nucleus, *Exp. Brain Res.*, 32: 565-578.

Baldissera, F. and Bruggencate, G. ten (1976) Rubrospinal effects on ventral spinocerebellar tract neurons, *Acta physiol. scand.*, 96: 233-249.

Baldissera, F. and Roberts, W.J. (1975) Effects on the ventral spinocerebellar tract neurons from Deiters' nucleus and the medial longitudinal fascicle in the cat, *Acta physiol. scand.*, 93: 228-249.

Baldissera, F. and Roberts, W.J. (1976) Effects of the vestibulospinal tract on transmission from primary afferents to ventral spinocerebellar tract neurons, *Acta physiol. scand.*, 96: 217-232.

Baldissera, F., Hultborn, H. and Illert, M. (1981) Integration in spinal neuronal systems. In V.B. Brooks (Ed.), *Handbook of Physiology, Section 1, The Nervous System, Vol. II, Motor Control*, Amer. Physiol. Soc., Bethesda, MD, pp. 509-595.

Banna, N.R. and Anderson, E.G. (1968) The effects of 5-hydroxytryptamine antagonists on spinal neuronal activity, *J. Pharmacol. exp. Ther.*, 162: 319-325.

Basbaum, A.I. and Fields, H.L. (1979) The origin of descending pathways in the dorsolateral funiculus of the spinal cord of the cat and rat: further studies studies on the anatomy of pain modulation, *J. comp. Neurol.*, 187: 513-532.

Basbaum, A.I., Clanton, C.H. and Fields, H.L. (1978) Three bulbospinal pathways from the rostral medulla of the cat: an autoradiographic study of pain modulating systems, *J. comp. Neurol.*, 178: 209-224.

Bertler, Å., Falck, B. and Rosengren, E. (1963) The direct demonstration of a barrier mechanism in the brain capillaries, *Acta pharmacol.*, 20: 317-321.

Bessou, P. and Laporte, Y. (1961) Étude des récepteurs musculaires innervés par les fibres afférentes du groupe III (fibres myelinisées fines), chez le chat, *Arch. ital. Biol.*, 99: 293-321.

Brown, A.G. (1973) Ascending and long spinal pathways: dorsal columns, spinocervical tract and spinothalamic tract. In A. Iggo (Ed.), *Somatosensory System. Handbook of Sensory Physiology, Vol. II*, Springer-Verlag, Berlin, pp. 315-338.

Carlsson, A., Magnusson, T. and Rosengren, E. (1963) 5-Hydroxytryptamine of the spinal cord normally and after transection, *Experientia*, 19: 359-360.

Carlsson, A., Falck, B., Fuxe, K. and Hillarp, N.-Å. (1964) Cellular localization of monoamines in the spinal cord, *Acta physiol. scand.*, 60: 112-119.

Carlsson, A., Corrodi, H., Fuxe, K. and Hökfelt, T. (1969) Effects of some antidepressant drugs on the depletion of intraneuronal brain catecholamine stores caused by 4α-dimethyl-meta-tyramine, *Europ. J. Pharmacol.*, 5: 367-373.

Carpenter, D., Engberg, I., Funkenstein, H. and Lundberg, A. (1963) Decerebrate control of reflexes to primary afferents, *Acta physiol. scand.*, 59: 424-437.

Carpenter, D., Engberg, I. and Lundberg, A. (1965) Differential supraspinal control of inhibitory and excitatory actions from the FRA to ascending spinal pathways, *Acta physiol. scand.*, 63: 103-110.

Carpenter, D., Engberg, I. and Lundberg, A. (1966) Primary afferent depolarization evoked from the brain stem and the cerebellum, *Arch. ital. Biol.*, 104: 73-85.

Cervero, F. and Iggo, A. (1980) The substantia gelatinosa of the spinal cord. A critical review, *Brain*, 103: 717-772.

Cervero, F., Iggo, A. and Molony, V. (1977) Responses of spinocervical tract neurones to noxious stimulation of the skin, *J. Physiol. (Lond.)*, 267: 537-558.

Chung, J.M., Kenshalo, Jr., D.R., Gerhart, K.D. and Willis, W.D. (1979) Excitation of primate spinothalamic neurons by cutaneous C-fiber volleys, *J. Neurophysiol.*, 42: 1354-1369.

Crone, C., Hultborn, H. and Mazières, L. (1982) Brain stem control of a spinal circuit mediating longlasting excitation from muscle spindle Ia afferents, *Acta physiol. scand.*, in press.

Dahlström, A. and Fuxe, K. (1965) Evidence for the existence of monoamine neurons in the central nervous system. II. Experimentally induced changes in the intraneuronal amine levels of bulbospinal neuron systems, *Acta physiol. scand.*, 64: Suppl. 247, 1-36.

Downman, C.B.B. and Hussein, A. (1958) Spinal tracts and supraspinal centres influencing visceromotor and allied reflexes in cats, *J. Physiol. (Lond.)*, 141: 489-499.

Eccles, R.M. and Lundberg, A. (1959a) Synaptic actions in motoneurones by afferents which may evoke the flexion reflex, *Arch. ital. Biol.*, 97: 199-221.

Eccles, R.M. and Lundberg, A. (1959b) Supraspinal control of interneurones mediating spinal reflexes, *J. Physiol. (Lond.)*, 147: 565-584.

Eccles, J.C., Kostyuk, P.G. and Schmidt, R.F. (1962) Presynaptic inhibition of the central actions of flexor reflex afferents, *J. Physiol. (Lond.)*, 161: 258-281.

Ekerot, C.-F., Larson, B. and Oscarsson, O. (1979) Information carried by the spinocerebellar paths. In R. Granit and O. Pompeiano (Eds.), *Reflex Control of Posture and Movement, Progress in Brain Research, Vol. 50*, Elsevier/North-Holland Biomedical Press, Amsterdam, pp. 79-90.

Emmelin, N. (1952) 'Paralytic secretion' of saliva. An example of supersensitivity after denervation, *Physiol. Rev.*, 32: 21-46.

Engberg, I. (1963) Effects from the pyramidal tract on plantar reflexes in the cat, *Acta physiol. scand.*, 59: Suppl. 213, 38.

Engberg, I., Lundberg, A. and Ryall, R.W. (1968a) Reticulospinal inhibition of transmission in reflex pathways, *J. Physiol. (Lond.)*, 194: 201-223.

Engberg, I., Lundberg, A. and Ryall, R.W. (1968b) Reticulospinal inhibition of interneurones, *J. Physiol. (Lond.)*, 194: 225-236.

Engberg, I., Lundberg, A. and Ryall, R.W. (1968c) The effect of reserpine on transmission in the spinal cord, *Acta physiol. scand.*, 72: 115-122.

Engberg, I., Lundberg, A. and Ryall, R.W. (1968d) Is the tonic decerebrate inhibition of reflex paths mediated by monoaminergic pathways? *Acta physiol. scand.*, 72: 123-133.

Fedina, L., Lundberg, A. and Vyklický, L. (1971) The effect of a noradrenaline liberator (4,alpha-dimethyl-meta-tyramine) on reflex transmission in spinal cats, *Acta physiol. scand.*, 83: 495-504.

Fields, H.L. and Basbaum, A.I. (1978) Brainstem control of spinal pain transmission neurons, *Ann. Rev. Physiol.*, 40: 217-248.

Foreman, R.D., Schmidt, R.F. and Willis, W.D. (1977) Convergence of muscle and cutaneous input onto primate spinothalamic tract neurons, *Brain Res.*, 124: 555-560.

Foreman, R.D., Schmidt, R.F. and Willis, W.D. (1979) Effects of mechanical and chemical stimulation of fine muscle afferents upon primate spinothalamic tract cells, *J. Physiol. (Lond.)*, 286: 215-231.

Fulton, J.F. (1926) *Muscular Contraction and Reflex Control of Movement*, Williams and Wilkins, Baltimore, MD, pp. 644.

Fulton, J.F., Liddell, E.G.T. and Rioch, D. McK. (1930) The influence of experimental lesions of the spinal cord upon the knee jerk. I. Acute lesions, *Brain*, 53: 311-326.

Gerhart, K.D., Wilcox, T.K., Chung, J.M. and Willis, W.D. (1981) Inhibition of nociceptive and nonnociceptive responses of primate spinothalamic cells by stimulation in medial brain stem, *J. Neurophysiol.*, 45: 121-136.

Grillner, S. (1981) Control of locomotion in bipeds, tetrapods, and fish. In V.B. Brooks (Ed.), *Handbook of Physiology, Section 1, The Nervous System, Vol. II*, Motor Control, Amer. Physiol. Soc., Bethesda, MD, pp. 1179-1236.

Grillner, S. and Shik, M.L. (1973) On the descending control of the lumbosacral spinal cord from the "mesencephalic locomotor region", *Acta physiol. scand.*, 87: 320-333.

Haber, L.H., Martin, R.F., Chung, J.M. and Willis, W.D. (1980) Inhibition and excitation of primate spinothalamic tract neurons by stimulation in region of nucleus reticularis gigantocellularis, *J. Neurophysiol.*, 43: 1578-1593.

Headley, P.M., Duggan, A.W. and Griersmith, B.T. (1978) Selective reduction by noradrenaline and 5-hydroxytryptamine of nociceptive responses of cat dorsal horn neurones, *Brain Res.*, 145: 185-189.

Holmqvist, B. (1961) Crossed spinal reflex actions evoked by volleys in somatic afferents, *Acta physiol. scand.*, 52: Suppl. 181, 1-67.

Holmqvist, B. and Lundberg, A. (1959) On the organization of the supraspinal inhibitory control of interneurones of various spinal reflex arcs, *Arch. ital. Biol.*, 97: 340-356.

Holmqvist, B. and Lundberg, A. (1961) Differential supraspinal control of synaptic actions evoked by volleys in the flexion afferents in alpha motoneurones, *Acta physiol. scand.*, 54: Suppl. 186.

Holmqvist, B., Lundberg, A. and Oscarsson, O. (1956) Functional organization of the dorsal spino-cerebellar tract in the cat. V. Further experiments on convergence of excitatory and inhibitory actions, *Acta physiol. scand.*, 38: 76-90.

Holmqvist, B., Lundberg, A. and Oscarsson, O. (1960) Supraspinal inhibitory control of transmission to three ascending spinal pathways influenced by the flexion reflex afferents, *Arch. ital. Biol.*, 98: 60-80.

Hongo, T. and Okada, M. (1967) Cortically evoked pre- and postsynaptic inhibition of impulse transmission to the dorsal spinocerebellar tract, *Exp. Brain Res.*, 3: 163-177.

Hongo, T., Jankowska, E. and Lundberg, A. (1966) Convergence of excitatory and inhibitory action on interneurones in the lumbosacral cord, *Exp. Brain Res.*, 1: 338-358.

Hongo, T., Jankowska, E. and Lundberg, A. (1972) The rubrospinal tract. III. Effects on primary afferent terminals, *Exp. Brain Res.*, 15: 39-53.

Hultborn, H. and Wigström, H. (1980) Motor response with long latency and maintained duration evoked by activity in Ia afferents. In J.E. Desmedt (Ed.), *Spinal and Supraspinal Mechanisms of Voluntary Motor Control and Locomotion, Progr. Clin. Neurophysiol., Vol. 8*, Karger, Basel, pp. 99-116.

Illert, M. and Lundberg, A. (1978) Collateral connections to the lateral reticular nucleus from cervical propriospinal neurons projecting to forelimb motoneurons in the cat, *Neurosci. Lett.*, 7: 167-172.

Illert, M., Jankowska, E., Lundberg, A. and Odutola, A. (1981) Integration in descending motor pathways controlling the forelimb in the cat. 7. Effects from the reticular formation on C3–C4 propriospinal neurons, *Exp. Brain Res.*, 42: 269-281.

Ito, M., Udo, M. and Mano, N. (1970) Long inhibitory and excitatory pathways converging onto cat reticular and Deiters' neurons and their relevance to reticulofugal axons, *J. Neurophysiol.*, 33: 210-226.

Jankowska, E. and Lundberg, A. (1981) Interneurons in the spinal cord, *Trends NeuroSci.*, 4: 230-233.

Jankowska, E., Jukes, M.G.M., Lund, S. and Lundberg, A. (1967) The effect of DOPA on the spinal cord. 5. Reciprocal organization of pathways transmitting excitatory action to alpha motoneurones of flexors and extensors, *Acta physiol. scand.*, 70: 369-388.

Jankowska, E., Lund, S., Lundberg, A. and Pompeiano, O. (1968) Inhibitory effects evoked through ventral reticulospinal pathways, *Arch. ital. Biol.*, 106: 124-140.

Jeneskog, T. and Johansson, H. (1977) The rubro-bulbospinal path. A descending system known to influence dynamic fusimotor neurons and its interaction with distal cutaneous afferents in the control of flexor reflex afferent pathways, *Exp. Brain Res.*, 27: 161-179.

Job, C. (1953) Ueber autogene Inhibition und Reflexumkehr bei spinalisierten und decerebrierten Katzen, *Pflügers Arch. ges. Physiol.*, 256: 406-418.

Jurna, I. and Lundberg, A. (1968) The influence of an inhibitor of dopamine-beta-hydroxylase on the effect of DOPA on transmission in the spinal cord. In *Structure and Functions of Inhibitory Neuronal Mechanisms*, Pergamon Press, Oxford, pp. 469-472.

Kenshalo, Jr., D.R., Leonard, R.B., Chung, J.M. and Willis, W.D. (1979) Responses of primate spinothalamic neurons to graded and to repeated noxious heat stimuli, *J. Neurophysiol.*, 42: 1370-1389.

Kenshalo, Jr., D.R., Giesler, Jr., G.J., Leonard, R.B. and Willis, W.D. (1980) Responses of neurons in primate ventral posterior lateral nucleus to noxious stimuli, *J. Neurophysiol.*, 43: 1594-1614.

Kniffki, K.-D., Mense, S. and Schmidt, R.F. (1977) The spinocervical tract as a possible pathway for muscular nociception, *J. Physiol. (Paris)*, 73: 359-366.

Kniffki, K.-D., Mense, S. and Schmidt, R.F. (1981a) Muscle receptors with fine afferent fibres which may evoke circulatory reflexes, *Circulat. Res.*, in press.

Kniffki, K.,-D., Schomburg, E.D. and Steffens, H. (1981b) Convergence in segmental reflex pathways from fine muscle afferents and cutaneous or group II muscle afferents to α-motoneurons, *Brain Res.*, 218: 342-346.

Kuno, M. and Perl, E.R. (1960) Alteration of spinal reflexes by interaction with suprasegmental and dorsal root activity, *J. Physiol. (Lond.)*, 151: 103-122.

Laporte, Y., Lundberg, A. and Oscarsson, O. (1956) Functional organization of the dorsal spino-cerebellar tract in the cat. II. Single fibre recording in Flechsig's fasciculus on electrical stimulation of various peripheral nerves, *Acta physiol. scand.*, 36: 188-203.

Liddell, E.G.T., Matthes, K., Oldberg, E. and Ruch, T.C. (1932) Reflex release of flexor muscles by spinal section, *Brain*, 55: 239-246.

Lindström, S. (1973) Recurrent control from motor axon collaterals of Ia inhibitory pathways in the spinal cord of the cat, *Acta physiol. scand.*, Suppl. 392.

Lund, S., Lundberg, A. and Vyklický, L. (1965) Inhibitory action from the flexor reflex afferents on transmission to Ia afferents, *Acta physiol. scand.*, 64: 345-355.

Lundberg, A. (1959) Integrative significance of patterns of connections made by muscle afferents in the spinal cord, In *Symp. XXI Int. Physiol. Congr.*, Buenos Aires, pp. 1-5.

Lundberg, A. (1964a) Ascending spinal hindlimb pathways in the cat. In J.C. Eccles and J.P. Schadé (Eds.), *Physiology of Spinal Neurons, Progress in Brain Research, Vol. 12*, Elsevier, Amsterdam, pp. 135-163.

Lundberg, A. (1964b) Supraspinal control of transmission in reflex paths to motoneurons and primary afferents. In J.C. Eccles and J.P. Schadé (Eds.), *Physiology of Spinal Neurons, Progress in Brain Research, Vol. 12*, Elsevier, Amsterdam, pp. 197-221.

Lundberg, A. (1965) *Monoamines and spinal reflexes. Essays in Physiology*, Springer Verlag, Berlin, pp. 186-190.

Lundberg, A. (1966) Integration in the reflex pathway. In R. Granit (Ed.), *Muscular Afferents and Motor Control*, Almqvist and Wiksell, Stockholm, pp. 275-305.

Lundberg, A. (1975) The control of spinal mechanisms from the brain. In D.B. Tower (Ed.), *The Nervous System, Vol. 1*, Raven Press, New York, pp. 253-265.

Lundberg, A. (1979) Multisensory control of spinal reflex pathways. In R. Granit and O. Pompeiano (Eds.), *Reflex Control of Posture and Movement, Progress in Brain Research, Vol. 50*, Elsevier/North-Holland Biomedical Press, Amsterdam, pp. 11-28.

Lundberg, A. (1981) Half-centres revisited. In J. Szentágothai, M. Palkovits and J. Hamori (Eds.), *Regulatory Functions of the CNS Motion and Organization Principles, Advanc. Physiol. Sci., Vol. 1*, Akademiai Kiado, Budapest, pp. 155-167.

Lundberg, A. and Oscarsson, O. (1960) Functional organization of the dorsal spino-cerebellar tract in the cat. VII. Identification of units by antidromic activation from the cerebellar cortex with recognition of five functional subdivisions, *Acta physiol. scand.*, 50: 356-374.

Lundberg, A. and Oscarsson, O. (1961) Three ascending spinal pathways in the dorsal part of the lateral funiculus, *Acta physiol. scand.*, 51: 1-16.

Lundberg, A. and Oscarsson, O. (1962) Two ascending spinal pathways in the ventral part of the cord, *Acta physiol. scand.*, 54: 270-286.

Lundberg, A. and Vyklický, L. (1963) Inhibitory interaction between spinal reflexes to primary afferents, *Experientia*, 19: 247-248.

Lundberg, A. and Vyklciký, L. (1966) Inhibition of transmission to primary afferents by electrical stimulation of the brain stem, *Arch. ital. Biol.*, 104: 86-97.

Lundberg, A. and Weight, F. (1971) Functional organization of connexions to the ventral spinocerebellar tract, *Exp. Brain Res.*, 12: 295-316.

Lundberg, A., Norrsell, U. and Voorhoeve, P. (1963) Effects from the sensorimotor cortex on ascending spinal pathways, *Acta physiol. scand.*, 59: 462-473.

Magni, F. and Oscarsson, O. (1961) Cerebral control of transmission to the ventral spinocerebellar tract, *Arch. ital. Biol.*, 99: 369-396.

Magnusson, T. and Rosengren, E. (1963) Catecholamines of the spinal cord normally and after transection, *Experientia*, 19: 229-230.

Martin, R.F., Jordan, L.M. and Willis, W.D. (1978) Differential projections of cat medullary raphe neurons demonstrated by retrograde labelling following spinal cord lesions, *J. comp. Neurol.*, 182: 77-88.

Mendell, L.M. (1966) Physiological properties of unmyelinated fiber projection to the spinal cord, *Exp. Neurol.*, 16: 316-332.

Moore, R.Y. and Bloom, F.E. (1979) Central catecholamine neuron systems: anatomy and physiology of the norepinephrine and epinephrine systems, *Ann. Rev. Neurosci.*, 2: 113-168.

Mori, S., Nisimura, H.I. and Aoki, (1980) Brain stem activation of the spinal stepping generator. In J.A. Hobson, and M.A.B. Brazier (Eds.), *The Reticular Formation Revisited, Vol. 6*, Raven Press, New York, pp. 241-259.

Nygren, L.-G. and Olson, L. (1976) On spinal noradrenaline receptor supersensitivity: correlation between nerve terminal densities and flexor reflexes various times after intracisternal 6-hydroxydopamine, *Brain Res.*, 116: 455-470.

Nygren, L.-G. and Olson, L. (1977) A new major projection from locus coeruleus: The main source of noradrenergic nerve terminals in the ventral and dorsal columns of the spinal cord, *Brain Res.*, 132: 85-93.

Oscarsson, O. (1957) Functional organization of the ventral spinocerebellar tract in the cat. II. Connections with muscle, joint, and skin nerve afferents and effects on adequate stimulation of various receptors, *Acta physiol. scand.*, 42: Suppl. 146, 1-107.

Oscarsson, O. (1960) Functional organization of the ventral spinocerebellar tract in the cat. III. Supraspinal control of VSCT units of I-type, *Acta physiol. scand.*, 49: 171-183.

Oscarsson, O. (1973) Functional organization of spino-cerebellar paths. In A. Iggo (Ed.) *Handbook of Sensory Physiology, Vol. II, Somatosensory System*, Springer, Berlin, pp. 339-380.

Paintal, A.S. (1960) Functional analysis of group III afferent fibers of mammalian muscles, *J. Physiol. (Lond.)*, 152: 250-270.

Pilyavsky, A.I., Gokin, A.P. and Yakhnitsa, I.A. (1981) Locus coeruleus rhythmic stimulation influence on spinal inhibition evoked by flexor reflex afferents activation in cat, *J. Neurofiziol.*, 13: 187-195 (in Russian).

Poitras, D. and Parent, A. (1978) Atlas of the distribution of monoamine-containing nerve cell bodies in the brain stem of the cat, *J. comp. Neurol.*, 187: 85-96.

Rudomin, P. and Dutton, H. (1969) Effects of muscle and cutaneous afferent nerve volleys on excitability fluctuations of Ia terminals, *J. Neurophysiol.*, 32: 158-169.

Schmidt, R.F. (1971) Presynaptic inhibition in the vertebrate central nervous system, *Ergebn. Physiol.*, 63: 20-101.

Sherrington, C.S. (1906) *The Integrative Action of the Nervous System*, Yale University Press, New Haven, CT.

Sherrington, C.S. and Sowton, S.C.M. (1915) Observations on reflex responses to single break-shocks, *J. Physiol. (Lond.)*, 49: 331-348.

Shibuya, T. and Anderson, E.G. (1968) The influence of chronic cord transection on the effects of 5-hydroxytryptophan, 1-tryptophan and pargyline on spinal neuronal activity, *J. Pharmacol. exp. Ther.*, 164: 185-190.

Smirnov, K.A. and Potekhina, I.L. (1974) Localization and properties of reticulo-spinal neurons with axons descending in the dorsolateral parts of the spinal cord, *J. Neurofiziol.*, 6: 266-272, (in Russian).

Steeves, J.D., Schmidt, B.J., Skovgaard, B.J. and Jordan, L.M. (1980) Effect of noradrenaline and 5-hydroxytryptamine depletion on locomotion in the cat, *Brain Res.*, 185: 349-362.

Tohyama, M., Sakai, K., Salvert, D., Touret, M. and Jouvet, M. (1979a) Spinal projections from the lower brain stem in the cat as demonstrated by the horseradish peroxidase technique. I. Origins of the reticulospinal tracts and their funicular trajectories, *Brain Res.*, 173: 383-403.

Tohyama, M., Sakai, K., Touret, M., Salvert, D. and Jouvet, M. (1979b) Spinal projections from the lower brain stem in the cat as demonstrated by the horseradish peroxidase technique. II. Projections from the dorsolateral pontine tegmentum and raphe nuclei, *Brain Res.*, 176: 215-231.

Torvik, A. and Brodal, A. (1957) The origin of the reticulospinal fibres in the cat. An experimental study, *Anat. Rec.*, 128: 113-137.

Trevino, D.L., Maunz, R.A., Bryan, R.N. and Willis, W.D. (1972) Location of cells of origin of the spinothalamic tract in the lumbar enlargement of cat, *Exp. Neurol.*, 34: 64-77.

Wiklund, L., Leger, L. and Persson, M. (1981) Monoamine cell distribution in the cat brain stem. A fluorescence histochemical study with quantification of indolaminergic and locus coeruleus cell group, *J. comp. Neurol.*, 203: 613-647.

Willis, W.D. (1976) Spinothalamic system: Physiological aspects. In J.J. Bonica and D. Albe-Fessard (Eds.), *Advances in Pain Research and Therapy, Vol. I*, Raven Press, New York, pp. 215-223.

Willis, W.D. (1979) Effects of high threshold muscle afferent volleys on ascending pathways. In R. Granit and O. Pompeiano (Eds.), *Reflex Control of Posture and Movement, Progress in Brain Research, Vol. 50*, Elsevier/North-Holland Biomedical Press, Amsterdam, pp. 105-111.

Willis, W.D., Haber, L.H. and Martin, R.F. (1977) Inhibition of spinothalamic tract cells and interneurons by brain stem stimulation in the monkey, *J. Neurophysiol.*, 40: 968-981.

Wolstencroft, J.H. (1980) The role of raphe and medial reticular neurons in control systems related to nociceptive inputs. In J.A. Hobson and M.A.B. Brazier (Eds.), *The Reticular Formation Revisited*. Raven Press, New York, pp. 349-371.

Yakhnitsa, I.A. (1981) Changes in segmental reflexes evoked by stimulation of locus coeruleus and potentiation of cathecholamines, *J. Neurofiziol.*, 13: 39-47, (in Russian).

Yakhnitsa, I.A., Bulgakova, N.V. and Pilyavsky, A.I. (1981) Influence of drugs increasing or reducing background firing of locus coeruleus neurons on some types of spinal inhibition in cat, *J. Neurofiziol.*, 13: 247-256, (in Russian).

Brain Stem Control of Spinal Mechanisms
– B. Sjölund and A. Björklund, editors
© 1982 Elsevier Biomedical Press

9

The Reticulospinal System and Its Role in Generating Vestibular and Visuomotor Reflexes

BARRY W. PETERSON and KIKURO FUKUSHIMA

Department of Physiology, Northwestern University Medical School, Chicago, IL, U.S.A. and Department of Physiology, Hokkaido University School of Medicine, Sapporo, Japan

I. Introduction

Until recently anatomical and physiological studies provided different views of the complexity of reticulospinal systems. Physiologists studying responses to electrical stimulation of the pontomedullary reticular core described a wide variety of effects, including activation or inhibition of somatomotor and autonomic systems (Lloyd, 1941; Magoun and Rhines, 1946; Rhines and Magoun, 1946; Sprague and Chambers, 1954; Henry and Caleresu, 1974a, b, c; Mackel, 1979), modification of spinal reflex pathways (Engberg et al., 1968a, b) and modulation of ascending sensory information (Lundberg and Vyklicki, 1966; Basbaum et al., 1978). Anatomical studies relying on retrograde chromatolysis and degeneration techniques, on the other hand, had emphasized a relatively homogeneous descending reticulospinal system originating in the medial pontomedullary reticular formation and terminating primarily in spinal laminae V–IX (Torvik and Brodal, 1957; Petras, 1967). Only with the advent of studies based on anterograde and retrograde transport techniques has it become clear that there are multiple reticulospinal pathways each of which may be specialized to perform a specific subset of the physiological functions of the entire reticulospinal projection system (see Martin et al., 1981; Coulter et al., 1979; Walberg, and Kuypers and Huisman, this volume). A question that then arises is what function or functions can be appropriately ascribed to those reticulospinal projections originating from large neurons of the medial pontomedullary reticular formation. In this paper we review several lines of evidence that indicate that these projections play an important role in control of somatic musculature, and present new data on vestibular and tectal action on reticulospinal neurons that shed some light on the function of at least one component of the magnocellular reticulospinal projection system.

II. Projections from Medial Pontomedullary Reticular Formation to Spinal Motor Centers

II.1. Medial and lateral reticulospinal tracts

Neuroanatomical studies have revealed the presence of large-celled reticulospinal projections linking the medial pontomedullary reticular formation with the spinal ventral horn in a variety of species (Torvik and Brodal, 1957; Petras, 1967; Martin et al., 1981; Coulter et al., 1979). The system has also been studied with electrophysiological techniques, primarily in the cat (Magni and Willis, 1964; Wolstencroft, 1964; Ito et al., 1970; Peterson et al., 1975b; Eccles et al., 1975; Shapovalov and Gurevitch, 1970). For consistency with the physiological data that will be presented later, the following description of the reticulospinal system focuses on data from the cat. In this species the magnocellular reticulospinal projections can be differentiated into three groups of descending fibers: one in the ventromedial funiculus (RSTm), one in the ipsilateral ventrolateral funiculus (RSTi) and one in the contralateral ventrolateral funiculus (RSTc). As shown in Figure 1B, RSTm originates primarily from neurons in the pons and in dorsorostral nucleus reticularis (n.r.) gigantocellularis, although a few RSTm neurons are found more caudally. The descending RSTm fibers run in or close to the medial longitudinal fasciculus (MLF), continue in the spinal ventromedial funiculus, and then terminate in Rexed's laminae VI–IX at all levels of the spinal cord. As indicated by the symbols in Figure 1B, the great majority of RSTm neurons project at least as far as the upper lumbar spinal cord, and there is no clear segregation of neurons that terminate at different spinal levels.

The anatomical organization of the lateral reticulospinal tracts, RSTi and RSTc, is somewhat more complex. As shown in Figure 1, both pathways originate from neurons in the medullary reticular formation. Medullary lesions destroying these neurons as well as passing RSTm fibers, produce fiber degeneration extending to all spinal levels and terminal degeneration in Rexed's laminae V–IX (Nyberg-Hansen, 1966; Petras, 1967). More recent observations employing the anterograde transport techniques (Martin et al., 1981; Huerta and Harting, 1982), indicate that a similar pattern of terminal labeling occurs when radioactive amino acids are placed in the medullary reticular formation. It thus appears that medullary reticulospinal projections cover the entire terminal area of RSTm fibers and, in addition, terminate heavily in regions at the base of the dorsal horn (which receives relatively few RSTm terminals). This extensive distribution of their terminals suggests that lateral reticulospinal fibers act upon a wider population of spinal neurons than do RSTm fibers, which have a more restricted area of termination.

As shown in Figure 1C, most RSTi fibers extend as far as the lumbar cord. There is, however, a significant group of RSTi neurons that project only to the neck (N cells), and these neurons have a distribution within the medullary re-

firing recorded prior to penetration of the neurons revealed that late firing produced by stimulation of the contralateral horizontal canal was associated with
long-latency (5–15 msec), slowly-rising, excitatory postsynaptic potentials
(EPSPs). Neurons which fired within 10 msec of the beginning of the train
exhibited shorter-latency, di- or trisynaptic EPSPs that began within 1.7–2
msec of the first effective shock, often superimposed on a slower EPSP. Several
neurons which failed to fire in response to stimulation of the ipsilateral horizontal canal exhibited di- or trisynaptic IPSPs upon intracellular recording.
Reticulospinal neurons thus may receive reciprocal excitation and inhibition
from the contralateral and ipsilateral horizontal canals. The contralateral
input consists of both shorter- and longer-latency components, indicating that
these neurons are a point of convergence of relatively direct and more complex,
integrative semicircular canal pathways. This convergence may represent the
neural substrate for combining, on the same population of reticulospinal
neurons, the low and high frequency components of the vestibulocollic reflex
signal discussed in the previous section.

Open and filled symbols in Figure 6 indicate the locations of reticulospinal
neurons that responded to stimulation of the ipsilateral and contralateral horizontal semicircular canals. The data in the figure and in Table I indicate that

TABLE I

FIRING OF RETICULOSPINAL NEURONS EVOKED BY TRAINS OF BIPOLAR CURRENT
PULSES APPLIED TO WIRES IMPLANTED CLOSE TO HORIZONTAL SEMICIRCULAR
CANAL AMPULLAE.

Within the population of 221 neurons studied, responses of 126 were observed following stimulation of both ipsolateral and contralateral canals: responses of 54 following contralateral stimulation only, and reponses of 41 following ipsilateral stimulation only.

	Projection		
	RSTm	RSTi	RSTc
Contralateral horizontal canal			
Latency range	1.7–20+	1.5–20+	6–20+
Fired at ≤ 10 msec	6	3	1
Fired later	41	5	3
No response	61	46	14
Ipsilateral horizontal canal			
Latency range	9–20+	over 20	over 20
Fired at ≤ 10 msec	1	0	0
Fired later	11	2	1
No response	70	39	13

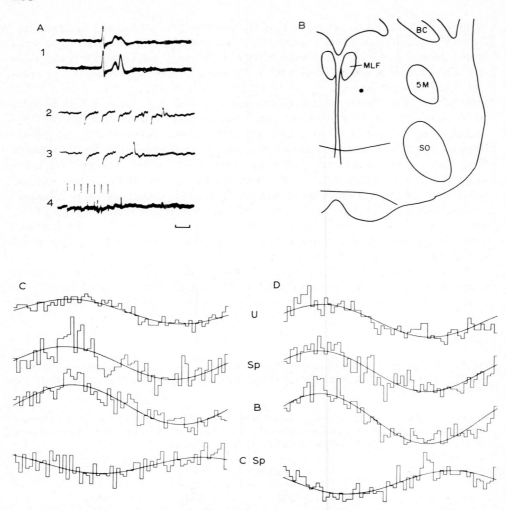

Figure 5. Reticulospinal neuron receiving convergent tectal and semicircular canal input. The neuron, whose location is shown in B, was identified as an RSTm neuron by its antidromic response to stimulation of ventromedial funiculus at C2 (A1, lower trace). In the upper trace, the neuron fails to respond to slightly weaker spinal stimulus. A2 and A3 show responses to trains of stimuli applied to anterior and posterior portions of the contralateral superior colliculus, respectively. A4 shows response to trains of stimuli applied to an electrode implanted close to the contralateral horizontal semicircular canal ampulla. Variation in action potential size was caused by movements of the brain stem. Time base for A1 is 1 msec, for A2 and 3 is 2 msec and for A4 is 5 msec. C and D, the responses of the neuron and neck muscles to sinusoidal polarization of contralateral horizontal semicircular canal afferents at 0.2 Hz (C) and 3.0 Hz (D). Modulation of unit activity (U) is in phase with activity of right splenius (Sp) and right biventer cervicis (B) muscles, and out of phase with left splenius muscle (C Sp). Abbreviations in B: BC, brachium conjunctivum; MLF, medial longitudinal fasciculus; SO, superior olive; 5M, trigeminal motor nucleus.

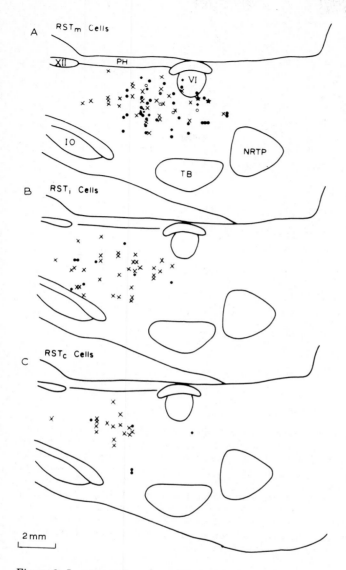

Figure 6. Locations of neurons responding to stimulation of horizontal semicircular canal nerves. Histologically determined locations of reticulospinal neurons whose responses to canal stimulation were observed with extracellular recording, are plotted on four schematic, parasagittal sections of the pontomedullary brain stem. RSTm neurons are shown in A, RSTi neurons in B, and RSTc neurons in C. Filled circles indicate neurons excited by stimulation of contralateral horizontal canal; open circles, neurons excited by ipsilateral horizontal canal; filled diamonds, neurons excited by both; and Xs, neurons excited by neither. Two neurons inhibited by stimulation of contralateral horizontal canal are shown by stars. Abbreviations: IO, inferior olive; NRTP, nucleus reticularis tegmenti pontis; PH, nucleus prepositus hypoglossi; TB, trapezoid body; VI, abducens nucleus, and XII, hypoglossal nucleus.

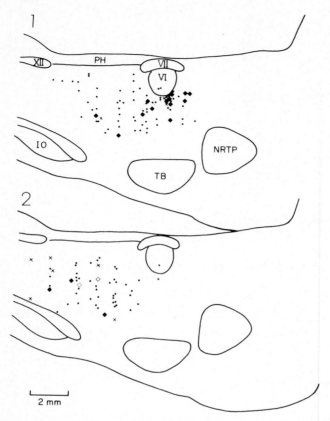

Figure 7. Locations of reticulospinal neurons that responded to canal polarization plotted on schematic parasagittal sections of the medial pontomedullary brain stem. Neurons modulated with phase lags are plotted with filled diamonds, and those with phase leads with open diamonds. Silent, non-responding neurons are shown as small dots, and spontaneously firing, non-responding neurons as Xs. Section 1 indicates responses of RSTm neurons to contralateral polarization; section 2, responses of RSTi-c neurons to contralateral polarization; section 3, responses of RSTm neurons to ipsilateral polarization; and section 4, responses of RSTi-c neurons to ipsilateral polarization. Abbreviations: IO, inferior olive; NRTP, nucleus reticularis tegmenti pontis; PH, prepositus hypoglossi nucleus; TB, trapezoid body; VI, abducens nucleus; VII, genu of facial nerve; XII, hypoglossal nucleus. (From Peterson et al., 1980, with permission.)

RSTm neurons, which are located in the region surrounding the abducens nucleus, are more likely to respond to such stimulation than are RSTi or RSTc neurons. This finding is of functional interest since it suggests that the reflex activity elicited by horizontal semicircular canal stimulation is carried by the widely divergent RSTm system which has direct access to neck, back and limb motoneurons (see Section II above). Activity of RSTm neurons may contribute both to gaze shifts and postural adjustments produced by horizontal canal activation.

Fukushima, Y., Igusa, Y. and Yoshida, K. (1977) Characteristics of responses of medial brain stem neurons to horizontal head angular acceleration and electrical stimulation of the labyrinth in the cat, *Brain Res.*, 120: 564-570.

Fukushima, K., Hirai, N. and Rapoport, S. (1979a) Direct excitation of neck flexor motoneurons by the interstitiospinal tract, *Brain Res.*, 160: 358-362.

Fukushima, K., Pitts, N.G. and Peterson, B.W. (1978) Direct excitation of neck motoneurons by interstitiospinal fibers, *Exp. Brain Res.*, 33: 565-581.

Fukushima, K., Pitts, N.G. and Peterson, B.W. (1979b) Interstitiospinal action on forelimb, hindlimb and back motoneurons, *Exp. Brain Res.*, 37: 605-608.

Fukushima, K., Murakami, S., Matsushima, J. and Kato, M. (1980) Vestibular responses and branching of interstitiospinal neurons, *Exp. brain Res.*, 40: 131-145.

Fukushima, K., Ohno, M., Murakami, S. and Kato, M. (1981) Effects of stimulation of frontal cortex, superior colliculus and neck muscle afferents on interstitiospinal neurons in the cat, *Exp. Brain Res.*, 44: 143-153.

Fukushima, K., Ohno, M., Takahashi, K. and Kato, M. (1982) Location and vestibular responses of interstitial and midbrain reticular neurons that project to the vestibular nuclei in the cat, *Exp. Brain Res.*, in press.

Grillner, S. and Lund, S. (1968) The origin of a descending pathway with monosynaptic action on flexor motoneurons, *Acta physiol. scand.*, 74: 274-284.

Guitton, D., Crommelinck, M. and Roucous, A. (1980) Stimulation of the superior colliculus in the alert cat. I. Eye movements and neck EMG activity evoked when the head is restrained, *Exp. Brain Res.*, 39: 63-73.

Harting, J.K. (1977) Descending pathways from the superior colliculus: an autoradiographic study in the rhesus monkey *(Macaca mulatta)*, *J. comp. Neurol.*, 173: 583-612.

Henry, J.L. and Calaresu, F.R. (1974a) Excitatory and inhibitory inputs from medullary nuclei projecting to spinal cardio-acceleratory neurons in the cat, *Exp. Brain Res.*, 20: 495-504.

Henry, J.L. and Calaresu, F.R. (1974b) Pathways from medullary nuclei to spinal cardio-acceleratory neurons in the cat, *Exp. Brain Res.*, 20: 505-514.

Henry, J.L. and Calaresu, F.R. (1974c) Origin and course of crossed medullary pathways to spinal sympathetic neurons in the cat, *Exp. Brain Res.*, 20: 515-526.

Hikosaka, O. and Kawakami, T. (1977) Inhibitory reticular neurons related to the quick phase of vestibular nystagmus: their location and projection, *Exp. Brain Res.*, 27: 377-396.

Hirai, N., Hwang, J.C. and Wilson, V.J. (1979) Comparison of dynamic properties of canal-evoked vestibulospinal reflexes of the neck and forelimb in the decerebrate cat, *Exp. Brain Res.*, 36: 393-397.

Horn, G. and Hill, R.M. (1966) Responsiveness to sensory stimulation of units in the superior colliculus and subadjacent tectotegmental regions of the rabbit, *Exp. Neurol.*, 14: 199-223.

Huerta, M.F. and Harting, J.K. (1982) Tectal control of spinal cord activity: neuroanatomical demonstration of pathways connecting superior colliculus with the cervical spinal cord grey. In H.G.J.M. Kuypers and G.F. Martin (Eds.), *Descending Pathways to the Spinal Cord, Progress in Brain Research, Vol. 57*, Elsevier Biomedical, Amsterdam, in press.

Illert, M., Jankowska, E., Lundberg, A. and Odutola, A. (1981) Integration in descending motor pathways controlling the forelimb in the cat. 7. Effects from the reticular formation on C3–C4 propriospinal neurones, *Exp. Brain Res.*, 42: 269-281.

Ito, M., Udo, M. and Mano, N. (1970) Long inhibitory and excitatory pathways converging onto cat's reticular and Deiters' neurons, and their relevance to the reticulofugal axons, *J. Neurophysiol.*, 33: 210-226.

Jankowska, E., Lund, S., Lundberg, A. and Pompeiano, O. (1968) Inhibitory effects evoked through ventral reticulospinal pathways, *Arch. ital. Biol.*, 106: 124-140.

Kawamura, K., Brodal, A. and Hoddevik, G. (1974) The projection of the superior colliculus onto the reticular formation of the brain stem. An experimental anatomical study in the cat, *Exp. Brain Res.*, 19: 1-19.

Ladpli, R. and Brodal, A. (1968) Experimental studies of commissural and reticular formation projections from the vestibular nuclei in the cat, *Brain Res.*, 8: 65-96.

Llinas, R. and Terzuolo, C.A. (1964) Mechanisms of supraspinal actions upon spinal cord activities. Reticular inhibitory mechanisms on alpha-extensor motoneurons, *J. Neurophysiol.*, 27: 579-591.

Lloyd, D.P.C. (1941) Activity in neurons of the bulbospinal correlation system, *J. Neurophysiol.*, 4: 115-134.

Lundberg, A. and Vyklicky, L. (1966) Inhibition of transmission to primary afferents by electrical stimulation of the brain stem, *Arch. ital. Biol.*, 104: 86-96.

Mackel, R. (1979) Segmental and descending control of the external urethral and anal sphincters in the cat, *J. Physiol. (Lond.)*, 294: 105-122.

Magni, F. and Willis, W.D. (1964) Cortical control of brain stem reticular neurons, *Arch. ital. Biol.*, 102: 418-433.

Magoun, H.W. and Rhines, R. (1946) An inhibitory mechanism in the bulbar reticular formation, *J. Neurophysiol.*, 9: 165-171.

Martin, G.F., Cabana, T., Humbertson, A.O., Laxson, L.C. and Fanneton, W.M. (1981) Spinal projections from the medullary reticular formation of the North American opossum: evidence for connectional heterogeneity, *J. comp. Neurol.*, 196: 663-682.

Maunz, R.A., Pitts, N.G. and Peterson, B.W. (1978) Cat spinoreticular neurons: locations, responses and changes in responses during repetitive stimulation, *Brain Res.*, 148: 365-379.

McCrea, R.A., Yoshida, K., Evinger, C. and Berthoz, A. (1981) The location, axonal orborization and termination sites of eye-movement-related secondary vestibular neurons demonstrated by intra-axonal HRP injection in the alert cat. In A.F. Fuchs and W. Becker (Eds.), *Progress in Oculomotor Research*, Elsevier/North-Holland, Amsterdam, pp. 379-386.

Mehler, W.R., Feferman, M.E. and Nauta, W.J.H. (1960) Ascending axon degeneration following anterolateral cordotomy. An experimental study in the monkey, *Brain*, 83: 719-750.

Nyberg-Hansen, R. (1966) Functional organization of descending supraspinal fibre systems to the spinal cord. Anatomical observations and physiological correlations, *Ergebn. Anat. Entwickl.-Gesch.*, 39: 1-48.

Peterson, B.W. (1977) Identification of reticulospinal projections that may participate in gaze control. In R. Baker and A. Berthoz (Eds.), *Control of Gaze by Brain Stem Neurons, Developments in Neuroscience, Vol. 1*, Elsevier/North-Holland, Amsterdam, pp. 143-152.

Peterson, B.W. (1979) Reticulo-motor pathways: their connections and possible roles in motor behavior. In H. Asanuma and V.J. Wilson (Eds.), *Integration in the Nervous System*, Igaku-Shoin, Tokyo, pp. 185-200.

Peterson, B.W. (1980) Participation of pontomedullary reticular neurons in specific motor activity. In J.A. Hobson and M.A.B. Brazier (Eds.), *The Reticular Formation Revisited*, Raven Press, New York, in press.

Peterson, B.W. and Abzug, C. (1975) Properties of projections from vestibular nuclei to medial reticular formation in the cat, *J. Neurophysiol.*, 38: 1421-1435.

Peterson, B.W., Anderson, M.E. and Filion, M. (1974) Responses of ponto-medullary reticular neurons to cortical, tectal and cutaneous stimuli, *Exp. Brain Res.*, 21: 19-44.

Peterson, B.W., Filion, M., Felpel, L.P. and Abzug, C. (1975a) Responses of medial reticular neurons to stimulation of the vestibular nerve, *Exp. Brain Res.*, 22: 335-350.

Peterson, B.W., Maunz, R.A., Pitts, N.G. and Mackel, R.G. (1975b) Patterns of projection and branching of reticulospinal neurons, *Exp. Brain Res.*, 23: 333-351.

Peterson, B.W., Franck, J.I., Pitts, N.G. and Daunton, N.G. (1976) Changes in responses of medial ponto-medullary reticular neurons during repetitive cutaneous, vestibular, cortical and tectal stimulation, *J. Neurophysiol.*, 39: 564-581.

Peterson, B.W., Pitts, N.G., Fukushima, K. and Mackel, R. (1978) Reticulospinal excitation and inhibition of neck motoneurons, *Exp. Brain Res.*, 32: 471-489.

Peterson, B.W., Pitts, N.G. and Fukushima, K. (1979) Reticulospinal connections with limb and axial motoneurons, *Exp. Brain Res.*, 36: 1-20.

Peterson, B.W., Fukushima, K., Hirai, N., Schor, R.H. and Wilson, V.J. (1980) Responses of vestibulospinal and reticulospinal neurons to sinusoidal vestibular stimulation, *J. Neurophysiol.*, 43: 1236-1250.

Peterson, B.W., Bilotto, G., Goldberg, J. and Wilson, V.J. (1982) Dynamics of vestibuloocular, vestibulocollic and cervicocollic reflexes, *Ann. N.Y. Acad. Sci.*, in press.

Petras, J.M. (1967) Cortical, tectal and tegmental fiber connections in the spinal cord of the cat, *Brain Res.*, 6: 275-324.

Rhines, R. and Magoun, H.W. (1946) Brain stem facilitation of cortical motor response, *J. Neurophysiol.*, 9: 219-229.

Rossi, G.F. and Brodal, A. (1957) Terminal distribution of spinoreticular fibers in the cat, *Arch. Neurol. Psychiat.*, 78: 439-453.

Roucoux, A., Guittan, D. and Crommelinck, M. (1980) Stimulation of the superior colliculus in the alert cat. II. Eye and head movements evoked when the head is unrestrained, *Exp. Brain Res.*, 39: 75-85.

Scheibel, M.E. and Scheibel, A.B. (1965) The response of reticular units to repetitive stimuli, *Arch. ital. Biol.*, 103: 279-299.

Segundo, J.P., Takenaka, T. and Encabo, H. (1967) Somatic sensory properties of bulbar reticular neurons, *J. Neurophysiol.*, 30: 1221-1238.

Shapovalov, A.I. and Gurevitch, N.R. (1970) Monosynaptic and disynaptic reticulospinal actions on lumbar motoneurons of the rat, *Brain Res.*, 21: 249-263.

Shimazu, H. and Precht, W. (1965) Tonic and kinetic responses of cat's vestibular neurons to horizontal angular acceleration, *J. Neurophysiol.*, 28: 989-1013.

Sprague, J.M. and Chambers, W.W. (1954) Control of posture by reticular formation and cerebellum in the intact, anesthetized and unanesthetized and in the decerebrated cat, *Amer. J. Physiol.*, 176: 52-64.

Spyer, K.M., Ghelarducci, B. and Pompeiano, O. (1974) Gravity responses of neurons in main reticular formation, *J. Neurophysiol.*, 37: 705-721.

Straschill, M. and Schick, F. (1977) Discharges of superior colliculus neurons during head and eye movement of the alert cat, *Exp. Brain Res.*, 27: 131-142.

Suzuki, J.I. and Cohen, B. (1964) Head, eye, body and limb movements from semicircular canal nerves, *Exp. Neurol.*, 10: 393-405.

Suzuki, J.I., Goto, K., Tokumasu, K. and Cohen, B. (1969) Implantation of electrodes near individual vestibular nerve branches in mammals, *Ann. Otol.*, 78: 815-826.

Torvik, A. and Brodal, A. (1957) The origin of reticulospinal fibers in the cat, *Anat. Rec.*, 128: 113-137.

Udo, M. and Mano, N. (1970) Discrimination of different spinal monosynaptic pathways converging onto reticular neurons, *J. Neurophysiol.*, 33: 227-238.

Wilson, V.J. and Melville Jones, G. (1979) *Mammalian Vestibular Physiology*, Plenum, New York.

Wilson, V.J. and Yoshida, M. (1969) Monosynaptic inhibition of neck motoneurons by the medial vestibular nucleus, *Exp. Brain Res.*, 9: 365-380.

Wilson, V.J., Yoshida, M. and Schor, R.H. (1970) Supraspinal monosynaptic excitation and inhibition of thoracic back motoneurons, *Exp. Brain Res.*, 11: 282-295.

Wilson, V.J., Peterson, B.W., Fukushima, K., Hirai, N. and Uchino, Y. (1979) Analysis of vestibulocollic reflexes by sinusoidal polarization of vestibular afferent fibers, *J. Neurophysiol.*, 42: 331-346.

Wolstencroft, J.H. (1964) Reticulospinal neurones, *J. Physiol. (Lond.)*, 174: 91-108.

Wurtz, R.H. and Goldberg, M.E. (1972) Activity of superior colliculus in behaving monkey III. Cells discharging before eye movements, *J. Neurophysiol.*, 35: 575-586.

ing the latter half of the second year (Forssberg unpublished observations; see also Burnett and Johnson, 1971; Sutherland et al., 1980). There is, therefore, no correlation between the initiation of unsupported locomotion and planti-grade gait, which implies that they are controlled by two separate neural processes. The development of unsupported locomotion is probably in part due to the maturation of the equilibrium system, since automatic postural reactions can be elicited in small children just able to stand erect without support (Forssberg and Nashner, 1982).

A model of the neural control of locomotion in man based on the ontogeny of locomotion would thus be more complex than during quadrupedal locomotion. Infant locomotion might reflect the autonomous activity of a spinal locomotor set which is programmed for quadrupedal locomotion and triggered from the periphery, similar to spinal locomotion. That the rhythm-generating circuits are located in the spinal cord is supported by the finding that anencephalic new-borns have a well-developed infant locomotion (see Peiper, 1961). At around two months of age, descending CPG-controlling circuits (see above) probably make functional contacts with the spinal locomotor network, and meanwhile the locomotor activity is depressed until around six months. It is still gener-ated by the spinal pattern generator which now is controlled by supraspinal structures. Around one year of age adaptive systems have matured enough to permit unsupported locomotion and also control some minor corrections

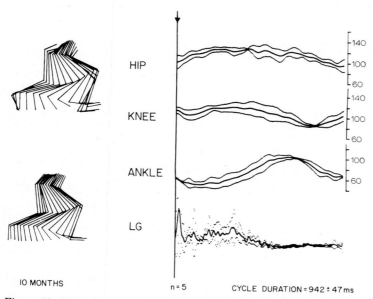

Figure 12. Movements and muscular activity of a 10-month-old boy walking on a treadmill belt. Averaged recordings from 5 step cycles. This boy could walk without external support 2 weeks after the recordings (for details see Fig. 11).

(Forssberg, unpublished observations). Finally, a neuronal system, unique for the human species, is formed somewhere in the CNS. It interacts with the spinal locomotor set and transforms the activity to an efficient plantigrade locomotor pattern.

Acknowledgements

These studies have been supported by the Swedish Medical Research Council (No. 19P-5639 and 4X-5925) and the Norrbacka Eugenia Stiftelsen. The valuable criticism of Drs. S. Grillner and A. McClellan is gratefully acknowledged.

References

Andersson, O. and Grillner, S. (1981) Peripheral control of the cats' step cycle. I. Phase dependent effects of ramp-movements of the hip during "fictive locomotion", *Acta physiol. scand.*, 113: 89-101.

Andersson, O., Forssberg, H., Grillner, S. and Lindquist, M. (1978a) Phasic gain control of the transmission in cutaneous reflex pathways to motoneurons during "fictive" locomotion, *Brain Res.*, 149: 503-507.

Andersson, O., Grillner, S., Lindquist, M. and Zomlefer, M. (1978b) Peripheral control of the spinal pattern generators for locomotion in cat, *Brain Res.*, 150: 625-630.

Andersson, O., Forssberg, H., Grillner, S. and Wallén, P. (1981) Peripheral feedback mechanisms acting on the central pattern generators for locomotion in fish and cat, *Canad. J. Physiol. Pharmacol.*, 59: 713-726.

Arshavsky, Y.I., Berkenblit, M.B., Fukson, O.I., Gelfand, I.M. and Orlovsky, G.N. (1972a) Recordings of neurons of the dorsal spinocerebellar tract during evoked locomotion, *Brain Res.*, 43: 272-275.

Arshavsky, Y.I., Berkenblit, M.B., Fukson, O.I., Gelfand, I.M. and Orlovsky, G.N. (1972b) Origin of modulation in neurons of the ventral spinocerebellar tract during locomotion, *Brain Res.*, 43: 276-279.

Arshavsky, Y.I., Gelfand, I.M., Orlovsky, G.N. and Pavlova, G.A. (1978a) Messages conveyed by spinocerebellar pathways during scratching in the cat. I. Activity of neurons of the lateral reticular nucleus, *Brain Res.*, 151: 479-492.

Arshavsky, Y.I., Gelfand, I.M., Orlovsky, G.N. and Pavlova, G.A. (1978b) Messages conveyed by spinocerebellar pathways during scratching in the cat. II. Activity of neurones of the ventral spinocerebellar tract, *Brain Res.*, 151: 493-506.

Bernstein, N. (1967) *The Coordination and Regulation of Movements*, Pergamon Press, Oxford.

Bruner, J.S. and Bruner, B.M. (1968) On voluntary action and its hierarchical structure, *Int. J. Psychol.*, 3: 239-255.

Budakova, N.N. (1973) Stepping movements in the spinal cat due to DOPA administration, *Fiziol. Zh. USSR*, 59: 1190-1198.

Burnett, C.N. and Johnson, E.W. (1971) Development of gait in childhood: Part II, *Devel. Med. Child. Neurol.*, 13: 207-215.

Duysens, J. and Loeb, G.E. (1980) Modulation of ipsi- and contralateral reflex responses in unrestrained walking cats, *J. Neurophysiol.*, 44: 1024-1037.

Duysens, J. and Pearson, K.G. (1980) Inhibition of flexor burst generation by loading ankle extensor muscles in walking cats, *Brain Res.*, 187: 321-332.

Easton, T.A. (1972) On the normal use of reflexes, *Amer. Sci.*, 60: 591-599.

Eberhardt, H.D., Inman, V.T. and Bresler, B. (1954) The principal elements in human locomotion. In P.E. Klopsteg and P.D. Wilson (Eds.), *Human Limbs and Their Substitutes*, pp. 437-471.

Eidelberg, E., Story, J.L., Walden, J.G. and Meyer, B.L. (1981) Anatomical correlates of return of locomotor function after partial spinal cord lesions in cats, *Exp. Brain Res.*, 42: 81-88.

Forssberg, H. (1979a) Stumbling corrective reaction: A phase dependent compensatory reaction during locomotion, *J. Neurophysiol.*, 42: 936-953.

Forssberg, H. (1979b) On integrative motor functions in the cat's spinal cord, *Acta physiol. scand.*, Suppl. 474.

Forssberg, H. (1980) Infant locomotion – an inherited motor program for locomotion, *Acta physiol. scand.*, 109: C10.

Forssberg, H. and Grillner, S. (1973) The locomotion of the acute spinal cat injected with clonidine i.v., *Brain Res.*, 50: 184-186.

Forssberg, H. and Nashner, L.M. (1982) Ontogenetic development of postural control in man: adaptation to altered support and visual conditions during stance, *J. Neurosci.*, in press.

Forssberg, H. and Wallberg, H. (1980) Infant locomotion – a preliminary movement and electromyographic study. In K. Berg and B. Eriksson (Eds.), *International Series on Sport Sciences, Vol. 10: Children and Exercise IX*, University Park Press, Baltimore, pp. 32-40.

Forssberg, H., Grillner, S. and Rossignol, S. (1975) Phase dependent reflex reversal during walking in chronic spinal cats, *Brain Res.*, 85: 103-107.

Forssberg, H., Grillner, S. and Rossignol, S. (1977) Phasic gain control of reflexes from the dorsum of the paw during locomotion, *Brain Res.*, 132: 121-139.

Forssberg, H., Grillner, S. and Halbertsma, J. (1980a) The locomotion of the low spinal cat. I. Coordination within a hindlimb, *Acta physiol. scand.*, 108: 269-281.

Forssberg, H., Grillner, S., Halbertsma, J. and Rossignol, S. (1980b) The locomotion of the low spinal cat. II. Interlimb coordination, *Acta physiol. scand.*, 108: 283-295.

Freusberg, A. (1874) Reflexbewegungen beim Hunde. *Pflügers Arch. ges. Physiol.*, 9: 358-391.

Grillner, S. (1969) Supraspinal and segmental control of static and dynamic γ-motoneurons in the cat, *Acta physiol. scand.*, Suppl. 327.

Grillner, S. (1981) Control of locomotion in bipeds, tetrapods and fish. In V. Brooks (Ed.), *Handbook of Physiology: The Nervous System, Vol. II, Motor Control*, Chap. 26.

Grillner, S. and Lund, S. (1968) The origin of the descending pathway with monosynaptic action on flexor motoneurons, *Acta physiol. scand.*, 74: 274-284.

Grillner, S. and Rossignol, S. (1978) On the initiation of the swing phase of locomotion in chronic spinal cats, *Brain Res.*, 146: 269-277.

Grillner, S. and Shik, M.L. (1973) On the descending control of the lumbosacral spinal cord from the "mesencephalic locomotor region", *Acta physiol. scand.*, 87: 320-333.

Grillner, S. and Zangger, P. (1975) How detailed is the central pattern generation for locomotion? *Brain Res.*, 88: 367-371.

Grillner, S. and Zangger, P. (1979) On the central generation of locomotion in the low spinal cat, *Exp. Brain Res.*, 34: 241-262.

Grillner, S., Hongo, T. and Lund, S. (1970) The vestibulospinal tract. Effects on α-motoneurones in the lumbosacral spinal cord in the cat, *Exp. Brain Res.*, 10: 94-120.

Grillner, S., Halbertsma, J., Nilsson, J. and Thorstensson, A. (1979) The adaptation to speed in human locomotion, *Brain Res.*, 165: 177-182.

Hinsey, J.S., Ranson, S.W. and McNattin, R.F. (1930) The role of hypothalamus and mesencephalon in locomotion, *Arch. Neurol. Psychiat.*, 23: 1-43.

Hongo, T., Jankowska, E. and Lundberg, A. (1972) The rubrospinal tract. IV. Effects on interneurones, *Exp. Brain Res.*, 15: 54-78.

Jankowska, E., Jukes, M.G.M., Lund, S. and Lundberg, A. (1967a) The effect of DOPA on the spinal cord. 5. Reciprocal organization of pathways transmitting excitatory action to alpha motoneurons of flexors and extensors, *Acta physiol. scand.*, 70: 369-388.

Jankowska, E., Jukes, M.G.M., Lund, S. and Lundberg, A. (1967b) The effect of DOPA on the spinal cord. 6. Half-centre organization of interneurones transmitting effects from the flexor reflex afferents, *Acta physiol. scand.*, 70: 398-402.

Kulagin, A.S. and Shik, M.L. (1970) Interaction of symmetrical limbs during controlled locomotion, *Biofizika*, 15: 164-170 (Engl transl. 171-178).

Manter, J.T. (1938) The dynamics of quadrupedal walking, *J. exp. Biol.*, 15: 522-540.

Morgan, W.W. and Huffman, R.D. (1980) Effect of cathecholaminergic and serotonergic neurotoxins on locomotor responses in cat, *Anat. Rec.*, 196: 129A-130A.

Mori, S., Shik, M.L. and Yagodnitsyn, A.S. (1977) Role of pontine tegmentum for locomotor control in mesencephalic cat, *J. Neurophysiol.*, 40: 284-295.

Mori, S., Nishimura, H. and Aoki, M. (1980) Brain stem activation of the spinal stepping generator. In J.A. Hobson and M.A.B. Brazier (Eds.), *The Reticular Formation Revisited*, Raven Press, New York, pp. 241-259.

Orlovsky, G.N. (1969) Spontaneous and induced locomotion of the thalamic cat, *Biofizika*, 14: 1095-1102.

Orlovsky, G.N. (1970) Work of the reticulospinal neurones during locomotion. *Biophysics* 15: 761-771. (English translation of *Biofizika*, 15: 728-737, 1970).

Orlovsky, G.N. (1972a) Activity of vestibulospinal neurons during locomotion, *Brain Res.*, 46: 85-98.

Orlovsky, G.N. (1972b) Activity of rubrospinal neurons during locomotion, *Brain Res.*, 46: 99-112.

Orlovsky, G.N. (1972c) The effect of different descending systems on flexor and extensor activity during locomotion, *Brain Res.*, 40: 359-371.

Orlovsky, G.N., Severin, F.V. and Shik, M.L. (1966) Effect of damage to cerebellum on the coordination of movement in the dog on running, *Biophysics*, 11: 578-588.

Peiper, A. (1961) *Cerebral Function in Infancy and Childhood*, Consultants Bureau, New York.

Piaget, J. (1954) *The Origins of Intelligence in Children*, W.W. Norton, New York.

Prochazka, A., Sontag, K.-H. and Wand, P. (1978) Motor reactions to perturbations of gait: proprioceptive and somesthetic involvement, *Neurosci. Lett.*, 7: 35-39.

Russell, D. and Zajac, F. (1979) Effects of stimulating Deiter's nucleus and medial longitudinal fasciculus on the timing of the fictive locomotor rhythm induced in cats by DOPA, *Brain Res.*, 177: 588-592.

Saunders, J.B., Inman, V.T. and Eberhardt, H.D. (1953) The major determinants in normal and pathological gait, *J. Bone Jt. Surg.*, 35A: 543-558.

Sherrington, C.S. (1910) Flexion-reflex of the limb, crossed extension-reflex and reflex stepping and standing, *J. Physiol. (Lond.)*, 40: 28-121.

Shik, M.L. (1980) Control of locomotion. In *Proc. 28th International Congress of Physiological Sciences*, Akademiai Kiado/Pergamon Press, pp. 143-148.

Shik, M.L. and Yagodnitsyn, A.S. (1977) The pontobulbar "locomotor strip", *Neurophysiologia* 9: 95-97 (in Russian).

Shik, M.L., Severin, F.V. and Orlovsky, G.N. (1966) Control of walking and running by means of electrical stimulation of the mid-brain. *Biophysics* 11: 756-765. (English translation of *Biofizika*, 11: 659-666).

Sirota, M.G. and Shik, M.L. (1973) The cat locomotion elicited through the electrode implanted in the midbrain, *Sechenow Physiol. J. USSR*, 59: 1314-1321 (in Russian).

Statham, L. and Murray, M.P. (1971) Early walking patterns of normal children, *Clin. Orthop.*, 79: 8-24.

Steeves, J.D. and Jordan, L.M. (1980) Localization of a descending pathway in the spinal cord which is necessary for controlled treadmill locomotion, *Neurosci. Lett.*, 20: 283-288.

Steeves, J.D., Jordan, L.M. and Lake, N. (1975) The close proximity of catecholamine containing cells to the "mesencephalic locomotor region" (MLR), *Brain Res.*, 100: 663-670.

Steeves, J.D., Schmidt, B.J., Skovgaard, B.J. and Jordan, L.M. (1980) Effect of noradrenaline and 5-hydroxytryptamine depletion on locomotion in the cat, *Brain Res.*, 185: 349-362.

Sutherland, D.H., Olsen, R., Cooper, L. and Woo, S.L.Y. (1980) The development of mature gait, *J. Bone Jt. Surg.*, 62A: 336-353.

Waller, W.H. (1940) Progression movements elicited by subthalamic stimulation, *J. Neurophysiol.*, 3: 300-307.

Wilson, V.J. and Yoshida, M. (1969) Comparison of effects of stimulation of Deiter's nucleus and medial longitudinal fasciculus on neck, forelimb and hindlimb motoneurons, *J. Neurophysiol.*, 32: 743-758.

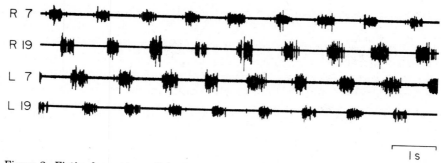

Figure 2. Fictive locomotor activity in an in vitro preparation of the lamprey spinal cord. Recordings were obtained from ventral roots of segments indicated (R, right side; L, left side). Numbering starts with the most rostral segment in the spinal cord piece, which consisted of 27 segments. The solution bathing the preparation contained 0.6 mM D-glutamate. Note the strict alternation between the bursts of the left and right ventral roots at the same level, and the lag between activation of the rostral and the caudal root of the same side. Time calibration as indicated. (From Cohen and Wallén, 1980, with permission.)

V. Descending and Ascending Control of Swimming Motor Activity in the Lamprey

The spinal central pattern generator (CPG) networks for swimming in the lamprey must normally be activated by higher order initiation neurons (e.g. descending pathways) as a result of, for instance, different sensory stimuli. One type of swimming, escape swimming, can be elicited in intact animals by mechanical pressure or by pinching applied to the head region or to the tail. It seemed reasonable that escape swimming motor activity might also be elicited by these stimuli in immobile, in vitro preparations, and thereby allow a detailed analysis of the initiation pathways for this response.

Mechanical stimuli applied to part of the rostral head region (snout) elicit several adaptive responses which are intended to remove the source of irritation. For example, animals often respond by turning away from the stimulus, followed by forward escape swimming (McClellan and Grillner, 1981). This has been analyzed with electromyographic (EMG) recordings.

In an in vitro brain stem–spinal cord preparation (Fig. 3A) consisting of the anterior head with the brain stem exposed and attached to the isolated spinal cord, mechanical stimulation applied to the head elicits escape swimming motor activity in ventral roots (Fig. 3C). Since there is no movement accompanying this motor activity, it is called "fictive escape swimming". The pattern includes a burst in the rostral ventral root contralateral to the stimulus followed by a pattern corresponding to the forward swimming (McClellan and Grillner, 1981).

Different parts of the brain stem–spinal cord preparation can be bathed in different solutions by partitioning the experimental dish into separate chambers (e.g. three, as in Fig. 3), isolated from each other by barriers sealed with vaseline. It is then possible to examine the characteristics of descending pathways, which initiate swimming by manipulating the ionic or pharmacological environment in the different chambers. For example, with a low Ca^{2+} solution in the middle chamber (Fig. 3A), blocking local chemical synaptic transmission stimulation of the snout still elicits swimming motor activity in ventral roots caudal to the block (3 and 4 in Fig. 3A). Thus, a significant part of the descending initiation pathways in the lamprey is direct. In contrast, it has been suggested that separate direct and serially connected descending pathways must both be active to initiate locomotion in the spinal cord of the cat (Shik, 1981).

In the brain stem–spinal cord preparation, electrical microstimulation in a strip traversing from the mesencephalon through the rhombencephalon, approximately 200–300 μm lateral to the mid-line (x's in Fig. 3B, left; more detail in Fig. 3B, right), is effective in eliciting well-coordinated swimming motor activity (Fig. 3D; cf. McClellan and Grillner, 1981). These regions are also restricted in depth. There appear to be similarities between the brain stem locomotor regions in the lamprey and those in fish, turtle, cats and monkeys (Kashin et al., 1974; Kazennikow et al., 1980; Shik et al., 1966; Mori et al., 1977; Eidelberg et al., 1981).

Many of the large, identifiable brain stem neurons also influence motor output in the spinal cord. The Mauthner cells receive sensory input from several cranial nerves and, when stimulated at high frequencies, produce a very weak caudal–rostral propagated bending of the body, possibly similar to backwards swimming (Rovainen, 1967a). The bulbar Müller cells (B group) receive sensory input from several cranial nerves, and stimulation of B_3 may also produce a very weak undulatory movement of the body (Rovainen, 1967a). Finally, some mesencephalic and bulbar Müller cells can increase the frequency of ongoing swimming motor activity elicited by D-glutamate (Cohen and Buchanan, 1980; Buchanan, 1981).

Escape swimming in the lamprey can also be elicited in intact or spinal animals by mechanical stimuli (pressure or pinching) applied to the tail. Application of the same type of stimulus to an in vitro preparation, consisting of part of the tail attached to the caudal spinal cord, elicits motor activity in the ventral roots organized as "fictive escape swimming" (McClellan and Grillner, 1981). This spinal cord preparation can also be partitioned into isolated chambers (see above). Sensory activation of fictive swimming with a low Ca^{2+} solution in the middle chamber indicates that a major part of the ascending initiation pathways are direct (McClellan and Grillner, 1981).

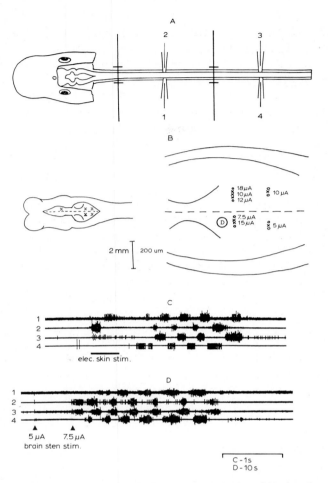

Figure 3. A, diagram of the brain stem–spinal cord preparation, consisting of the anterior part of the head with the brain stem exposed and attached to the spinal cord. Swimming motor activity is recorded from ventral roots with suction electrodes (1–4). The experimental chamber is partitioned here into three compartments, which are isolated from each other by barriers (two vertical lines) sealed with vaseline. B, regions in the mesencephalon and rhombencephalon (x's, left) where electrical stimulation (20 Hz, 1 msec pulses) has been found to elicit swimming motor activity. (The left region of the mesencephalon is probably also effective, but has not been studied yet.) Magnified view of the rhombencephalon (right) showing the positions of electrode tracks (50 μm separation) which were effective in eliciting swimming activity (x's with current thresholds), and those which were not effective (O's). C, electrical stimulation, through plate electrodes (around 10 mm²), of the left part of the snout (bar; 10 mA, 20 Hz, 5 msec pulses) first elicits a burst in ventral root 1, corresponding to turning away from the stimulus, followed by a forward escape swimming pattern. This is indicated by the alternation of ventral root bursts on opposite sides (1–2 and 3–4) and a rostral–caudal lag of ventral root bursts on the same side (1–4 and 2–3). D, swimming motor activity elicited by electrical microstimulation (20 Hz, 1 msec pulses) of the lowest threshold track (7.5 μA) marked "D" in part B (right). The swimming pattern was elicited at a threshold current of 7.5 μA, and adapted during maintained stimulation after several cycles.

VI. The Possible Role of Some Putative Transmitters in the Rhythmogenesis in the Spinal In Vitro Preparation

VI.1. Excitatory amino acids

Application of a variety of excitatory amino acids can elicit "fictive locomotion" in the spinal cord in vitro preparation (see above, Fig. 2; Poon, 1980; Cohen and Wallén, 1980). Excitatory amino acids may activate three distinctly different types of receptors (Watkins, 1981): kainate, quisqualate and N-methyl-D-aspartate (NMDA) receptors. The former two are thought to be preferentially activated by a synaptic release of L-glutamate and the latter type by aspartate. When NMDA receptor-activating substances such as N-methylasparate (50–200 μM) and D-glutamate are applied to the bath, they are very potent in releasing fictive locomotion (Grillner et al., 1981c). N-methylaspartate (NMA) is the most potent (Fig. 4). These effects are blocked by NMDA receptor blockers such as α-aminoadipate (Grillner et al., 1981c) and 2-aminophosphonovalerate (Grillner and Stokes, unpublished observations). Kainate does not release rhythmic activity (Poon, 1980). L-Glutamate gives an irregular burst activity

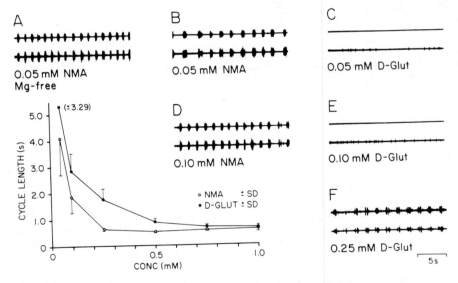

Figure 4. Comparison of the effects of N-methyl (DL) aspartate (NMA) and D-glutamate on the efferent activity recorded in two adjacent ventral roots (B–F). At 0.05 and 0.1 mM NMA is effective (B and D), but D-glutamate is only effective at concentrations of 0.25 mM (C, E and F). Time calibration in F applies to all records. The graph is from another experiment and shows that the cycle duration (± standard deviation, S.D.) is always longer with D-glutamate than with NMA at the same concentration. NMA itself is more potent when a Mg^{2+}-free solution is used (A) (cf. B). (From Grillner et al., 1981c, with permission.)

and a less potent effect than D-glutamate. If quisqualate is tried alone, it gives either a tonic efferent activity in the ventral roots or a feeble rhythmicity (Grillner and Wilén, unpublished observations). However, if small amounts of quisqualate are added to the bath during NMA-induced fictive locomotion, the effect of NMA may become potentiated, resulting in a higher burst rate.

In conclusion, NMDA receptor-activating substances release fictive locomotion, which must imply that cells that are part of, or have an input to, the pattern generator have NMDA receptors. These findings suggest the possibility that presumed aspartate-releasing neurons could normally be used to activate the pattern generator. Such neurons could be of the descending, intraspinal, or ascending type. It is noteworthy that the "giant interneurons" have recently been suggested to be aspartergic (Homma, 1981).

VI.2. Glycine and other putative transmitters

In a preparation in which fictive locomotion is continuously produced, the participation of other transmitters may be tested by adding receptor blockers to the bathing solution. If the burst production is dependent on the release of a certain transmitter, there should be a change of the pattern of burst activity if a blocker for this transmitter is administered. The glycine blocker strychnine in low dosages (Grillner and Wallén, 1980) increases the rate of bursting, and thus clearly the activity of the pattern generator. Conversely, if glycine is added to the bath the rate of bursting is depressed. This would suggest that neurons releasing glycine, or a transmitter that activates glycinergic receptors, are either part of the pattern generator circuitry or act on neurons that influence the degree of activity in the pattern generator.

GABA is another putative transmitter which is present in the spinal cord (Wald et al., 1981; cf. Homma and Rovainen, 1978). It probably does not play a role under these particular conditions, since the GABA blocker bicuculline can be administered in very high dosages without interfering with the burst production (Grillner and Wallén, 1980). The administration of GABA itself, however, does depress the burst rate.

The lamprey spinal cord contains a group of intraspinal serotonin (5-HT) neurons located just ventral to the central canal (Baumgarten, 1972). These neurons probably do not take part in the burst production under these conditions since the 5-HT-blocker methysergide can be given in high dosages without having any effect on rhythm production (Grillner et al., 1981c, and unpublished observations). The noradrenergic α-receptor blocker phenoxybenzamine does not influence the activity (Poon, 1980), nor does noradrenaline added to the bath. The effects that DOPA has been reported to have (Poon, 1980) may be related to its action as a weak agonist of glutamate (Watkins, 1978). The cholinergic blockers atropine and curare appear to have no effect on the rhythmic activity in the spinal preparation (Grillner et al., 1981c).

VII. Temperature and Ionic Composition of the In Vitro Bath

VII.1. The potassium concentration

The extracellular potassium concentration influences the membrane potential of the neurons and, thereby, their excitability. Neuronal activity may give rise to a rapid accumulation of extracellular potassium locally (Kriz et al., 1975), with an accompaning depolarization of the neurons in that particular region. Such factors have been considered as a possible factor in neuronal rhythmogenesis (Jankowska et al., 1967b; cf. Grillner, 1981).

If the potassium concentration is increased or decreased by 1.0 mM in the lamprey Ringer solution (2.1 mM) in the bath, the burst rate changes. An increased potassium level results in a significantly increased burst rate (e.g. by one-third), and a decrease has the reverse effect (Grillner and Wilén, unpublished observations). These moderate changes in potassium concentration should be compared to the large local intraspinal changes that result from a short series of nerve volleys, which can give potassium concentration increases of 6 mM (Kriz et al., 1975).

VII.2. Temperature changes

The burst rate is strongly affected by changes in the temperature of the in vitro bath. An increase from 3 to 15°C can double the burst rate, everything else being equal (Grillner and Wallén, 1980).

VIII. Intracellular Studies of Spinal Neurons

VIII.1. Motoneurons

The motoneurons supplying the segmental muscle fibers all undergo phasic depolarizations and hyperpolarizations in each swim cycle (Fig. 5), but only a certain proportion are sufficiently depolarized to generate action potentials (Russell and Wallén, 1980, and unpublished observations). In an intact lamprey, swimming at a low rate, EMG activity can be recorded primarily at the lateral aspect of the body, where the red "slow" muscle fibers are located, and little activity in the center of the muscle mass, where there are primarily white "fast" muscle fibers. It is therefore likely that motoneurons supplying red muscle fibers are active under these conditions (Wallén and Williams, 1982), and that the conditions are similar to those in fish (Hudson, 1973; Grillner, 1974; Grillner and Kashin, 1976). The motoneurons that generate action potentials under the in vitro conditions may also preferentially be of the "slow type".

To test the possibility of an inhibitory input to the motoneurons during the fictive "swim cycle", chloride was injected into the motoneurons. This resulted in a reversal of the hyperpolarizing part of the cycle into a depolarizing one, which means that in each swim cycle the hyperpolarizing phase is a result of phasic chloride-dependent IPSPs rather than being just a disfacilitation (Russell and Wallén, 1980, and unpublished observations). Following chloride injection, each "swim cycle" consists of two distinct depolarizing phases. This means that there is a true depolarizing phase generated by one set of excitatory interneurons followed by a true inhibitory phase generated by a set of inhibitory interneurons (Russell and Wallén, 1980, and unpublished observations). This mechanism can be described as a "push–pull arrangement", and it also occurs in other rhythmic innate movements in higher vertebrates (Sears, 1964; Edgerton et al., 1976).

Motoneurons that are assumed to supply the dorsal fin muscles (Cohen and

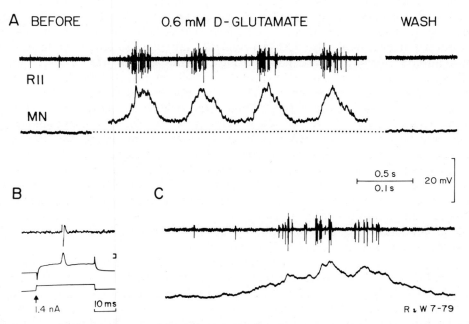

Figure 5. Intracellular variation in membrane potential of a motoneuron during fictive locomotion. Upper traces in A–C show the burst patterns in the ventral root of the same hemisegment in which the neuron is recorded. The lower traces are intracellular. In B, the cell is identified as a motoneuron by intracellular stimulation resulting in a ventral root spike (voltage calibration is 20 mV). A, shows the flat membrane potential before and after administration of D-glutamate, and in the middle panel the large rhythmic oscillations (around 20 mV, voltage calibration applies to A and C) during D-glutamate administration in the bath. C, shows one half-cycle with expanded time resolution, showing that peaks of depolarization in the intracellular record coincide with an increased number of spikes in the ventral root. (From Russell and Wallén, unpublished observations.)

Buchanan, 1980; Buchanan, 1981) are also phasically active in the spinal in vitro preparation, but they are phase-shifted by half a cycle, and thus active at the same time as the myotomal muscle fibers on the contralateral side. Motoneurons are presumably not part of the pattern generating circuits as no recurrent effects have been demonstrated (Teräväinen and Rovainen, 1971; Shapovalov, 1977).

VIII.2. Interneurons

A small proportion of the spinal cord "interneurons" is comprised of large identifiable neurons, which have been defined and investigated by Rovainen (e.g. 1974b). Cohen and Buchanan (1980) and Buchanan (1981) have studied these propriospinal interneurons during fictive locomotion. Two types of inhibitory interneurons have descending axons throughout a large part of the spinal cord, the "lateral interneurons" on the ipsilateral side and the "CC-interneurons" on the contralateral side. Both types have large membrane potential oscillations related to the efferent burst pattern. The former type is in phase with the efferent burst pattern, while the "CC-interneuron" has a phase lead over ipsilateral segmental bursts and its depolarization is terminated earlier. It has direct inhibitory connections to the crossed myotomal motoneurons along many segments and must consequently contribute to the hyperpolarization of the motoneurons in each swim cycle. Their quantitative importance for the motoneuronal hyperpolarization in the swim cycle, however, is not yet determined. The lack of correspondence between the shape of the segmental ventral root burst and the depolarization phase of the "CC-interneurons" is noteworthy in this context. The lateral interneuron is only present in the rostral part of the spinal cord, and it is therefore not necessary for the intersegmental coordination as it can be generated by any small section of the spinal cord independent of its position along the cord. It must be realized that, presumably, a large part of the projections of these propriospinal interneurons may be on local segmental interneurons that have not yet been described.

Sigvardt and Grillner (1981, and unpublished observations) have studied the morphology (intracellular Lucifer yellow injection; Stewart, 1978) and the phase relationship of the activity in segmental interneurons during fictive locomotion. A large number of interneurons are confined to one segment, and have no apparent axon, even when the cells have been well filled with Lucifer yellow. The "dendritic trees" of such neurons are often confined to one hemisegment and may be very simple or quite complex. During fictive locomotion such interneurons often exhibit phasic depolarizations of between 2 and 15 mV (Fig. 6), and most of them generate action potentials either spontaneously or as a result of current pulses. Many such interneurons have an activity pattern that closely corresponds to the burst pattern of the efferent ipsilateral bursts. Even the amplitude of the depolarization phases follows closely the form of the rectified and filtered ventral root bursts. Other interneurons have a pattern that solution to block chemical synaptic transmission. If the rostral end of the cord was divided into thin fascicles, spike activity (Fig. 11) could be recorded within lateral fascicles, but not within the medial fascicles, including the dorsal columns. These neurons in the lateral fascicles responded both to stepwise and sinusoidal lateral movements of the cord. As the same pattern of activity can be obtained both in "Ringer" and in Ca^{2+}-free solutions, it is likely that the neurons studied are themselves mechanosensitive, rather than being synaptically activated from such neurons. When single units were recorded, it could be shown that each one could be activated from a circumscribed area along the lateral margin of the cord by very gentle tapping with a fine glass rod. When the adjoining area was stretched or unloaded (Grillner et al., 1982) the unit reacted like a typical stretch receptor neuron.

The spinal cord of the lamprey thus contains intraspinal mechanosensitive elements. It would seem unlikely that the axons from which we recorded belong to afferent neurons, as they do not have branches in the dorsal column. It thus appears likely that there are neurons with axons in the lateral funiculus of the cord and with a localized mechanosensitive area along the lateral margin of the spinal cord. The only neuron with its cell body in this region is the edge cell, which has dendritic branches ramifying in the rostrocaudal direction along the lateral margin of the cord (Tretjakoff, 1909; Rovainen, 1974b). This type of neuron would seem eminently well suited to serve as a mechanoreceptor neuron.

XI. Concluding Remarks

The lamprey spinal cord in isolation can generate the motor pattern that is used during locomotion. The motoneurons are driven in each swim cycle by an alternating excitatory and inhibitory input. The motor pattern is generated by local interneuronal circuits as the motor pattern can be generated with a few segments of the spinal cord. A large number of interneurons in the spinal cord are phasically depolarized during fictive locomotion, some in phase with the ventral root burst, others with a phase lead or phase lag in relation to the bursts, and a few that may be strictly reciprocal. Many of these interneurons are strictly local and have no axon; despite this fact, they generate action potentials. It is likely that glycinergic neurons directly or indirectly contribute to the pattern generator circuits, and an activation of NMDA receptors can activate these circuits. The exact interneuronal circuit responsible for the pattern generation has not yet been defined.

The pattern generator can also be activated by stimulation of the brain stem or by mechanical stimuli applied to the head or the tailfin in the intact lamprey. The pattern generator circuits are also influenced by peripheral feedback circuits in a similar manner to higher vertebrates. Part of this feedback is exerted by mechanosensitive neurons located within the spinal cord.

Summary

The lamprey nervous system can be maintained in vitro for several days. Stimulation of the brain stem in a very circumscribed region can elicit a motor pattern that would have resulted in locomotion had the nervous system still been connected to the muscles. The spinal cord in isolation can also produce "fictive locomotion", for instance during administration of N-methyl-D-aspartate receptor stimulating agents, in the in vitro bath. The spinal pattern generator is dependent on glycinergic mechanisms, and is activating each motoneuron in "a push–pull mode" with periods of excitation followed by a chloride-dependent inhibition. The pattern generator is composed of local segmental interneurons. A number of local interneurons active during fictive locomotion have no axons, but their detailed pattern of connections is still not yet determined. The pattern generator is influenced by movement-related feedback, part of which is elicited by intraspinal mechanosensitive neurons.

Acknowledgements

This project has been supported by the Swedish Medical Research Council, Project No. 3026, Magnus Bergvalls Stiftelse and KI's fonder. K. Sigvardt has been supported by the Swedish Medical Research Council, A. McClellan from NIH (F32-NS06321-01) and T. Williams from the Royal Society, London. The dedicated help of Mrs. I. Klingebrant is gratefully acknowledged.

References

Andersson, O., Forssberg, H., Grillner, S. and Wallén, P. (1981) Peripheral feedback mechanisms acting on the central pattern generators for locomotion in fish and cat, *Canad. J. Physiol. Pharmacol.*, 59: 713-726.

Baumgarten, H.G. (1972) Biogenic monoamines in the cyclostome and lower vertebrate brain, *Progr. Histochem. Cytochem.*, 4: 1-90.

Buchanan, J.T. (1981) *Identification of cc Interneurons and Studies of Swimming Activity in the Lamprey*, PhD Thesis, Washington University, St. Louis, Mo.

Cohen, A.H. and Buchanan, J.T. (1980) Activity of identified spinal neurons in lamprey during "fictive swimming", *Soc. Neurosci. Abstr.*, 6: 369.

Cohen, A.H. and Wallén, P. (1978) Rhythmic locomotor activity induced in an in vitro preparation of the lamprey spinal cord, *Neurosci. Lett.*, Suppl. 1: S92.

Cohen, A.H. and Wallén, P. (1980) The neuronal correlate of locomotion in fish. "Fictive swimming" induced in an in vitro preparation of the lamprey spinal cord, *Exp. Brain Res.*, 41: 11-18.

Delcomyn, F. (1980) Neural basis of rhythmic behavior in animals, *Science*, 210: 492-498.

Edgerton, V.R., Grillner, S., Sjöström, A. and Zangger, P. (1976) Central generation of locomotion in vertebrates. In R. Herman, S. Grillner, P. Stein and D. Stuart (Eds.), *Neural Control of Locomotion, Vol. 18*, Plenum Press, New York, pp. 439-464.

Eidelberg, E., Walden, J.G. and Nguyen, L.H. (1981) Locomotor control in macaque monkeys, *Brain*, 104: 647-664.

II.1. Effect of spinal transection in the neonatal rat

The acute period. Except for primitive vestibular and locomotor reactions, few responses of the hindquarters were influenced by cephalic stimulation at birth. These responses disappeared after surgery in the neonatal operates and never reappeared. Other than these behavioral deficits, the only other hindlimb response affected by the surgery was the flexed posture of the proximal musculature, which was not seen during the first postoperative day. Wriggling, flexion reflexes, urogenital responses including urination and defecation, and the scratch response, were evident after recovery from anesthesia. Thus, the spinal shock seen immediately after surgery was minimal.

During the next three postoperative weeks, additional responses appeared in the hindlimbs of neonatal operates. There were a number of similarities with normal response ontogeny and, in general, the actual time of appearance of many responses was synchronized with the appearance of these responses in unoperated littermates. However, certain responses did not disappear as in normal response ontogeny, certain responses appeared earlier, and, in certain cases, there was a delay of 4–5 days in the appearance of responses in neonatal operates.

The first postoperative week. By the end of the first postoperative week generalized avoidance reactions, such as a long-lasting wriggling of the hindquarters after pinching the tail, were the major responses seen in the isolated hindquarters of neonatal operates. These responses continued throughout the entire postoperative survival period. In the hindquarters of unoperated littermates, these generalized avoidance responses disappeared suddenly between 6 and 8 days of age and were replaced with responses resembling those of the adult.

By 4–5 postoperative days in neonatal operates the hindlimbs began to support the hindquarters, and the feet rested on their plantar surfaces. In unoperated littermates this posture normally occurred between 9 and 10 days of age. The coordination of the hindlimbs of neonatal operates remained poor in other situations, just as in littermate controls. Locomotor responses began in unoperated animals by 6–8 days of age, several days before stepping was seen in neonatal operates.

The second postoperative week. A urogenital response, seen at birth in the rat (Stelzner, 1971), disappeared in both neonatal operates and normal littermates between 10 and 12 days of age. Also, the posture of the hindlimbs of both intact littermates and neonatal operates resembled the normal adult posture by the end of the second postoperative (and postnatal) week. Both hindlimbs were held beside the body and the feet rested only on their ventral pads supporting the hindquarters. It was usually not until the end of the second postoperative week that stepping responses were seen in the hindlimbs of neonatal operates as the forelimbs pulled the hindquarters forward. On the other hand, in unoperated littermates locomotor responses of the hindlimbs were almost mature by this age. Although stepping and hopping responses could be elicited at 10–12 postoperative days, other coordinated responses of the hindlimbs such as the placing reactions remained poorly developed in both neonatal operates and unoperated littermates.

The third postoperative week. Stepping became a major response during this period. Many short, laterally directed steps, not coordinated with the forelimbs, gave the neonatal operates a waddling gait. There was also rapid development of hindlimb coordination between 15 and 21 postoperative days that was most apparent when the operates were tested on a grid with variably spaced openings. By 17–18 postoperative days, increased extensor tone and struggling movements were seen when a hindlimb fell through a grid opening. When the ventral pads came in contact with a grid bar there was a rapid bilateral extensor movement (extensor thrust response) that often bounced the animal off the grid surface. By 21 postoperative days hindlimb replacement was rapid and extensor thrust was a major reaction. The hindfeet were seen to palpate the grid surface and made fine adjustments on it. A discrete placing response, similar to tactile placing, also was first elicited at the same time. All of these responses were mature by 16–18 days of age in littermate controls, indicating a delay in the appearance of these responses by several days in neonatal operates. Except for an overall decrease in the responsiveness of the hindquarters seen at long survival periods, there were few further behavioral changes for as long as a year after surgery.

II.2. Effect of spinal transection in the weanling rat

The effect of mid-thoracic spinal transection in weanling rats produced similar effects to those found after the same surgery in adults (Sugar and Gerard, 1940). Few responses were seen during the first 2 or 3 postoperative days, indicating that spinal shock was greater in the weanling operate than in the neonatal operate. It was necessary to manually evacuate the urinary bladder of these animals for the first 7–10 postoperative days. Over the last half of the first postoperative week scratching, flexion reflexes and brief wriggling appeared. With increasing time, choreoathetoid-like movements and flexor and extensor spasms appeared – behaviors which were seldom observed in neonatal operates. Other responses found in neonatal operates, such as hindlimb support and tactile placing, were never observed, even with postoperative recovery periods of up to one year. Figure 1 shows the posture of a chronic neonatal operate (a) and a chronic weanling operate (b). Table I summarizes the behavioral differences in the hindlimbs of adult animals spinally transected at the neonatal and weanling stages of development. It can be seen in Table I that a large number of responses survive or are spared by a spinal transection at the neonatal stage of development which are lost if the same lesion is made in a weanling or adult animal.

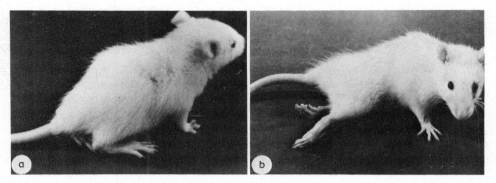

Figure 1. A neonatal operate at the weanling stage of development (a) and a chronic weanling operate (b). (Taken from Stelzner, 1982, with permission.)

TABLE I

HINDLIMB BEHAVIORS OF SPINALLY TRANSECTED RATS

Neonatal operates		Weanling operates	
1.	Spinal shock minimal	1.	Spinal shock pronounced
2.	Wriggling – long lasting	2.	Wriggling – brief
3.	Spontaneous responses common: scratch, flexion reflexes – spasms infrequent	3.	Spasms and choreoathetoid movements common: scratch, flexion reflexes present
4.	Hindlimb support	4.	–
5.	Locomotor responses: stepping, hopping	5.	–
6.	Hindlimb replacement	6.	–
7.	Hindlimb palpitations	7.	–
8.	Extensor thrust responses	8.	–
9.	"Tactile" placing	9.	–

II.3. Age or stage of maturation when responses are no longer spared after spinal transection

To determine when sparing of function no longer occurs, the spinal cord of rats at several different ages (newborn, 9 days of age, 12 days, 18 days, 21 days and adult) was mid-thoracically transected (Weber and Stelzner, 1977). The immediate effects of surgery, the postoperative recovery and development of responses, and the chronic behaviors of the hindlimbs were tested. These responses were evaluated using a rating system from 1 (maximal response depression) to 4 (responses of a mature neonatal operate) developed from the results of our first study. Seven different classes of behavior (posture, locomotion, placing, etc.) were evaluated by two individuals who rated the behavior independently and without knowledge of the animal's age at the time of surgery or postoperative recovery time. A high correlation ($r = 0.88$) was found between the scores of the two raters. To analyze the data we also divided the postoperative recovery period into 4 stages:

Stage 1 (Period of spinal shock): the first two postoperative days when responses are most depressed

Stage 2 (Recovery period): the remainder of the first postoperative week when response recovery in the weanling transected animals is complete

Stage 3 (Developmental period): from 8 to 28 days postoperatively when response ontogeny in the normal and neonatally transected animals is still taking place

Stage 4 (Chronic period): the period after 28 postoperative days when responses are stable for all groups of spinally transected rats

Figure 2, taken from our original study (Weber and Stelzner, 1977), graphically presents the summed median scores of all the categories of responses to give an estimate of the total amount of behavioral recovery. On the ordinate it is apparent that a fully recovered rat would have a score of 56 (7 different behavioral categories, a value of 4 indicating full recovery and the summed scores of two raters). Notice the clear discontinuity in the median scores between the newborn, 9-day and 12-day groups and the older groups; there were highly significant differences between animals operated on at 12 days or less and animals operated on at 15 days or older. During stage 1, the period of spinal shock, the responses of the hindlimbs of newborn, 9-day and 12-day operates

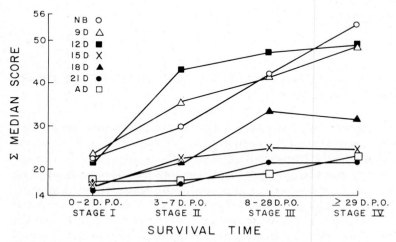

Figure 2. Behavioral recovery at different ages following spinal transection. Set text for details. (From Weber and Stelzner, 1977, with permission.)

were equivalent, and there was less spinal shock than in the animals operated at 15 days or later. Recovery (stage 2) appeared greater for the 9-day and 12-day groups, since many of the behaviors which recovered in these two groups by 7 postoperative days had not yet developed in the neonatal operates or their littermate controls by 7 days of age. These responses had been lost in the 9- and 12-day groups during stage 1. Thus, there was greater sparing of function and reduced spinal shock in animals spinally transected before 15 days of age.

III. Development of Dorsal Root, Descending, and Intrinsic Connections in the Lumbosacral Spinal Cord

The previous section described an inverse relationship between the initial amount of spinal shock (response depression) and the final development and recovery of responses in the isolated spinal cord and hindquarters of the post-natal rat. The development of spinal shock in some way appears to have per-manently changed the functioning of the isolated spinal cord. As stated in the Introduction, most studies of the adult CNS have assumed that the amount of spinal shock is related to the amount of influence the cut axons had on spinal circuitry prior to surgery (Chambers et al., 1973; Sherrington, 1947). Because the amount of spinal shock is a function of age, we wanted to determine if it was related to the maturity of axonal connections at the time of injury. We asked whether there was a temporal relationship between the maturation of dorsal root, descending, and intrinsic connections and the increased spinal shock and decreased behavioral recovery we had observed to begin near post-natal day 15.

III.1. Dorsal root connections

We analyzed the development of dorsal root connections in the lumbosacral spinal cord using a lesion–degeneration analysis after intradural section of dorsal roots in the neonatal and weanling rat (Gilbert and Stelzner, 1979). As others have found, the rate of axonal degeneration in the neonate is much more rapid than in the adult. Otherwise, dorsal root connections were fully mature at birth. The distribution of degeneration in the lumbosacral spinal cord of the neonatal rat was similar to that found in the weanling or adult, as was previously shown by Cajal (1911) using the Golgi technique. In our study, many examples of electron-dense degenerating synaptic endings were seen with the electron microscope in projection zones of the dorsal root, confirming the presence of dorsal root connections at birth.

III.2. Descending connections

We also analyzed the development of descending connections in the lumbosacral spinal cord using the lesion–degeneration analysis after mid-thoracic spinal hemisection (Gilbert and Stelzner, 1979). Although the rate of degeneration was identical to that found after dorsal root section, unlike dorsal root distribution, the distribution of degeneration after thoracic hemisection was incomplete in the neonatal animal. After spinal hemisection, no degeneration was found either at the base of the dorsal funiculus, which is where the corticospinal tract descends in the rat, or in the dorsal horn or intermediate nucleus of Cajal, which are projection zones of the corticospinal tract. Other investigators, using the anterograde transport of [³H]amino acids, the degeneration method and the neurofibrillar technique (DeMyer, 1967; Donatelle, 1977; Hicks and D'Amato, 1975; Wise et al., 1979), have also reported that the corticospinal tract has not reached the lumbosacral spinal cord during the neonatal period in the rat.

Although the detailed development of specific descending pathways from the rat brain stem has not been reported, most brain stem pathways have probably arrived in the lumbosacral spinal cord during the neonatal period. Unlike the cerebral cortex (Armstrong-James and Johnson, 1970; Deza and Eidelberg, 1967; Eayrs and Goodhead, 1959; Wise et al., 1979), the reticular formation is relatively mature at birth in the rat and at least certain descending reticulospinal axons are present (Das and Hine, 1972). Central monoamine neurons form in the brain stem during the later portion of prenatal life, and most descending monoamine pathways have also been traced into the spinal cord prior to birth (Seiger and Olson, 1973). The retrograde cell loss of magnocellular neurons of the red nucleus that is found after mid-thoracic spinal hemisection in the neonatal rat (Prendergast and Stelzner, 1976), also shows that the rubrospinal tract has at least reached this position in the spinal cord at birth. Although the evidence is more indirect, the vestibular reactions seen in the hindlimbs while the rat pup is righting or being tilted suggest that the vestibulospinal tract is also present and functioning in the lumbosacral spinal cord at birth.

Our light microscopic results and the data in the above paragraph suggest that most descending nerve tracts are in a position to form synaptic connections in the lumbosacral spinal cord of the newborn rat. However, we were surprised that no sign of electron-dense degenerating synaptic endings could be found in either the ventromedial gray (lamina VIII) or the lateral gray (laminae VI–VII) after neonatal hemisection. This was true even though we use a large number of different postoperative survival periods (8 h–3 days): periods when degeneration in these areas was visible using the light microscope. There are two probable reasons for this finding. A number of reports have shown that the appearance of synapses in a target area is often delayed for a variable period once axons have arrived near it (Rakic, 1977; Wise and

androgen production on the development of these reflexes are controlled. The basis for the lack of recovery of this type of reflex is presently unknown, but it does show a limit to the plasticity found in the developing spinal cord.

If synaptic reorganization is responsible for the sparing of function that is seen in the isolated spinal cord, there should be a differential reorganization which is dependent on the age of the animal at the time of spinal transection. We have tested whether there are differences in the distribution or density of dorsal root axons in the lumbosacral spinal cord of adult rats spinally injured at the neonatal or weanling stages (Stelzner et al., 1979). In order to use each animal as its own control, we compared the two sides of the L5–S1 segments of the lumbosacral spinal cord in adult rats given a mid-thoracic hemisection at the neonatal or weanling stage. There was no evidence for a change in the distribution of dorsal root axons between the experimental (initially hemisected side) and control sides of the cord in either group of operates. A number of differences in our experimental design from previous experiments on the adult animal may have masked a small positive result (as in Liu and Chambers, 1958; McCouch et al., 1958; Murray and Goldberger, 1974). However, in rats spinally hemisected at the neonatal stage, a significantly greater density of dorsal root degeneration was found within the intermediate nucleus of Cajal on the experimental side using coded material and a blind analysis. This difference was not detected in weanling operates. Controls indicated that the increased density of degeneration in neonatal operates was not due to compression resulting from shrinkage of the nucleus or to degeneration remaining from the initial hemisection. We concluded that this difference was due to an increased density of dorsal root axons which could only be detected in the neonatal operates. This growth was quantitatively abnormal; it was restricted to an area where the dorsal root normally projects and where there is normally an overlap with descending connections. This morphological plasticity coincides with the sparing of function we have found. Whether this abnormal growth occurs after a lesion at 12 days but not after 15 days of age, when the sparing of function effect ends, is not yet known. We also do not know whether this sparing of function is related to the abnormal dorsal root growth or is more closely related to changes in intrinsic synaptic development. Our results indicate that synaptic reorganization does take place to a greater extent after spinal injury in neonatal operates than in weanling operates. Further experiments will show whether synaptic reorganization is the mechanism responsible for sparing of function in the isolated spinal cord of young rats.

V. Summary and Conclusions

(1) Previous studies show that the amount of spinal shock and subsequent reflex recovery seen after spinal transection are inversely related to one another. Both of these factors are dependent on the amount of descending in-

fluence on spinal circuitry found prior to spinal transection.

(2) Our studies show that if spinal transection is made before the time descending connections are mature (early operates; before 15 days of age in the rat), spinal shock is minimal, most reflexes present prior to the lesion recover, and other reflexes develop at approximately the same time as in unoperated littermates. Many responses are present (spared) in these early operates that remain absent in animals spinally transected at older ages (adult operates).

(3) These age-related behavioral differences found in the isolated hindquarters are not due to the generation or regeneration of descending axons through the site of spinal lesion.

(4) These data from early operates suggest that spinal circuitry underlying reflexes in the isolated hindquarters in different classes of vertebrates are more similar than data from adult operates of these species have shown.

(5) There are two possible explanations supported by the data to explain the age-related differences in reflexes found after isolating the spinal cord: (a) the first is that spinal shock is an indication of the pathological effect of removal of descending influences on the circuits underlying spinal reflexes. This circuitry remains intact but is permanently depressed after spinal transection in the adult, but not in the early operate; (b) the second explanation is that the amount of spinal shock seen at different stages of development indicates the functional maturity of descending and local connections at the time of injury. There is greater synaptic reorganization of connections still being formed in the isolated spinal cord so that the circuits underlying the spared reflexes continue to operate "normally".

Both of these explanations may be partially correct since they are not mutually exclusive. In fact, the spinal circuitry underlying the behavioral differences between early and adult operates may remain permanently depressed in adult operates because synaptic reorganization at this stage of development is not sufficient to completely overcome the loss of descending connections.

(6) The increased influence of descending connections on spinal reflex circuits seen during both phylogeny and ontogeny, appears necessary to fully maintain the intrinsic functioning of the spinal cord once this influence is present. However, our data suggest that both spinal reflexes and the intrinsic functioning of the spinal cord are able to operate independently of descending influences, if these influences are not allowed to form.

Acknowledgements

I would like to thank Dr. James A. Horel and Dr. Eric D. Weber for their comments on an early draft of this manuscript, and Ms. Judith A. Strauss for photographic assistance. My own work that is discussed in this paper was supported by NIH Grants NS16105, NS14096 and NS10579.

References

Altman, J. and Sudarshan, K. (1975) Postnatal development of locomotion in the laboratory rat, *Anim. Behav.*, 23: 896-920.

Amassian, V.E. and Ross, R.J. (1978a) Developing role of sensorimotor cortex and pyramidal tract neurons in kittens, *J. Physiol. (Paris)*, 74: 165-184.

Amassian, V.E. and Ross, R.J. (1978b) Electrophysiological correlates of the developing higher sensorimotor control system. *J. Physiol. (Paris)*, 74: 185-201.

Anderson, L.S., Black, R.G., Abraham, J. and Ward, A.A. (1971) Neuronal hyperactivity in experimental trigeminal deafferentation, *J. Neurosurg.*, 35: 444-452.

Armstrong-James, M. and Johnson, R. (1970) Quantitative studies of postnatal changes in synapses in rat superficial motor cerebral cortex: an electron microscopical study, *Z. Zellforsch.*, 110: 559-568.

Beck, C.H. and Chambers, W.W. (1970) Speed, accuracy, and strength of forelimb movements after unilateral pyramidotomy in rhesus monkeys, *J. comp. physiol. Psychol.*, 70: 1-22.

Bernstein, D.R. and Stelzner, D.J. (1980) Developmental plasticity of the corticospinal tract (CST) following midthoracic spinal cord "over-hemisection" in the neonatal rat, *Soc. Neurosci. Abstr.*, 6: 683.

Bernstein, D.R. and Stelzner, D.J. (1981) Corticospinal tract (CST) plasticity in the early postnatal rat, *Soc. Neurosci. Abstr.*, 7: 678.

Bernstein, D.R., Bechard, D.E. and Stelzner, D.J. (1981) Neuritic growth maintained near the lesion site long after spinal cord transection in the newborn rat, *Neurosci. Lett.*, 26: 55-60.

Bernstein, J.J., Gelderd, J.B. and Bernstein, M.E. (1974) Alteration of neuronal synaptic complement during regeneration and axonal sprouting of rat spinal cord, *Exp. Neurol.*, 44: 470-482.

Bernstein, M.E. and Bernstein, J.J. (1977) Synaptic frequency alteration on rat ventral horn neurons in the first segment proximal to spinal cord hemisection: an ultrastructural statistical study of regenerative capacity, *J. Neurocytol.*, 6: 85-102.

Bignall, K.E. (1974) Ontogeny of levels of neural organization: the righting reflex as a model, *Exp. Neurol.*, 42: 566-573.

Bignall, K.E. and Schramm, L. (1974) Behavior of chronically decerebrated kittens, *Exp. Neurol.*, 42: 519-531.

Bogen, J.E. and Campbell, B. (1962) Recovery of foreleg placing after ipsilateral frontal lobectomy in the hemicerebrectomized cat, *Science*, 135: 309-310.

Bregman, B.S. and Goldberger, M.E. (1980) Infant lesion effect: result of neonatal and adult hemisection in cats, *Soc. Neurosci. Abstr.*, 6: 206.

Bregman, B.W. and Goldberger, M.E. (1981) Characteristics of a corticospinal tract with an aberrant trajectory, *Soc. Neurosci. Abstr.*, 7: 180.

Brooks, C.M. (1933) Studies on the cerebral cortex. II. Localized representation of hopping reactions in the rat and their normal management by small cortical remnants, *Arch. Neurol. Psychiat.*, 30: 40-74.

Brooks, C.M. and Peck, M.E. (1940) Effects of various cortical lesions on development of placing and hopping reactions in the rat, *J. Neurophysiol.*, 3: 66-73.

Bruce, I.C. and Tatton, W.G. (1980a) Sequential output–input maturation of kitten motor cortex, *Exp. Brain Res.*, 39: 411-419.

Bruce, I.C. and Tatton, W.G. (1980b) Synchronous development of motor cortical output to different muscles in the kitten, *Exp. Brain Res.*, 40: 349-353.

Cajal, S. Ramón y (1911) *Histologie du Système Nerveux de l'Homme et des Vertébrés*, A. Maloine, Paris.

Castro, A.J. (1975) Ipsilateral corticospinal projections after large lesions of the cerebral hemisphere in neonatal rats, *Exp. Neurol.*, 46: 1-8.

Castro, A.J. (1977) Limb preference after lesions of the cerebral hemisphere in adult and neonatal rats, *Physiol. Behav.*, 18: 605-608.

318

Chambers, W.W. (1955) Structural regeneration in the mammalian central nervous system in relation to age. In W.F. Windle (Ed.), *Regeneration in the Central Nervous System*, C.C. Thomas, Springfield, IL, pp. 135-147.

Chambers, W.W., Liu, C.N., McCouch, G.P. and D'Aquili, E. (1966) Descending tracts and spinal shock in the cat, *Brain*, 89: 377-390.

Chambers, W.W., Liu, C.N. and McCouch, G.P. (1973) Anatomical and physiological correlates of plasticity in the central nervous system, *Brain Behav. Evol.*, 8: 5-26.

Cummings, J.P., Bernstein, D.R. and Stelzner, D.J. (1981) Further evidence that sparing of function after spinal cord transection in the neonatal rat is not due to axonal generation or regeneration, *Exp. Neurol.*, in press.

Das, G.D. and Hine, R.J. (1972) Nature and significance of spontaneous degeneration of axons in the pyramidal tract, *Z. Anat. Entwickl.-Gesch.*, 136: 98-114.

DeMyer, W. (1967) Ontogenesis of the rat corticospinal tract. Normal events and effects of intrauterine neurosurgical lesions, *Arch. Neurol.*, 16: 203-211.

DeMyer, W.E. (1973) Development of axonal pathways after neurosurgical lesions in the septum of the fetal rat: fornix ventralis, commissure of the fornix ventralis, corpus callosum and anterior commissure, *J. comp. Neurol.*, 166: 49-73.

Devor, M. (1975) Neuroplasticity in the sparing or deterioration of function after early olfactory tract lesions, *Science*, 190: 998-1000.

Devor, M. (1976) Neuroplasticity in the rearrangement of olfactory tract fibers after neonatal transection in hamsters, *J. comp. Neurol.*, 166: 49-73.

Deza, L. and Eidelberg, E. (1967) Development of cortical electrical activity in the rat, *Exp. Neurol.*, 16: 425-438.

Donatelle, J.M. (1977) Growth of the corticospinal tract and the development of placing reactions in the postnatal rat, *J. comp. Neurol.*, 175: 207-232.

Eayrs, J.T. and Goodhead, B. (1959) Postnatal development of the cerebral cortex in the rat, *J. Anat. (Lond.)*, 93: 385-402.

Eidelberg, E., Straehley, D., Erspamer, R. and Watkins, C.J. (1977) Relationship between residual hind limb-assisted locomotion and surviving axons after incomplete spinal cord injuries, *Exp. Neurol.*, 56: 312-322.

Forssberg, H. (1979) On integrative motor functions in the cat's spinal cord, *Acta physiol. scand.*, Suppl. 474: 1-56.

Forssberg, H. and Grillner, S. (1973) The locomotion of the acute spinal cat injected with clonidine I.V., *Brain Res.*, 50: 184-186.

Forssberg, H., Grillner, S. and Sjöström, A. (1974) Tactile placing reactions in chronic spinal kittens, *Acta physiol. scand.*, 92: 114-120.

Forssberg, H., Grillner, S. and Halbertsma, J. (1980a) The locomotion of the low spinal cat. I. Coordination within a hind limb, *Acta physiol. scand.*, 108: 269-281.

Forssberg, H., Grillner, S., Halbertsma, J. and Rossignol, S. (1980b) The locomotion of the low spinal cat. II. Interlimb coordination, *Acta physiol. scand.*, 108: 283-295.

Fox, M.W. (1966) The clinical significance of age differences in the effects of decerebration and spinal cord transection in the dog, *J. small anim. Pract.*, 7: 91-98.

Fukson, O.I., Berkinblit, M.B. and Feldman, A.G. (1980) The spinal frog takes into account the scheme of its body during the wiping reflex, *Science*, 209: 1261-1263.

Gall, C. and Lynch, G. (1981) Fiber architecture of the dentate gyrus following ablation of the entorhinal cortex in rats of different ages: evidence for two forms of axon sprouting in the immature brain, *Neuroscience*, 5: 903-910.

Gelfan, S. (1963) Neurons and synapse population in the spinal cord. Indication of role in total integration, *Nature (Lond.)*, 198: 162-163.

Gerard, R.W. and Grinker, R.R. (1931) Regenerative possibilities of the central nervous system, *Arch. Neurol. Psychiat.*, 26: 469-484.

Gilbert, M. and Stelzner, D.J. (1979) The development of descending and dorsal root connections in the lumbosacral spinal cord of the postnatal rat, *J. comp. Neurol.*, 184: 821-838.

Brain Stem Control of Spinal Mechanisms
– B. Sjölund and A. Björklund, editors
© 1982 Elsevier Biomedical Press

13

Central Nervous Control of Arm Movement in Stroke Patients

G.R. HAMMOND, S. MILLER and P.M. ROBERTSON

Department of Anatomy, University of Newcastle upon Tyne, NE1 7RU, U.K.

I. Introduction

It is commonly accepted that the disorder of voluntary movement of the arm observed in stroke patients results from interruption of corticofugal nerve fibers, since most lesions occur in the cerebral hemisphere or internal capsule. However, these corticofugal fibers project not only to the spinal cord but also to regions of the brain stem from which other spinal motor projections originate (Kuypers, 1973). It is therefore concluded that the spinal motor centers controlling arm movement are partly deprived morphologically and/or functionally of projections from various supraspinal centers. The recovery of voluntary movement following the hemiplegia of stroke is frequently accompanied by the development of increased muscle tone, resistance to passive muscle stretch (spasticity) and increased tendon reflexes (see Twitchell, 1951; Lance, 1980). With the arm, the ability to perform voluntary movement usually returns in a shoulder to wrist sequence in the form of total flexor and extensor synergic patterns, which preclude independent movements at single joints; smooth transitions between flexor and extensor movements present particular difficulties (Twitchell, 1951; Brunnström, 1970; Bobath, 1978; De Souza et al., 1980).

In a task involving the turning of a cranked wheel mounted horizontally on a table, patterns of activity of muscles of the shoulder and arm have been studied in normal subjects and stroke patients (Gandy, 1980; Gandy et al., 1980; Robertson, 1980). The task was chosen since the movements are repetitive, contain elements of reaching and retrieving and involve the massed flexion and extension muscle synergies observed in stroke patients. In the previous studies of normal subjects performing the task, consistent patterns of muscle activity in the arm have been observed. The present study describes preliminary observations on stroke patients, and has been briefly reported (Hammond et al., 1981).

II. The Task

The subject sits in an anatomically standardized position at the table in which the cranked wheel is set. He is required to turn the cranked wheel a number of revolutions in each direction with each arm. The axis of the wheel is so placed that the subject has to lean forward one radius of the crank, 12.5 cm, in order to reach the further circumference (Fig. 1). For normal subjects an added frictional load equivalent to 1.8 Nm is applied to the wheel; for 9 of the 10 patients tested the added load would have made the task too difficult and was excluded. Surface electromyograms (EMG) from a number of arm and shoulder muscles are recorded with crank wheel position (see Fig. 4). The process of data reduction is given in Figure 2.

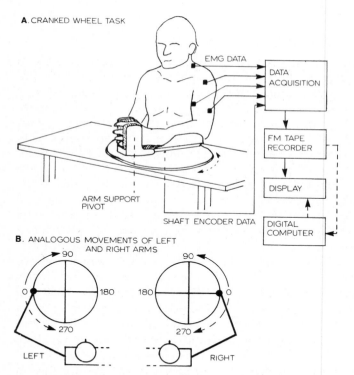

Figure 1. Cranked wheel task. A, diagram showing subject sitting at a table in which cranked wheel is set. The hand is held between layers of foam plastic in a clamp mounted on a pivot set at a radius of 12.5 cm from the center of the wheel. The arm support is integral with the hand clamp. The wheel position and surface EMG data were recorded on magnetic tape for off-line computer analysis. B, analogous mirror image movements of each arm are obtained by the positioning indicated. (From Van Hof and Mohn, 1981, with permission.)

NORMAL (R. ARM, CW).   EMG & WHEEL

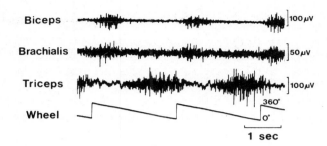

AVERAGED IEMG. Normalized to wheel position

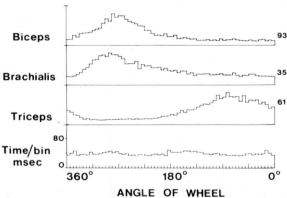

Figure 2. Data reduction and recordings obtained in a normal subject. Top, raw EMGs and crank-ed wheel position, recorded as a resetable DC voltage. Bottom, rectified and integrated electro-myograms (IEMG) from 20 revolutions averaged with respect to cranked wheel position, in which each revolution is subdivided into 64 equal position bins. The time per position bin trace indicates the average time spent in each position bin and provides a measure of the regularity of rotation. (From Van Hof and Mohn, 1981, with permission.)

III. Selection of Subjects and Patients

Ten normal subjects (5 male and 5 female) ranging in age from 19 to 35 years, mean 24 years, were tested. In this series they were not aged-matched to the 10 stroke patients tested, who were attending a hospital outpatient physiothera-py department. The patients (9 male and 1 female) ranged in age from 19 to 73 years, mean 53 years, and had suffered a single stroke, cardiovascular accident with hemiplegia of more than 24 h duration. Their selection was based on their ability to perform the task and their lack of marked cognitive and perceptual deficits.

IV. Comparison of Muscle Activity in Normal Subjects and Hemiplegic Patients

The EMG patterns for analogous arm movements of normal subjects are similar on right and left sides (Fig. 3; see also previous study, Gandy, 1980). In the unaffected arm of stroke patients the EMG patterns are comparable to those of normal subjects and serve as individual controls for the affected arm (Figs. 4 and 5, see also Gandy, 1980).

In general, the patients, who had widely differing degrees of motor deficit, turned the wheel more slowly and less evenly with the affected arm, and the

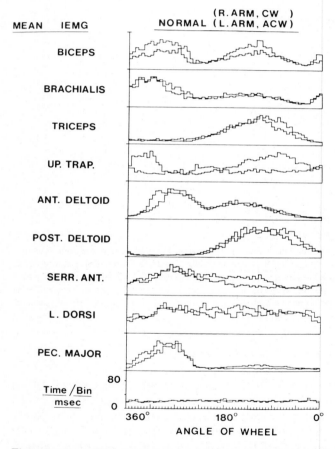

Figure 3. Analogous mirror image movements. Overplot of patterns in the right arm clockwise (CW) and left arm anticlockwise (ACW) directions in same normal subject to show equivalence of these mirror image movements.

EMG traces were less well modulated for the affected side (Fig. 4). There was a marked tendency to pause or slow consistently at one or two points of crank position during each cycle. These points corresponded approximately to the transitions of flexor and extensor muscle activity and were also noted by Gandy (1980). In the example of an individual patient (Fig. 5) one slowing point in the turning of the wheel is present at approximately 180°. The activity of the triceps here shows a marked phasic modulation with the crank position, but that of the biceps remains relatively unmodulated. Inspection of the raw data from which the integrated averaged EMG traces were obtained confirms this observation. In fact, the continuous unmodulated biceps activity was sufficient to cause an inappropriate flexion movement during the extensor phase, when, on this occasion, triceps activity momentarily decreased.

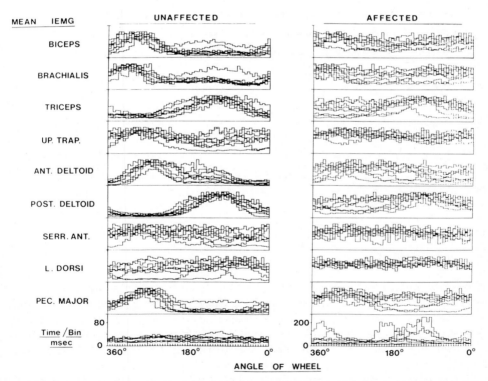

Figure 4. Mean integrated EMGs (IEMG) and time per wheel position bin versus wheel position. Overplots of averages obtained during 10–20 revolutions of the wheel in 8 hemiplegic stroke patients performing functionally analogous arm movements.

328

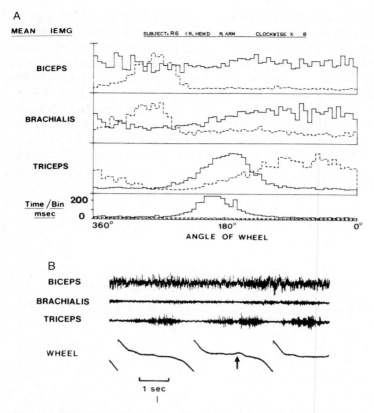

Figure 5. Recordings from a right hemiplegic stroke patient. A, averaged integrated electromyograms (IEMG) of 8 revolutions of wheel. Solid lines indicate affected side, broken lines unaffected side. Note pausing indicated by peak in time per position trace of affected side. B, sample of raw EMG and wheel position data from which averaged traces were derived. Note the position of temporary reversal of rotation of wheel (arrow).

V. Conclusions

The EMG patterns obtained during the task from the affected arms of stroke patients differed in several respects from those of their unaffected arms and from those of normal subjects. In particular, transitions between flexion and extension were prolonged, and abnormal co-contraction of antagonist muscles occurred. It was as if the mechanisms for turning off the activities of different muscles in the appropriate parts of the cycle had been impaired (Fig. 5B).

These features of disordered movement control are consistent with the hypothesis that, in stroke, there is an interruption of descending projections to spinal motor centers, including those interneurons responsible for reciprocal inhibition between antagonist motoneurons. In the cat, propriospinal neurons in C3–4 segments, thought to relay descending motor commands regarding reaching movements of the forelimb, project not only to agonist motoneurons but also to interneurons mediating reciprocal inhibition to antagonist motoneurons (Illert and Tanaka, 1978; Alstermark et al., 1981). In lumbo-sacral segments reciprocal inhibitory interneurons receive detailed projection from several areas of brainstem and cerebral cortex (Hultborn et al., 1976). In stroke patients disordered reciprocal inhibitory mechanisms between triceps surae and pretibial motoneurons have in fact been observed (Yanasigawa et al., 1976; Yanasigawa, 1980). It may also be of relevance that, when a subject initiates a voluntary movement, the gain of reciprocal inhibition is adjusted approximately 50 msec prior to the discharge of the appropriate motoneurons (Tanaka, 1980), and somewhat similar adjustments of reciprocal inhibition have been reported for hand movements (Day et al., 1981).

It is therefore tentatively proposed that part of the motor deficit after stroke may lie in the disordered supraspinal control of spinal interneurons responsible for reciprocal inhibition.

Acknowledgements

Support from the Medical Research Council and The Chest, Heart and Stroke Association of the United Kingdom is gratefully acknowledged.

References

Alstermark, B., Lundberg, A., Norrsell, U. and Sybirska, E. (1981) Integration in descending motor pathways controlling the forelimb in the cat. 9. Differential behavioural defects after spinal cord lesions interrupting defined pathways from higher centres to motoneurones, *Exp. Brain Res.*, 42: 299-318.

Bobath, B., (1978) *Adult Hemiplegia: Evaluation and Treatment,* 2nd edn., Heinemann, London.

Brunnström,. S. (1970) *Movement Therapy in Hemiplegia,* Harper and Row, New York.

Day, B.L., Marsden, C.D., Obeso, J.A. and Rothwell, J.C. (1981) Peripheral and central mechanisms of reciprocal inhibition in the human forearm, *J. Physiol. (Lond.),* 317: 59-60P.

De Souza, L.H., Langton Hewer, R. and Miller, S. (1980) Assessment of recovery of arm control in hemiplegic stroke patients. 1. Arm function tests, *Int. Rehab. Med.,* 2: 3-9.

Gandy, M. (1980) *The Dynamic Relationship Between the Electromyogram and Patterns of Muscular Activity in a Study of Arm Movement in Normal Subjects and Hemiplegic Patients,* Ph. D. Thesis (unpublished), Bristol University, 217 pp.

Gandy, M., Johnson, S.W., Lynn, P.A., Reed, G.A.L. and Miller, S. (1980) Acquisition and analysis of electromyographic data associated with dynamic movements of the arm, *Med. Biol. Engng. Comput.,* 18: 57-64.

Hammond, G.R., Miller, S., Potts, M.J. and Robertson, P.M. (1981) Central nervous control of arm movement in stroke patients, *J. Physiol. (Lond.),* 317: 61-62P.

Hultborn, H., Illert, M. and Santini, M. (1976) Convergence on interneurones mediating the reciprocal Ia inhibition of motoneurones. 3. Effects from supraspinal pathways, *Acta physiol. scand.,* 96: 368-391.

Illert, M. and Tanaka, R. (1978) Integration in descending motor pathways controlling the fore-limb in the cat. 4. Corticospinal inhibition of forelimb motoneurons mediated by short proprio-spinal neurones, *Exp. Brain Res.*, 31: 131-141.

Kuypers, H.G.J.M. (1973) The anatomical organization of the descending pathways and their con-tributions to motor control especially in primates, *New Develop. EMG. clin. Neurophysiol.*, 3: 38-68.

Lance, J.W. (1980) Symposium synopsis. In R.G. Feldman, R.R. Young and W.P. Koella (Eds.), *Spasticity: Disordered Motor Control*, Year Book Medical Publishers, Chicago, pp. 485-494.

Robertson, P.M. (1980) *An Investigation of Arm and Shoulder Movements and Underlying Muscle Activity in Normal Subjects and Stroke Patients*, Bachelor of Medical Science (Honours) Thesis (unpublished), Newcastle upon Tyne University, 96 pp.

Tanaka, R. (1980) Inhibitory mechanism in reciprocal innervation in voluntary movements. In J.E. Desmedt (Ed.), *Spinal and Supraspinal Mechanisms of Voluntary Motor Control and Loco-motion, Progr. in Clin. Neurophysiol.*, Vol., 8, Karger, Basel, pp. 117-128.

Twitchell, T.E. (1951) The restoration of motor function following hemiplegia in man, *Brain*, 74: 443-480.

Van Hof, M.W. and Mohn, G. (Eds.) (1981) *Functional Recovery from Brain Damage*, Elsevier/North-Holland, Amsterdam.

Yanasigawa, N. (1980) Reciprocal reflex connections in motor disorders in man. In J.E. Desmedt (Ed.), *Spinal and Supraspinal Mechanisms of Voluntary Control and Locomotion, Progr. in Clin. Neurophysiol. Vol. 8*, Karger, Basel, pp. 129-141.

Yanasigawa, N., Tanaka, R. and Ito, Z. (1976) Reciprocal Ia inhibition in spastic hemiplegia in man, *Brain*, 99: 555-574.

Brain Stem Control of Spinal Mechanisms
– B. Sjölund and A. Björklund, editors
© 1982 Elsevier Biomedical Press

14

An Engineering Approach to the Central Nervous Control of Dynamic Limb Movement

C.S. CHANDLER, J.R. HEWIT*, S. MILLER and N. TAN*

*Departments of Anatomy and *Mechanical Engineering, University of Newcastle upon Tyne, NE1 7RU, U.K.*

I. Introduction

Dynamic movement control of several coordinated limb segments presents a challenge both in the design of control systems for robotic arms and in the study of limb control in man and other mammals (Chandler et al., 1981). Current robot controller designs treat the coordination of multisegment limbs largely by kinematics. Dynamic factors such as the masses of the segments and interactive effects (e.g. Coriolis forces) tend to be ignored. The dexterity of human arms in real time is generally superior to that of currently available robots (Benati et al., 1980), despite the greater number of degrees of freedom in the human arm and the considerable neuromuscular time delays (synaptic and conduction delays and the delays in force production by the muscle).

The dynamic equations describing a manipulator operation with varying inertial loads and in the face of unexpected perturbations are very complex, and may be undefined when operating in unfamiliar or unstructured environments. Engineering approaches to meet these problems often involve the use of some model to give nominal controller actions together with a degree of feedback to provide compensation for inevitable model discrepancies. Several methods have been proposed (Albus, 1975; Hewit and Padovan, 1978; Horn and Raibert, 1978; Luh et al., 1980a, b), but none approaches the performance of the human arm. Some utilize trajectory planning appropriate to the task and compute controller actions in advance, but such methods are unsuitable for anything other than strictly repetitive tasks.

In contrast, neurophysiological studies have concentrated more on the individual components of the motor system and movements at one joint, rather than with the simultaneous coordinated control of several limb segments which is necessary to drive the hand quickly along some desired trajectory.

II. Invariant Control

This new method of robotic control (Hewit and Burdess, 1981) offers advantages over other proposed systems and may be of value in understanding some of the principles underlying the coordination of human limbs. It is based upon the principle of invariance (Greensite, 1970), and is a means of providing coordinated movement control of several limb segments along a selected trajectory in the presence of external forces and varying limb inertia. Consider the arm as a system with two sets of forces acting on it: one, the controlled applied forces; and the other, the external perturbing forces (Fig. 1a). If the perturbing forces can be measured and fed forward via an appropriate transfer function (WG^{-1}), their effects can be nullified. An indirect measure of the perturbing forces has been shown to be sufficient (Hewit and Burdess, 1981). In the simplest case, if the arm is treated as a single known mass, and its acceleration and the applied force measured, then the perturbing forces can be estimated and nullified (Fig. 1b). The overall system is thereby made invariant with respect to the perturbing force.

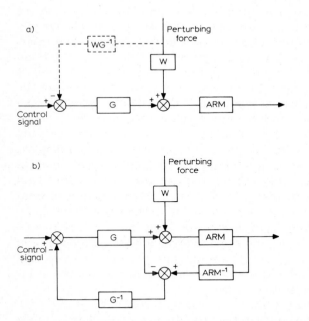

Figure 1. Invariant control. a, ideal case where the perturbing force is measured directly and fed forward to nullify its effect. b, usual case where the perturbing force is measured indirectly then fed forward.

tained of the control of transmission to these paths exerted by descending systems. This will be described in some detail below.

II. The Ventral Spino-Olivocerebellar System

In chloralose-anesthetized cats with only one ventral funiculus intact (Fig. 1A) characteristic, sharply rising field potentials can be recorded from the surface of the cerebellar anterior lobe upon electrical stimulation of dissected nerves from the four limbs (Fig. 1B). These potentials represent the climbing fiber-evoked depolarizations in Purkinje cell populations beneath the recording electrode (Eccles et al., 1967; Armstrong and Harvey 1968). The potentials are distributed in narrow sagittal zones (width 0.2–1 mm) over the anterior (and posterior) lobes as shown by the hatched areas in Figure 1A (Oscarsson, 1968; Oscarsson and Sjölund, 1974, 1977a). Each of these sagittal zones represents the termination area of cells within one subdivision of the inferior olivary nucleus (Armstrong, et al., 1974; Groenewegen and Voogd, 1977; Oscarsson and Sjölund, 1977b; Groenewegen et al., 1979). In the ventral spino-olivocerebellar system, these cells have monosynaptic connections from the spinal tract axons (Armstrong and Harvey, 1968; Oscarsson, 1968; Oscarsson and Sjölund, 1977c; Armstrong and Schild, 1980).

Based on receptive fields, latencies on electrical nerve stimulation, properties of olivary relays and termination areas in the cerebellar cortex, four VF-SOCPs transmitting information from the hindlimbs were distinguished and labeled according to their termination zones as the a-, b-, c_1- and c_3-VF-SOCPs (Oscarsson and Sjölund, 1977a, c). As shown in Figure 1, the a-VF-SOCP receives information from the ipsilateral hindlimb via polysynaptic connections to the spinal tract cells and projects to a vermal zone close to the midline, whereas the two paths projecting information from the same limb to the pars intermedia, the c_1- and c_3-VF-SOCPs, are (at least partly) monosynaptically activated at the segmental level. The b-VF-SOCP receives polysynaptically transmitted information from both hindlimbs and projects to the lateral vermis (b-lat. in Fig. 1B). A fifth path is the forelimb component of the b-VF-SOCP, signalling information from both forelimbs to the medial part of the b-zone (b-

---

Figure 1. SOCPs ascending through ventral funiculus (from Oscarsson and Sjölund, 1977a–c, with permission). A, termination zones (c_3, c_1, b, and a) of VF-SOCPs in lobules IV and V of the cerebellar anterior lobe. The receptive fields of different paths are indicated (see key). Inf. coll., inferior colliculus. B, responses recorded from the surface of the c_1-zone, the lateral (b-lat.) and medial (b-med.) parts of the b-zone, and the a-zone on stimulation of ipsilateral and contralateral (i, c) ulnar and sciatic nerves (Uln, Sci) in a preparation with the spinal cord interrupted at C3 except for the contralateral ventral funiculus (inset, A). Superimposed traces, positivity upward. Higher amplification in records from the a zone. C, tentative organization of the paths. FRA, flexion reflex afferents, Inf. olive, inferior olive.

med. in Fig. 1B). In the following sections, results relating to the four hindlimb paths will be discussed.

III. Influence of the Noradrenergic System

The transmission from the FRA to segmental reflex arcs in acute spinal cats can be radically changed by the administration of the noradrenaline precursor l-DOPA (Andén et al., 1966b; Jankowska et al., 1967) or of stimulants of central α-receptors such as clonidine (Forssberg and Grillner, 1973). l-DOPA acts by liberation of pre-existing stores of noradrenaline from the terminals of presumably coerulospinal fibers (Andén et al., 1966a; Jurna and Lundberg, 1968; Lundberg, this volume). This depresses the short latency transmission from the FRA to motoneurons and to primary afferent terminals as well as to some spinal neurons with axons ascending in the ventrolateral funiculi (Andén et al., 1966b). Clonidine likewise depresses the transmission from the FRA to motoneurons but not that to primary afferent terminals (Andersson and Sjölund, 1978; Lundberg, this volume).

To investigate whether the changes in activity at the segmental level here described are reflected in the four ascending VF-SOCPs, i.e. to see if these paths monitor the activity in lower motor centers, the climbing fiber-evoked responses (CFRs) in the cerebellar cortex evoked via these paths were measured during the administration of clonidine and l-DOPA (Fig. 2). The preparations were chloralose-anesthetized cats with only one ventral funiculus intact at the third cervical segment (Fig. 2A). Electrical stimulation of the sciatic nerves was used at 20 times threshold of the largest myelinated fibers to evoke segmental reflex responses as well as ascending activity. As a check of the transmission through the inferior olive, direct stimulation of the tract fibers was employed (VFC$_3$ in Fig. 2A) just distal to the spinal lesion.

A typical experiment with clonidine and DOPA administration is shown in

Figure 2.A, recording and stimulating arrangements. (See text, section III). A spinal lesion sparing only the contralateral ventral funiculus was made at C3. Stimulation of sciatic nerves (Sci) and contralateral ventral funiculus at C3 (VFC3). Recording from dorsal root filament (dorsal root), flexor nerve and from four positions on the cerebellar surface. Course of VF-SOCPs and reticulospinal control path indicated. Projection zones of the a-, c$_1$- and c$_3$-VF-SOCPs indicated by vertical hatching; b-zone, oblique hatching. In the diagram of cerebellum dotted lines indicate borders between vermis and pars intermedia (p. intermed.), and hyphenated lines, midline. Inf. olive, inferior olive; I.C., inferior colliculus. B–E, potentials recorded simultaneously from cerebellar surface (zones a and b), from ipsilateral tenuissimus nerve (Flexor) and from filament of ipsilateral L7 dorsal root (DrL7) on stimulation of contralateral ventral funiculus (cVFC3) at 2.0 mA (upper set of traces), of ipsilateral sciatic (iSci) nerve (middle set) and of contralateral sciatic (cSci) nerve (lower set). Drugs were given i.v. with 1 h intervals. Records were formed by superposition of 5–15 traces. Arrows in A indicate measured amplitudes of potentials. All voltage calibration bars are 200 μV, all time bars are 10msec.

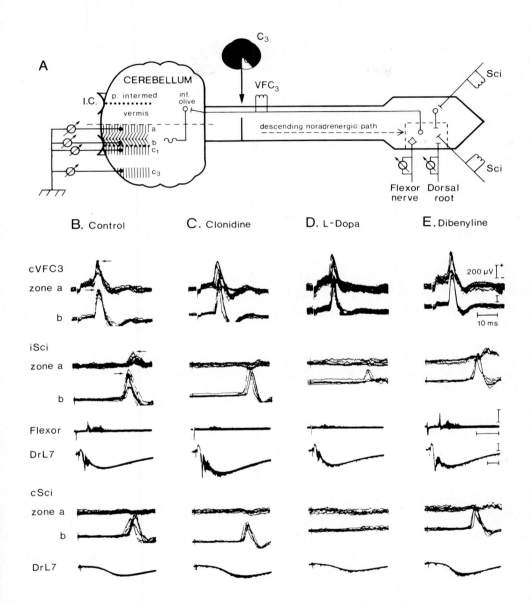

A

C₃

CEREBELLUM

I.C.   p. intermed.   inf. olive

vermis

VFC₃

descending noradrenergic path

Sci

Sci

Flexor nerve   Dorsal root

a
b
c₁
c₃

B. Control   **C.** Clonidine   **D.** L-Dopa   **E.** Dibenyline

cVFC3
zone a

b

200 µV

10 ms

iSci
zone a

b

Flexor

DrL7

cSci
zone a

b

DrL7

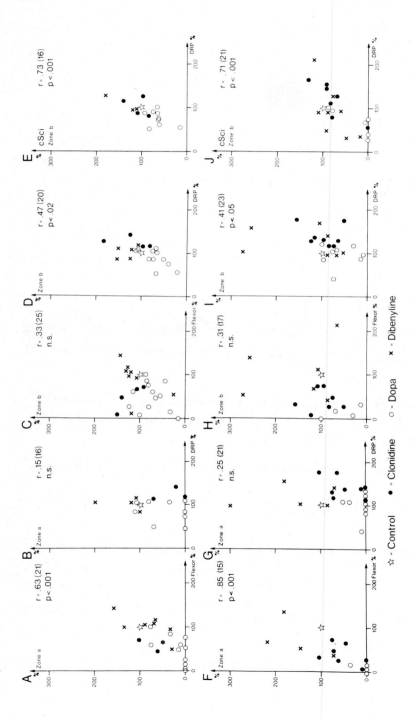

Figure 2B–E. Here, simultaneous recordings from the a- and b-zones are displayed as 5–10 superimposed sweeps. The sharply rising CFRs are easily recognized, both on direct tract stimulation (cVFC3) and on stimulation of the ipsilateral sciatic (iSci) nerve and, in the b-zone, of the contralateral sciatic (cSci) nerve as well. Below, the simultaneously recorded neurogram from the tenuissimus (flexor) nerve and the dorsal root potential (DRP) from a L7 rootlet (DrL7), reflecting primary afferent depolarization (PAD), are shown. As seen in Fig. 2B, the administration of the α-agonist clonidine (0.4 mg/kg i.v.) depressed the flexion reflex, whereas the DRP was somewhat enhanced. At the same time a suppression of the CFRs was seen in the a-zone, while the bilaterally evoked CFRs in the b-zone were unchanged. One hour later during the same experiment, while the long-lasting clonidine effect still remained, l-DOPA was given (100 mg/kg i.v.; D). This depressed also the CFRs of the b-zone as well as the DRPs, notably those evoked from the contralateral sciatic nerve (cf. below). The CFRs of the c_1- and c_3-zones did not change appreciably (not shown). The α-receptor blocking agent Dibenyline (20 mg/kg) reversed all the effect completely, as demonstrated in E. During the experiment, little or no changes occurred in the olivary transmission (Fig. 2, top).

Using the pharmacological manipulations described, corresponding alterations of segmental and cerebellar responses were searched for in two series of experiments. In both series the amplitudes of the stable integrated flexor neurograms and the DRPs were measured from superimposed records obtained 15–30 min after administration of the drugs. In one series (n = 14) the amplitudes of the fluctuating CFRs were measured from superimposed records as the maximal height reached repeatedly (arrows, Fig. 2B). However, the marked fluctuations of the amplitudes of the CFRs in some termination areas occasionally made the amplitude measurements uncertain. Therefore, a second series of experiments (n = 8) was made where the CFRs were averaged over 5–15 min to minimize amplitude variations not related to the pharmacological manipulations. After correction for slow changes in the transmission through the inferior olive and the recording conditions at the cerebellar surface the amplitudes of the CFRs and of the segmental responses were transformed into percent of controls. The different possible combinations of cerebellar and segmental responses were then plotted in the correlograms of Figures 3 and 4. The

Figure 3. Correlograms of maximal amplitudes of CFRs (A–E) from first series of experiments and mean amplitudes of CFRs (F–J) from second series in a- and b-zones versus size of integrated flexor neurograms (A, C, F, H) and of DRPs from ipsilateral L7 dorsal rootlets (B, D, G, I), on stimulation of the ipsilateral sciatic nerve and in b-zone versus size of DRP from ipsilateral L7 dorsal rootlet (E, J) on stimulation of the contralateral sciatic nerve. Each value was obtained during one of the conditions given in the key (control, clonidine, l-DOPA, Dibenyline). All values are expressed as percent of control. Control conditions are only given once in each correlogram and were excluded from the statistical calculations. r, Spearman rank correlation coefficient; numbers within brackets give number of observations; P, level of significance; n.s., no significance.

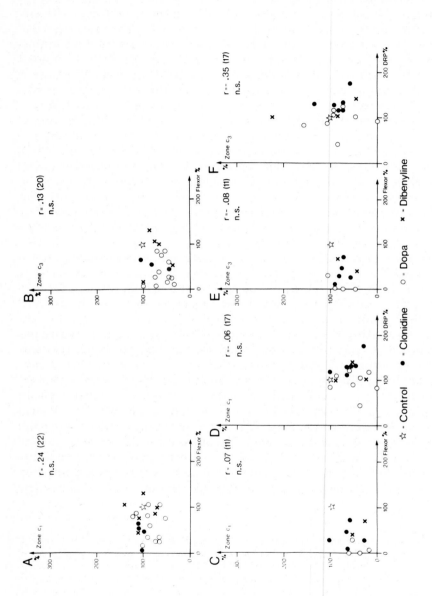

upper graphs in these figures show the correlations to maximal CFRs (first experimental series), and the lower graphs show the correlations to mean CFRs (second experimental series). One point represents the maximal (mean) amplitude of the CFRs in one of the zones against the size of the simultaneously recorded flexor neurogram or DRP. All responses could not, however, be followed throughout all manipulations in every experiment due to difficulties to maintain optimal record conditions. A statistical analysis using the Spearman rank correlation test (Siegel, 1956) was performed on the different correlations.

III.1. The a-VF-SOCP

The correlograms of Figure 3A–B and F–G give the results from stimulation of the ipsilateral sciatic nerve and plotting the CFR amplitudes of the a-zone against the segmental responses. After clonidine (filled circles), the CFR was depressed as was the flexion reflex, whereas the DRP was enhanced. l-DOPA (open circles) depressed all types of responses relative to their amplitudes under clonidine, whereas Dibenyline (crosses) restored the responses to a varying degree. Accordingly, there was a strong (positive) correlation between the amplitude of the CFR evoked via the a-VF-SOCP and the size of the flexion reflex only ($r = 0.63$–0.85; $P < 0.001$).

III.2. The b-VF-SOCP

The responses obtained from the b-zone on stimulation of the ipsilateral sciatic nerve are plotted against the segmental responses in Figure 3C–D and H–I. After clonidine, the DRP regularly increased in size, whereas the CFR amplitude decreased or increased in equal number of cases. l-DOPA diminished all responses relative to their size under clonidine and Dibenyline reversed all changes. The statistical analysis indicated a weak correlation of the amplitude of the CFR in the b-zone to the size of the DRP ($r = 0.41$–0.47; $P < 0.05$–0.02) but not to the size of the flexor neurogram. However, it is known that the short-latency DRP that can be recorded from filaments adjacent to those carrying the incoming nerve volley represents mainly a depolarization in cutaneous afferents evoked by cutaneous afferents (Carpenter et al., 1963). On the other hand, the DRP of longer latency that can be recorded at some distance from the entry zone and from contralateral dorsal root filaments reflects the PAD in the FRA induced by the FRA (cf. Fig. 2). There is partial occlusion between these two types of PAD on the side ipsilateral to stimulation, and the present DRP

Figure 4. Correlograms of maximal amplitudes of CFRs (A, B) from first series of experiments and of mean amplitudes of CFRs (C–F) from second series in c_1- and c_3-zones versus size of integrated flexor neurograms (A, B, C, E) and of DRPs from ipsilateral L7 dorsal rootlets (D, F). Ipsilateral sciatic nerve was stimulated. Conditions, symbols and abbreviations as in Figure 3.

recordings presumably represent a mixture of both types. As shown in Figure 2, the contralateral sciatic nerve was stimulated in most experiments to give a DRP reflecting only the FRA-induced PAD in the FRA, as well as a CFR evoked via the b-VF-SOCP with its bilateral receptive field. The correlation between these latter events was indeed found to be strong (Fig. 3E–J; $r = 0.71$–0.73; $P < 0.001$). These results were confirmed by stimulation of the sural nerve on the recording side, allowing separation of the two ipsilateral DRP components (Andersson and Sjölund, 1978).

III.3. The c_1- and c_3-VF-SOCPs

The CFRs evoked via the c_1- and c_3-VF-SOCPs by stimulation of the ipsilateral sciatic nerve often decreased somewhat in size during the experiments (Fig. 4). This decrease was more marked for the mean CFRs (C–F) than for the maximal CFRs (Fig. 4A and B) but was generally not reversed by Dibenyline. Accordingly, no covariations with the pronounced changes of the segmental responses induced by the pharmacological manipulations were established for these CFRs. As can be seen in Figure 4, this finding was confirmed in the statistical analysis.

   In summary, the results obtained with pharmacological activation or simulation of the descending noradrenergic system indicate a close parallellism between the control of the transmission from the FRA to the a-VF-SOCP and to motoneurons and of the transmission from the FRA to the b-VF-SOCP and to the PAD-generating mechanism influencing the FRA. The transmission to the c_1- and c_3-VF-SOCPs seems, however, to escape control from the noradrenergic system.

IV. Release from Tonic Inhibition in Decerebrate Preparations

In decerebrate preparations there is a tonic inhibition of the transmission from the FRA to motoneurons (Eccles and Lundberg, 1959b), to primary afferents (Carpenter et al., 1963) and to some neurons with axons ascending in the ventrolateral funiculi of the spinal cord (Holmqvist et al., 1960; Oscarsson, 1960). This inhibition is probably exerted at the interneuronal level (Engberg et al., 1968a, b) and is not dependent upon activity in descending noradrenergic paths (Engberg et al., 1968c). To explore further the influence of descending control systems on the four VF-SOCPs, a series of experiments (n = 17) was performed on decerebrate, unanesthetized cats. The dorsolateral funiculi (Dlfs) were initially spared in these preparations (Fig. 5A), since they contain the paths responsible for the tonic inhibition (Holmqvist and Lundberg, 1959b; Engberg et al., 1968a).

   In the experiment shown in Figure 5B, simultaneous recordings are shown of CFRs from the c_3-, c_1- and b-zones, of an integrated neurogram from the ipsilateral tenuissimus (flexor) nerve and of the DRP from an ipsilateral L7 rootlet. In part I, the spinal tract was stimulated at C3, evoking sharply rising CFRs in all the three zones. Stimulation of the ipsilateral sciatic nerve (II) evoked a flexor discharge and a DRP as well as CFRs in the c_3- and c_1-zones (arrowheads), but not in the b-zone. Stimulation of the contralateral sciatic nerve (III) evoked only a small DRP. However, after transection of both Dlfs (IV–VI), there was an increase of the flexor discharge and of the contralaterally evoked DRP (cf. Carpenter et al., 1963). At the same time a CFR appeared in the b-zone both on stimulation of the ipsilateral (V) and the contralateral (VI) sciatic nerves, whereas the CFRs evoked on tract stimulation remained unchanged (IV), as did the CFRs in the c_3- and c_1-zones on both tract and nerve stimulation (IV–V).

To improve the transmission in the a-VF-SOCP, which is often suppressed at the olivary level in the unanesthetized decerebrate preparations (Oscarsson and Sjölund, 1977a), a small amount of chloralose (10–20 mg/kg) was given to nine of the decerebrate cats before recording. It was then usually possible to evoke CFRs also in the a-zone on tract stimulation as shown in Fig. 5C, part I. Recordings are shown from the c_1-zone in the same cat for comparison. On nerve stimulation (Fig. 5C part II) there was a large CFR in the c_1-zone whereas no response was seen in the a-zone. After transection of the Dlfs at Th12 there was a marked release of the transmission to the flexor nerve and at the same time a CFR appeared in the a-zone (Fig. 5C part IV).

Summarizing the results from all the experiments in the series, there was after the transection of the Dlfs a significant release of the transmission from the FRA to flexor motoneurons (n = 16; $P < 0.01$; Student's t-test) and of the contralaterally evoked DRP (n = 16; $P < 0.01$), but not of the ipsilaterally evoked DRP (n = 16). Furthermore, the mean CFR amplitudes grew significantly in the a- and b-zones (n =11; $P < 0.02$ and n = 16; $P < 0.02$, respectively). In 7 of 9 of the cats with a more than 10% increase of the transmission via the b-VF-SOCP, there was a large simultaneous release of the contralaterally evoked DRP. On the other hand, the mean size of the CFRs in the c_1- and c_3-zones did not change significantly with the Dlf lesions (n = 17 and n = 14, respectively).

V. Effects on Stimulation of Tracts in the Ipsilateral Half of the Spinal Cord

As discussed in the previous section, inhibitory actions on segmental reflex paths activated by the FRA are carried through the Dlfs in the dorsal reticulospinal system (Engberg et al., 1968a) which is tonically active in the decerebrate preparation. However, inhibitory actions are also mediated via a reticulospinal pathway in the ventral quadrant (Vq) of the spinal cord but this path is not tonically active in the decerebrate state (Jankowska et al., 1968). The effects of weak continuous stimulation of the fascicles containing these paths were examined and compared in 11 chloralose-anesthetized cats with the neuraxis intact and a lesion sparing only one ventral funiculus in the lumbar cord (cf. Fig. 1).

In the experiment shown in Figure 6A–D, stimulation of the ipsilateral sciatic nerve (A) evoked CFRs in all the termination zones, and evoked a DRP and a discharge in the flexor nerve. Stimulation of the contralateral sciatic nerve evoked a CFR in the b-zone and a DRP with a long latency (Fig. 6B). On conditioning the responses evoked from the ipsilateral nerve with a 100 Hz impulse train (Fig. 6C) at 0.3 mA to the dissected Dlf, there was a marked depression and an increased latency of the CFR in the b-zone, and the CFR in the a-zone almost disappeared. The responses in the c_1- and c_3-zones were not changed. At the same time, the flexor discharge and the DRP were reduced in size when evoked from the ipsilateral side and stimulation of the contralateral sciatic nerve did not evoke any DRP at all (Fig. 6D). The diagrams in Figure 6I–K show the effects of trains of Dlf stimulation (black bars in Fig. 6K) on the segmental and cerebellar responses. The CFRs in the a- and b-zones were regularly inhibited along with the segmental responses whereas the CFRs in the c_1- and c_3-zones did not change appreciably. On the other hand, continuous stimulation of the ipsilateral Vq at weak strength markedly suppressed the CFRs in the a- and b-zones without much effect on the segmental responses (Fig. 6E–H). The CFRs in the c_1- and c_3-zones were not changed by this stimulation. The same pattern was observed in all the cats studied.

In addition to the inhibitory descending paths mentioned previously, there are, within the funiculi stimulated in the present experiments, also several descending paths exciting interneurons mediating FRA effects to segmental and ascending paths. These are the rubrospinal tract (Hongo et al., 1969; Bal-

---

Figure 5.A, stimulation and recording arrangements (See text, section IV). A spinal lesion of the dorsal funiculi was made at C3 to interrupt other paths to the anterior lobe. Hatched areas were interrupted during the experiment (at C3 or Th12–13). SS control, supraspinal control. B, potentials recorded from surface of cerebellar anterior lobe in indicated projection zones (b, c_1, c_3) on stimulation of contralateral ventral funiculus at C3 (cVFC3; strength 0.5 mA) and ipsilateral (iSci) and contralateral (cSci) sciatic nerves at 20T. On nerve stimulation, the discharge in the ipsilateral tenuissimus nerve was monitored after rectification and integration (Flexor), and the DRP was recorded from an ipsilateral L7 dorsal rootlet (DRL7). Recordings before (I–III) and after (IV–VI) interruption of both dorsolateral funiculi (DLFs) at C3. Records formed by 3–7 superimposed sweeps. Positivity signalled upwards in all figures. Upper calibrations (VI) for cerebellar recordings, lower for segmental recordings. (Voltage calibration refers to DR record only.) Arrowheads, when present, indicate start of CFRs and interrupted lines indicate baselines in all figures. Unanesthetized decerebrate preparation. C, potentials recorded from the a- and c_1-zones on stimulation of contralateral ventral funiculus at C3 (cVFC3; strength 0.5 mA) and of ipsilateral sciatic nerve (iSci) at 4T. DRL6, L6 dorsal rootlet. Recordings before (I–II) and after (III–IV) lesions in both dorsolateral funiculi at Th12. All voltage calibrations are 200 uV. Calibration in I refer to recordings on tract stimulation; in II, to recordings on nerve stimulation (cf., Fig. 1). Decerebrate preparation under light (20 mg/kg) chloralose anesthesia.

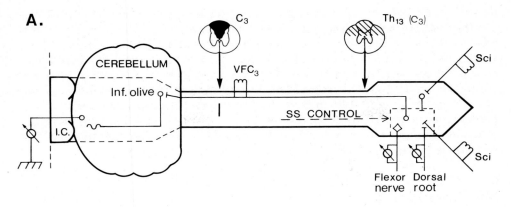

A.

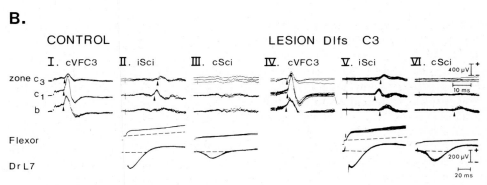

B.

CONTROL   LESION DIfs C3

Ⅰ. cVFC3   Ⅱ. iSci   Ⅲ. cSci   Ⅳ. cVFC3   Ⅴ. iSci   Ⅵ. cSci

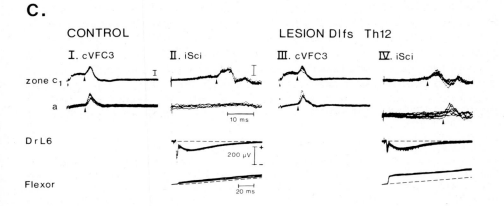

C.

CONTROL   LESION DIfs Th12

Ⅰ. cVFC3   Ⅱ. iSci   Ⅲ. cVFC3   Ⅳ. iSci

dissera et al., 1971; Baldissera and ten Bruggencate, 1976) and the lateral vestibulospinal tract (ten Bruggencate and Lundberg, 1974; Baldissera and Roberts, 1976) as well as the corticospinal tract (Lundberg and Voorhoeve, 1962; Lundberg et al., 1963). In the present experiments it was regularly possible to evoke CFRs in the a- and b-zones, as well as segmental responses, by short trains of stimuli to the dissected Dlf. Stimulation of the dissected Vq, on the other hand, produced CFRs in the a- and b-zones without any concomitant segmental responses. All observations (for Dlf, n = 11 and for Vq, n = 6) indicated that the segmental links to the a- and b-VF-SOCPs are polysynaptic. No CFRs were seen in the c_1- or c_3-zones with either form of stimulation.

VI. Comments

The present investigation has shown a highly differentiated control from the various descending systems tested onto a group of seemingly homogeneous spino-olivary paths that cross at the segmental level and ascend to make monosynaptic contacts with neurons of the inferior olivary nucleus (Brodal et al., 1950; Armstrong and Harvey, 1968; Oscarsson and Sjölund, 1977c). This differentiation is reflected in the actions of the noradrenergic system with separate controls on the transmission from the FRA to the a-VF-SOCP paralleling that to motoneurons, and on the transmission from the FRA to the b-VF-SOCP paralleling that to the mechanism generating PAD in the FRA, as well as in the lack of effects on the transmission to the c_1- and c_3-VF-SOCPs. A similar picture was obtained when manipulating the tonic descending inhibition in the decerebrate preparation, exerted by the dorsal reticulospinal path, and when stimulating dissected funiculi containing descending inhibitory and excitatory paths. As regards the hypothesis concerning the information carried by the VF-SOCPs, the results indicate that only the a- and b-VF-SOCPs carry information about the activity in lower motor centers (cf Lundberg, 1959, 1964; Oscarsson, 1968, 1973), whereas the c_1- and c_3-VF-SOCPs, monosynaptically activated from primary afferents (Oscarsson and Sjölund, 1977c), would forward information mainly related to peripheral events (Andersson and Sjölund, 1978). The c_1- and c_3-VF-SOCPs do in fact represent the first known FRA-acti-

Figure 6.A–H, potentials evoked and recorded as in Fig. 5 from two experiments (A–D and E–H). In C–D, the dissected (Th12) ipsilateral dorsolateral funiculus (iDlf) was stimulated continuously at 100 Hz (strength 0.3 mA). In G–H, the dissected (Th12) ipsilateral ventral quadrant (iVq) was stimulated continuously at 150 Hz (strength 0.2 mA). All voltage calibrations are 200 μV. Calibrations shown in D are for all recordings except for b-recordings in E–H, which are given in H. I–K, simultaneously recorded amplitudes of segmental (I) and cerebellar (J–K) responses on stimulation of ipsilateral sciatic nerve at 20T and expressed as percent of maximum. The iDlf was stimulated (100 Hz; 0.3 mA) intermittently (black bars). Same experiment as in A–D. Chloralose anesthesia.

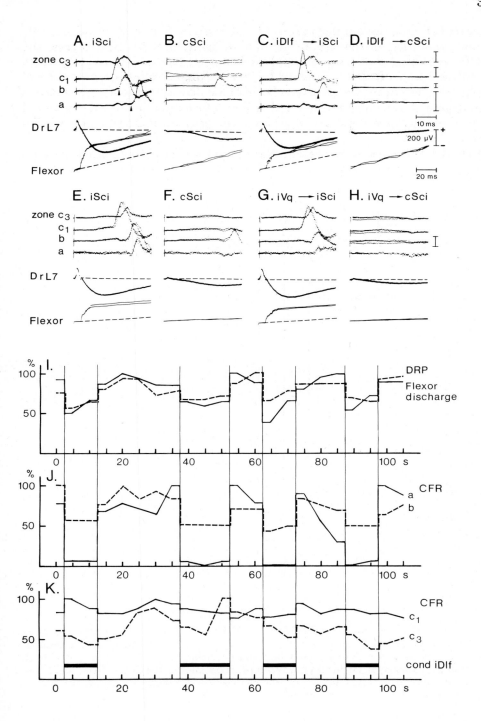

vated paths escaping supraspinal control (Sjölund, 1978) and, provided their spatial resolution is comparable to that in their forelimb equivalents, the SOCPs ascending via the dorsolateral (and dorsal) funiculi (Larson et al., 1969; Ekerot and Larson, 1979), it might be justified to distinguish a new class of cerebellar afferent information, combining modality convergence (the FRA), a high degree of spatial resolution and lack of information about interneuronal activity. A tentative summary diagram of the present findings is given in Figure 7.

As to the relevance of the present findings to the descending control of soma-

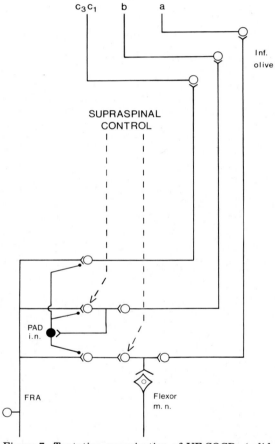

Figure 7. Tentative organization of VF-SOCPs (solid lines). Input from flexor reflex afferents (FRA) to all paths (contralateral input to b-path not shown). Minimum number of segmental interneurones indicated for each path. Descending control systems (Supraspinal control; interrupted lines) influence segmental mechanisms which may share interneurons with the a- and b-VF-SOCPs, as suggested in text. PAD i.n., interneuron mediating primary afferent depolarization; m.n., motoneuron; Inf. olive, inferior olive.

tosensory systems (see Le Bars et al., this volume; Willis, this volume), it is highly interesting that the cells of origin of the spino-olivary tracts studied occur in laminae IV–VIII of the spinal cord (Armstrong and Schild, 1980), thus overlapping the location of the spinothalamic tract cells in the cat (Carstens and Trevino, 1978). Furthermore, the spino-olivary tract cells receive an input from the FRA which might be equivalent to the "wide dynamic range" or "convergent" input to many spinothalamic tract cells (Mendell, 1966; Menetrey et al., 1977) even if there is no conclusive evidence of the participation of nociceptors in FRA actions (Lundberg, this volume). It is also well known that some spinothalamic tracts neurons have axons ascending in the ventral funiculus (e.g. Kerr, 1975) and the determination of spinal conduction velocities of spino-olivary fibers in the cat (Oscarsson and Sjölund, 1977c) agrees well (40 m/sec) with those of spinothalamic fibers in the same species (Holloway et al., 1978). Finally, Brodal et al. (1950) emphasize that the spino-olivary fibers in the cat are probably collaterals of ascending fibers of unknown destination. Even if there is no evidence that spino-olivary fibers and spinothalamic fibers belong to the same population, it is tempting to speculate that they might have a similar organization at the spinal level and that different groups of spinothalamic neurons are subject to different supraspinal control, as are the VF-SOCPs. This is in fact supported by the findings that some inhibitory descending mechanisms strongly influence "convergent" but not "non-convergent" neurons in the rat (Le Bars et al., 1979).

Extending the parallelism between spinocerebellar and spinothalamic pathways even further, could it be that some spinothalamic pathways monitor the activity in segmental interneuronal chains rather than external events as is probably the case with many spinocerebellar pathways (cf. Lundberg, 1959, 1964; Oscarsson, 1973)? Monitoring the activity in such interneurons would provide the cerebral cortex with information about the reflex activity elicited by somatosensory (e.g. nociceptive) stimuli, as well as about the activity in segmental inhibitory mechanisms acting on somatosensory pathways. This information may well be crucial for the correct interpretation of environmental stimuli.

Acknowledgements

Supported by grants from the Swedish MRC (No. 05658) and from the Medical Faculty, University of Lund. I am indebted to Dr. O. Oscarsson for valuable comments on the manuscript.

356

References

Andén, N.-E., Jukes, M.G.M. and Lundberg, A. (1966a) The effect of DOPA on the spinal cord. 2. A pharmacological analysis *Acta physiol. scand.*, 67: 387-397.

Andén, N.-E., Jukes, M.G.M., Lundberg, A. and Vyklicky, L. (1966b) The effect of DOPA on the spinal cord. 1. Influence on transmission from primary afferents, *Acta physiol. scand.*, 67: 373-386.

Andersson, G. and Sjölund, B. (1978) The ventral spino-olivocerebellar system in the cat. IV. Spinal transmission after administration of clonidine and l-DOPA *Exp. Brain Res.*, 33: 227-240.

Armstrong, D.M. (1974) Functional significance of connections of the inferior olive, *Physiol. Rev.*, 54: 358-417.

Armstrong, D.M. and Harvey, R.J. (1968) Responses of a spino-olivocerebellar pathway in the cat. *J. Physiol. (Lond.)*, 194: 147-168.

Armstrong, D.M. and Schild, R.F. (1980) Location in the spinal cord of neurons projecting directly to the inferior olive in the cat. In J. Courville, C. de Montigny and Y. Lamarre (Eds.), *The Inferior Olivary Nucleus. Anatomy and Physiology*, Raven Press, New York. pp. 125-143.

Armstrong, D.M., Harvey, R.J. and Schild, R.F. (1974) Topographical localization in the olivo-cerebellar projection: an electrophysiological study in the cat, *J. comp. Neurol.*, 154: 287-302.

Baldissera, F. and ten Bruggencate, G. (1976) Rubrospinal effects on ventral spinocerebellar tract neurones, *Acta physiol. scand.*, 96: 233-249.

Baldissera, F. and Roberts, W.J. (1976) Effects from the vestibulospinal tract on transmission from primary afferents to ventral spinocerebellar tract neurones, *Acta physiol. scand.*, 96: 217-232.

Baldissera, F., ten Bruggencate, G. and Lundberg, A. (1971) Rubrospinal monosynaptic connexion with last-order interneurones of polysynaptic reflex paths, *Brain Res.*, 27: 390-392.

Brodal, A., Walberg, F. and Blackstad, T. (1950) Termination of spinal afferents to inferior olive in cat, *J. Neurophysiol.*, 13: 431-454.

ten Bruggencate, G. and Lundberg, A. (1974) Facilitatory interaction in transmission to motoneurones from vestibulospinal fibres and contralateral primary afferents, *Exp. Brain Res.*, 19: 248-270.

Carpenter, D., Engberg, I., Funkenstein, H. and Lundberg, A. (1963) Decerebrate control of reflexes to primary afferents *Acta physiol. scand.*, 59: 424-437.

Carstens, E. and Trevino, D.L. (1978) Laminar origins of spinothalamic projections in the cat as determined by the retrograde transport of horseradish peroxidase, *J. comp. Neurol.*, 182: 151-166.

Eccles, R.M. and Lundberg, A. (1959a) Synaptic actions in motoneurones by afferents which may evoke the flexion reflex. *Arch. ital. Biol.*, 97: 199-220.

Eccles, R.M. and Lundberg, A. (1959b) Supraspinal control of interneurones mediating spinal reflexes, *J. Physiol. (Lond.)*, 147: 565-584.

Eccles, J.C., Ito, M. and Szentágothai, J. (1967) *The Cerebellum as a Neuronal Machine*, Springer, Berlin.

Ekerot, C.-F. and Larson, B. (1979) The dorsal spino-olivocerebellar system in the cat. II. Somatotopical organization, *Exp. Brain Res.*, 36: 219-232.

Ekerot, C.-F., Larson, B. and Oscarsson, O. (1979) Information carried by the spinocerebellar paths. In R. Granit and O. Pompeiano (Eds.), *Reflex Control of Posture and Movement, Progr. Brain Research, Vol. 50*, Elsevier/North-Holland Biomedical Press, Amsterdam, pp. 79-90.

Engberg, I., Lundberg, A. and Ryall, R.W. (1968a) Reticulospinal inhibition of transmission in reflex pathways, *J. Physiol. (Lond.)*, 194: 201-223.

Engberg, I., Lundberg, A. and Ryall, R.W. (1968b) Reticulospinal inhibition of interneurones, *J. Physiol. (Lond.)*, 194: 225-236.

Engberg, I., Lundberg, A. and Ryall, R.W. (1968c) Is the tonic decerebrate inhibition of reflex paths mediated by monoaminergic pathways? *Acta physiol. scand.*, 72: 123-133.

Forssberg, H. and Grillner, S. (1973) The locomotion of the acute spinal cat injected with clonidine i.v., *Brain Res.*, 50: 184-186.

neurons in n. raphe magnus. The area of stimulation in the anterior lobe is shown in Figure 2B. From this area inhibition was more frequently observed, as shown for the raphespinal neuron in Figure 2A. The inhibition in some neurons may have been monosynaptic, as in Figure 2A, since the latency was less than 1.0 msec. The excitation was of much longer latency (e.g. 25 msec) and presumably polysynaptic, since a train of pulses was required. This is the only input we found which gave a significant proportion of inhibitory responses (West and Wolstencroft, unpublished experiments).

IV.4. Motor inputs to raphespinal neurons

The experiments described show that raphespinal neurons receive both mono-synaptic and polysynaptic excitation from the red nucleus, monosynaptic and polysynaptic excitation from areas 4 and 6 of the motor cortex, and polysynap-tic excitation via the red nucleus from areas 1, 2, 3 and 5 of the cortex. A preli-minary study suggests that they also receive an inhibitory input from the cere-bellum. This finding is summarized in Figure 3.

The inputs from the motor cortex and red nucleus appear to provide non-spe-cific excitation in that n. raphe neurons respond to many different movements, although these are mainly flexor. Excitation of raphespinal neurons is likely to occur during most of the movements produced by the red nucleus and motor cortex. A possible function for this excitation, in suppressing peripheral refle-xes to allow descending commands to proceed uninterrupted, is discussed in the following section on sensorimotor integration.

It is of some interest that the cerebellum may have an inhibitory influence on raphe neurons. It could thus be used in motor programmes to switch raphe-spinal activity on and off.

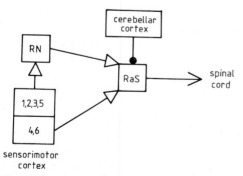

Figure 3. Diagram showing excitatory inputs (—▷) to raphespinal neurons (RaS) from the red nucleus (RN) and sensorimotor cortex: areas 4 and 6 direct, and areas 1, 2, 3 and 5 via red nucleus. An inhibitory input (—●) from the cerebellar cortex is also shown.

V. Raphe and Sensorimotor Integration

The lowest level of sensorimotor integration occurs in the spinal cord or in simple cranial reflexes such as the jaw-opening reflex. We shall discuss first the influence of the raphe on the spinal flexion reflex and then consider the influence of other supraspinal regions involved in motor control.

V.1. Descending inhibition of the flexor withdrawal reflex

The flexion reflex is a basic spinal motor response to sensory stimulation of the foot and leg; withdrawal can protect the extremity from damage by noxious stimuli. It is well known that, in the decerebrate animal, there is usually a powerful descending inhibition of this reflex, so that it can only be elicited by very strong stimuli or not at all. The source of this descending inhibition has been the subject of many investigations, particularly by Lundberg and his colleagues (Holmquist and Lundberg, 1961; Lundberg, 1964; Carpenter et al., 1965), who concluded that it came from a group of neurons in the midline of the brain stem and the adjacent ventromedial reticular formation. They termed this descending system the "dorsal reticulospinal system" (Engberg et al., 1968). From their description of the effective stimulation sites and the dorsolateral route taken by the axons in the spinal cord, it appears that raphespinal neurons are a major part of this system.

Most investigations of this type of descending inhibition have been made by recording from interneurons which respond to stimuli producing flexion (flexor reflex afferents (FRA) interneurons in Lundberg's terminology) or by recording from motoneurons of flexor muscles. One difficulty is that the pathway for the flexion withdrawal reflex has not yet been identified, and there are a variety of different types of interneurons which respond to inputs producing flexion, e.g. spinothalamic, spinoreticular and spinocervical tract neurons, to mention some.

We have reinvestigated the origin of the descending inhibition of the withdrawal reflex in the unanesthetized decerebrate and decerebellate cat by making lesions in the brain stem and measuring changes both in the reflex threshold to controlled pinch and in the latency to withdrawal following thermal stimulation of the foot pad. To obtain an estimate of the descending inhibition, these measurements were made in the hind legs before and after cold block of the cord at T13–L1.

Lesions in the locus coeruleus, medial and lateral vestibular nuclei, and lateral or ventrolateral reticular formation had little or no effect on the threshold for, or latency of, the withdrawal reflex. A transverse section at the junction between the pons and the midbrain reduced or abolished the extensor rigidity but did not reduce the descending inhibition. However, a transection of the medial brain stem, similar to that used by Holmquist and Lundberg (1961), reduced threshold and latency of the reflex to the levels seen after cold block of spinal neurons from the motor cortex (Magni and Willis, 1964) and the red nucleus (West and Wolstencroft, unpublished experiments).

An hypothesis concerning one possible role of the raphe is shown as a model in Figure 6B. If we consider Figure 6A, this hypothesis indicates that the flexor reflex may be facilitated by a supraspinal loop through the reticular formation and back via the fast medial reticulospinal neurons which can excite flexor motoneurons. Indeed, this is suggested by the results of Doughterty et al. (1970), who obtained evidence for a ventral descending facilitatory influence on flexor withdrawal in the decerebrate cat following a dorsal transection of the thoracic cord. Under these conditions, the reticulospinal neurons would take part in flexor withdrawal, as shown in Figure 6A. However, now let us consider what would happen when both reticulospinal and raphespinal neurons are facilitated from the motor cortex or red nucleus, as in Figure 6B. Nociceptor inputs to both flexor motoneurons and reticulospinal neurons would be switched off by the raphe and the reticulospinal neurons would respond exclusively to the descending excitatory influence from motor cortex and red nucleus. The reticulospinal activity would add a facilitatory influence to the corticospinal and rubrospinal actions on flexor motoneurons. The raphespinal activation would also ensure that the flexor command from the motor cortex would proceed uninterrupted by peripheral inputs which could produce a different pattern of spinal motor activity if their actions were not suppressed (see Wolstencroft, 1980).

V.6. *Descending inhibition: different types*

Descending inhibition by the "dorsal reticulospinal system" appears to originate both from the raphe and from medial areas of the ventral reticular formation up to about 3 mm from the midline (see Fig. 2G in Engberg et al., 1968). Thus the inhibition is partly raphespinal and partly reticulospinal. However, inhibition of the withdrawal reflex in the decerebrate cat, as shown both by lesions and by stimulation, is obtained from a more limited region of the brain stem, in the midline raphe and immediately adjacent ventromedial reticular formation less than 1.5 mm lateral to the midline. Inhibition of the flexion withdrawal reflex to cutaneous nociceptor stimulation may thus arise from a more limited region than does the inhibition of transmission in the flexor reflex afferent pathway from high threshold muscle afferents, as studied by Engberg et al. (1968), although both regions are at the same rostro-caudal level.

Hall et al. (1981) have claimed that descending inhibition does not arise from n. raphe magnus since widespread lesions of the raphe did not reduce the descending inhibition of the responses of dorsal horn neurons to C-fiber stimulation in the barbiturate-anesthetized cat. However, it is clear that they were studying a different type of inhibition, since raphe and medial reticular neurons are silenced by barbiturates. In their preparation there would be no activity in raphespinal neurons and thus no descending inhibition from this source.

V.7. Raphespinal neurons: problems

Only a part of the raphe complex, i.e. n. raphe magnus and n. raphe pallidus, is responsible for descending control of nociceptor inputs, but raphespinal neurons also occur in n. raphe pontis and n. raphe obscurus. The role of these projections is not known, but there is suggestive evidence for an involvement in motor control. Thus Mori et al. (1980) found that stimulation in n. raphe pontis in the mesencephalic cat could either facilitate or inhibit, depending on electrode depth, both hind limb postural tonus and the stepping movements produced by stimulation of the locomotor region in the mesencephalon. The raphespinal fibers from n. raphe obscurus descend in ventral quadrants of the cord and terminate mainly in the ventral horn (Martin et al., 1978). Although there is no spinal projection from n. raphe medianus, stimulation of this nucleus in the rat was observed to potentiate the lumbar ventral root monosynaptic response to dorsal root stimulation at the same time as it inhibited the polysynaptic response (Barasi and Roberts, 1974). Results such as these suggest that the role of raphespinal neurons in motor control deserves further investigation.

Another problem concerning the raphespinal projection is the respective role of fibers with different conduction velocities and with different transmitters. Raphespinal fibers from n. raphe magnus have a very wide range of conduction velocities (West and Wolstencroft, 1977b), so that activity in the dorsal horn induced by the fastest fibers (67 m/sec) may end long before activity induced by the slowest fibers (1.25 m/sec) begins, if they are both activated simultaneously. It is possible that the long time-course of the descending inhibition following n. raphe magnus stimulation is due to activity arriving over a long time period due to the range of conduction velocities. Alternatively, the slow non-myelinated fibers, presumably tryptaminergic, may inhibit a different type of input than the fast fibers. Conceivably, the slower fibers inhibit the slower inputs. There is no shortage of problems to be investigated.

VI. Summary

The function of the descending actions of n. raphe magnus and n. raphe pallidus in suppressing responses to nociceptor inputs has been investigated. This problem has been approached by studying the influence of other brain regions and of peripheral inputs on raphe neurons and by investigating the role of the raphe in descending inhibition of the flexion withdrawal reflex in the decerebrate cat.

Raphespinal neurons receive an excitatory input from both low threshold (touch, tap, hair movement) and high threshold (noxious pinch and heat) cutaneous afferents. They respond to peripheral nerve and dorsal column inputs at stimulation rates and intensities used to obtain pain relief in man. Thus it is possible that raphespinal activation may contribute to the pain control achieved by these methods of stimulation.

Descending inhibition of the flexion withdrawal reflex in the decerebrate cat was abolished by a lesion of n. raphe magnus, n. raphe pallidus and the immediately adjacent ventromedial reticular formation. Tonic activity in raphespinal neurons occurred simultaneously with a lack of response to noxious mechanical and thermal stimulation immediately after decerebration. From about 9 to 18 h after decerebration, raphe activity gradually declined and withdrawal reflex thresholds and latencies fell. The duration of the flexor motoneuron response, as determined from EMG recordings, became much longer as raphe activity declined. Thus raphespinal neurons may control the strength and duration of the flexor response in withdrawal. Raphespinal neurons appeared to be unresponsive to nociceptor mechanical and thermal spinal inputs immediately after decerebration but became responsive after the descending inhibition had declined. This suggests that they suppress their own inputs from nociceptive spinal neurons. Nucleus raphe magnus also suppressed nociceptor responses in the medial reticular formation.

Raphespinal and other raphe neurons can be excited by stimulation of the red nucleus and the sensorimotor cortex. There is a direct input to n. raphe magnus from areas 4 and 6 and an indirect input via the red nucleus from areas 1, 2, 3 and 5. There is also an inhibitory input from the cerebellar cortex. One function of the raphe may be to prevent responses to cutaneous stimulation from interfering with descending motor commands to spinal neurons.

Raphe activity can thus control both the ascending transmission of nociceptive information and the strength and duration of flexor responses to nociceptor cutaneous inputs. Raphespinal neurons may be used by descending motor control systems to switch off flexor responses to inputs from the legs and feet or to vary the responsiveness of flexor motoneurons to their cutaneous inputs. In this way the bulbar raphe nuclei can play a role in sensorimotor integration.

Acknowledgement

This work was supported by the Medical Research Council.

References

Barasi, S. and Roberts, M.H.T. (1974) The modification of lumbar motoneuron excitability by stimulation of a putative 5-hydroxytryptamine pathway, *Brit. J. Pharmacol.*, 52: 339-348.
Basbaum, A.I., Clanton C.H. and Fields, H.L. (1978) Three bulbospinal pathways from the rostral

medulla of the cat: an autoradiographic study of pain modulating systems, *J. comp. Neurol.*, 178: 209-224.

Beall, J.E., Martin, R.F., Applebaum, A.E. and Willis, W.D. (1976) Inhibition of primate spinothalamic tract neurons by stimulation in the region of the nucleus raphe magnus, *Brain Res.*, 114: 328-333.

Belcher, G., Ryall, R.W. and Schaffner, R. (1978) The differential effects of 5-hydroxytryptamine, noradrenaline and raphe stimulation on nociceptive and non-nociceptive dorsal horn interneurons in the cat, *Brain Res.*, 151: 307-321.

Berman, A.L. (1968) *The Brainstem of the Cat*, University of Wisconsin Press, Madison.

Bobillier, P., Petitjean, F., Salvert, D., Ligier, M. and Seguin, S. (1976) Differential projections of the nucleus raphe dorsalis and nucleus raphe centralis as revealed by autoradiography, *Brain Res.*, 85: 205-210.

Brodal, A., Walberg, F. and Taber, E. (1960) The raphe nuclei of the brain stem in the cat. II. Efferent connections, *J. comp. Neurol.*, 114: 239-259.

Cajal, S. Ramón y (1909) *Histologie du Système Nerveux de l'Homme et des Vertébrés, Vols. I and II*, Maloine, Paris.

Carpenter, D., Engberg, I. and Lundberg, A. (1965) Differential supraspinal control of inhibitory and excitatory actions from the FRA to ascending spinal pathways, *Acta physiol. scand.*, 63: 103-110.

Chambers, W.W., Liu, C.N., McCouch, G.P. and D'Aquili, E. (1966) Descending tracts and spinal shock in the cat, *Brain*, 89: 377-390.

Dougherty, M., Shea, S., Liu, E.N. and Chambers, W.W. (1970) Effects of spinal cord lesions on cutaneously elicited reflexes in the decerebrate cat. Tonic bulbospinal and spinobulbar inhibitory systems, *Exp. Neurol.*, 26: 551-570.

Duggan, A.W. and Griersmith, B.T. (1979) Inhibition of the spinal transmission of nociceptive information by supraspinal stimulation in the cat, *Pain*, 6: 149-161.

Engberg, I., Lundberg, A. and Ryall, R.W. (1968) Reticulospinal inhibition of transmission in reflex pathways, *J. Physiol. (Lond.)*, 194: 201-223.

Fields, H.L. and Anderson, S.D. (1978) Evidence that raphe-spinal neurons mediate opiate and midbrain stimulation-produced analgesias, *Pain*, 5: 333-349.

Fields, H.L., Basbaum, A.I., Clanton, C.H. and Anderson, S.D. (1977) Nucleus raphe magnus inhibition of spinal cord dorsal horn neurons, *Brain Res.*, 126: 441-453.

Gerhart, K.D., Wilcox, T.K., Chung, J.M. and Willis, W.D. (1981) Inhibition of nociceptive and non-nociceptive responses of primate spinothalamic cells by stimulation in medial brain stem, *J. Neurophysiol.*, 45: 121-136.

Giesler, G.J., Gerhart, K.D., Yezierski, R.P., Wilcox, T.K. and Willis, W.D. (1981) Postsynaptic inhibition of primate spinothalamic neurons by stimulation in nucleus raphe magnus, *Brain Res.*, 204: 184-188.

Guilbaud, G., Oliveras, J.L., Giesler, G. and Besson, J.M. (1977) Effects induced by stimulation of the centralis inferior nucleus of the raphe on dorsal horn interneurons in cat spinal cord, *Brain Res.*, 126: 355-360.

Hall, J.G., Duggan, A.W., Johnson, S.M. and Morton, C.R. (1981) Medullary raphe lesions do not reduce descending inhibition of dorsal horn neurons of the cat, *Neurosci. Lett.*, 25: 25-29.

Hayes, N.L. and Rustioni, A. (1981) Descending projections from brainstem and sensorimotor cortex to spinal enlargements in the cat. Single and double retrograde tracer studies, *Exp. Brain Res.*, 41: 89-107.

Holmquist, B. and Lundberg, A. (1961) Differential supraspinal control of synaptic actions evoked by volleys in the flexion reflex afferents in alpha motoneurons, *Acta physiol. scand.*, 84: Suppl. 186.

Huisman, A.M., Kuypers, H.G.J.M. and Verburgh, C.A. (1981) Quantitative differences in collateralization of the descending spinal pathways from red nucleus and other brain stem cell groups in rat as demonstrated with the multiple fluorescent retrograde tracer technique, *Brain Res.*, 209: 271-286.

Jankowska, E., Lund, S., Lundberg, A. and Pompeiano, O. (1968) Inhibitory effects evoked through ventral reticulospinal pathways, *Arch. ital. Biol.*, 106: 124-140.

Jouvet, M. (1968) Insomnia and decrease of cerebral 5-hydroxytryptamine after destruction of the raphe system in the cat, *Advanc. Pharmacol.*, 613: 265-279.

Kuypers, H.G.J.M. and Maisky, V.A. (1975) Retrograde axonal transport of horseradish peroxidase from spinal cord to brain stem cell groups in the cat, *Neurosci. Lett.*, 1: 9-14.

Kuypers, H.G.J.M. and Maisky, V.A. (1977) Funicular trajectones of descending pathways in cat, *Brain Res.*, 136: 159-165.

Le Bars, D., Dickenson, A.H. and Besson, J.M. (1979a) Diffuse noxious inhibitory controls (DNIC). I. Effects on dorsal horn convergent neurons in the rat, *Pain*, 6: 283-304.

Le Bars, D., Dickenson, A.H. and Besson, J.M. (1979b) Diffuse noxious inhibitory controls (DNIC). II. Lack of effect on non-convergent neurons, supraspinal involvement and theoretical implications, *Pain*, 6: 305-327.

Liebeskind, J.C., Giesler, G.J. and Urca, G. (1976) Evidence pertaining to an endogenous mechanism of pain inhibition in the central nervous system. In Y. Zotterman (Ed.), *Sensory Functions of the Skin*, Pergamon Press, Oxford, pp. 561-573.

Lovick, T.A. and Wolstencroft, J.H (1979a) Responses of medial reticular neurons to tooth pulp stimulation: evidence for a monosynaptic input, *J. Physiol. (Lond.)*, 292: 40-41P.

Lovick, T.A. and Wolstencroft, J.H. (1979b) A selective action of nucleus raphe magnus on tooth pulp inputs to medial reticular neurons, *J. Physiol. (Lond.)*, 293: 73-74P.

Lovick, T.A. and Wolstencroft, J.H. (1980) Inhibition from nucleus raphe magnus of tooth pulp responses in medial reticular neurons of the cat can be antagonized by bicuculline, *Neurosci. Lett.*, 19: 325-330.

Lovick, T.A. and Wolstencroft, J.H. (1982) Presynaptic control of tooth pulp input by raphe and reticular nuclei and the role of GABA. In B. Matthews and R.G. Hill (Eds.), *Anatomical, Physiological and Pharmacological Aspects of Trigeminal Pain*, Elsevier/North-Holland, Amsterdam, in press.

Lovick, T.A., West, D.C. and Wolstencroft, J.H. (1977) Interactions between brain stem raphe nuclei and the trigeminal nuclei. In D.J. Anderson and B. Matthews (Eds.), *Pain in the Trigeminal Region*, Elsevier/North-Holland, Amsterdam, pp. 307-317.

Lovick, T.A., West, D.C. and Wolstencroft, J.H. (1978a) Responses of raphespinal and other bulbar raphe neurons to stimulation of the periaqueductal gray in the cat, *Neurosci. Lett.*, 8: 45-49.

Lovick, T.A., West, D.C. and Wolstencroft, J.H. (1978b) Bulbar raphe neurons with projections to the spinal trigeminal nucleus and the lumbar cord in the cat, *J. Physiol. (Lond.)*, 277: 61-62P.

Lundberg, A. (1964) Supraspinal control of transmission in reflex paths to motoneurons and primary afferents. In J.C. Eccles and J.P. Schadé (Eds.), *Physiology of Spinal Neurons, Progress in Brain Research, Vol. 12*, Elsevier, Amsterdam, pp. 197-219.

Magni, F. and Willis, W.D. (1964) Cortical control of brain stem reticular neurons, *Arch. ital. Biol.*, 102: 418-433.

Martin, R.F., Jordan, L.M. and Willis, W.D. (1978) Differential projections of cat medullary raphe neurons demonstrated by retrograde labelling following spinal cord lesions, *J. comp. Neurol.*, 182: 77-88.

Martin, R.F., Haber, L.H. and Willis, W.D. (1979) Primary afferent depolarization of identified cutaneous fibers following stimulation in medial brain stem, *J. Neurophysiol.*, 42: 779-790.

Mayer, D.J., Wolfe, T.L., Akil, H., Carder, B. and Liebeskind, J.C. (1971) Analgesia from electrical stimulation in the brainstem of the rat, *Science*, 174: 1351-1354.

McCreery, D.B., Bloedel, J.R. and Hames, E.G. (1979) Effects of stimulating in the raphe nuclei and in reticular formation on response of spinothalamic neurons to mechanical stimuli, *J. Neurophysiol.*, 42: 166-182.

Meessen, H. and Olszewski, J. (1949) *A Cytoarchitectonic Atlas of the Rhombencephalon of the Rabbit*, S. Karger, Basel.

Menetrey, D., Chaouch, A. and Besson, J.M. (1979) Location and properties of lumbar spinoreticular tract neurons in the rat, *Neurosci. Lett.*, Suppl. 3: S262.

Moolenhaar, G.-M., Holloway, J.A. and Trouth, C.O. (1976) Responses of caudal raphe neurons to peripheral somatic stimulation, *Exp. Neurol.*, 53: 304-313.

Mori, S., Nishimura, H. and Aoki, M. (1980) Brain stem activation of the spinal stepping generator. In J.A. Hobson and M.A.B. Brazier (Eds.), *The Reticular Formation Revisited, Specifying Function for a Nonspecific System*, Raven Press, New York, pp. 241-259.

Oliveras, J.L., Redjemi, F., Guilbaud, G. and Besson, J.M. (1975) Analgesia induced by electrical stimulation of the inferior centralis nucleus of the raphe in the cat, *Pain*, 1: 139-145.

Pomeroy, S.L. and Behbehani, M.M. (1979) Physiologic evidence for a projection from periaqueductal gray to nucleus raphe magnus in the rat, *Brain Res.*, 176: 143-147.

Proudfit, H.K. and Anderson, E.G. (1974) New long latency bulbospinal evoked potentials blocked by serotonin antagonists, *Brain Res.*, 65: 542-546.

Reynolds, D.V. (1969) Surgery in the rat during electrical analgesia induced by focal brain stimulation, *Science*, 164: 444-445.

Rivot, J.P., Chaouch, A. and Besson, J.M. (1980) Nucleus raphe magnus modulation of response of rat dorsal horn neurons to unmyelinated fiber inputs: partial involvement of serotonergic pathways, *J. Neurophysiol.*, 44: 1039-1057.

Satoh, K. (1979) The origin of reticulospinal fibers in the rat: a HRP study, *J. Hirnforsch.*, 20: 313-332.

Sherrington, C. (1947) *The Integrative Action of the Nervous System*, Cambridge University Press, Cambridge, 433 pp.

Taber, E., Brodal, A. and Walberg, F. (1960) The raphe nuclei of the brain stem in the cat. I. Normal topography and cytoarchitecture and general discussion, *J. comp. Neurol.*, 114: 161-188.

West, D.C. and Wolstencroft, J.H. (1977a) Afferent inputs to raphespinal neurons, *Proc. Int. Union Physiol. Sci.*, 13: 809.

West, D.C. and Wolstencroft, J.H. (1977b) Location and conduction velocity of raphespinal neurons in nucleus raphe magnus and raphe pallidus in the cat, *Neurosci. Lett.*, 5: 147-151.

West, D.C. and Wolstencroft, J.H. (1978) Facilitation of raphespinal and other bulbar raphe neurons by stimulation of the sensorimotor cortex, *J. Physiol. (Lond.)*, 277: 47P.

West, D.C., Lovick, T.A. and Wolstencroft, J.H. (1982) An excitatory input to nucleus raphe magnus from the red nucleus, *Neurosci. Lett.*, 29: 31-34.

Wiklund, L., Léger, L. and Persson, M. (1982) Monoamine cell distribution in the cat brain stem. A fluorescence histochemical study with quantification of indolaminergic and locus coeruleus cell groups, *J. comp. Neurol.*, 203: 613-647.

Willis, W.D., Haber, L.H. and Martin, R.F. (1977) Inhibition of spinothalamic tract cells and interneurons by brain stem stimulation in the monkey, *J. Neurophysiol.*, 40: 968-981.

Wolstencroft, J.H. (1964) Reticulospinal neurons, *J. Physiol. (Lond.)*, 174: 91-108.

Wolstencroft, J.H. (1980) The role of raphe and medial reticular neurons in control systems related to nociceptive inputs. In J.A. Hobson and M.A.B. Brazier (Eds.), *The Reticular Formation Revisited*, Raven Press, New York, pp. 349-371.

Brain Stem Control of Spinal Mechanisms
– B. Sjölund and A. Björklund, editors
© 1982 Elsevier Biomedical Press

17

The Triggering of Bulbo-Spinal Serotonergic Inhibitory Controls by Noxious Peripheral Inputs

DANIEL LE BARS, ANTHONY H. DICKENSON* and JEAN-MARIE BESSON

*Unité de Recherches de Neurophysiologie Pharmacologique de l'INSERM, 2 rue d'Alésia, 75014 Paris, France and *Department of Neurophysiology and Neuropharmacology, National Institute for Medical Research, The Ridgeway, Mill Hill, London, NW7 1AA, U.K.*

I. Introduction

A great number of studies, both behavioral and electrophysiological, have underlined the role of descending control systems originating from the brain stem in the modulation of the transmission of nociceptive messages at the spinal level (for a review, see Willis and Coggeshall, 1978; Besson, 1980). All these experiments have been performed using paradigms, i.e. direct electrical stimulation of brain stem sites, which undoubtedly revealed the potentiality of such modulation, but did not give any information on its functional meanings. For instance, it is conceivable that the manner in which such systems are triggered during stimulation-produced analgesia (SPA) may well constitute an artificial situation which could shunt a more complex circuitry.

We will report here that at least some of these bulbospinal inhibitory controls could be triggered by noxious somatic inputs, thus suggesting their possible involvement in pain processes. This assertion is mainly based on the concept of diffuse noxious inhibitory controls (DNIC) which we have recently introduced (Le Bars et al., 1979a, 1979b). As we will report in the dorsal horn, DNIC act essentially upon convergent units, i.e. those cells receiving inputs from both low-threshold cutaneous mechanoreceptors and nociceptors, which are also designated as trigger (Melzack and Wall, 1965), wide dynamic range (Mendell, 1966), lamina V type (Wall, 1967), class II (Iggo, 1974), polymodal (Zimmermann, 1976) or multireceptive (Mokha et al., 1981) neurons. Convergent neurons probably play a major role in the transmission of painful messages since they can be activated by a great variety of painful stimuli from cutaneous, muscular and visceral origins, and some of them project in ascending pathways such as the spinothalamic, spinoreticular and spinocervical tracts (for a review, see Zimmermann, 1976, 1977; Dennis and Melzack, 1977; Price and Dubner, 1977; Willis and Coggeshall, 1978). In addition, their activities are strongly modulated by supraspinal and segmental inhibitory influences. One of their main characteristics is therefore the potential to be influenced by a large variety of converging excitatory and inhibitory processes. Without excluding a role for the noxious specific neurons located in the marginal layer (Christensen and Perl, 1970), it is believed that convergent neurons are of essential importance in the transmission and the integration of nociceptive messages at the spinal level.

II. General Characteristics of Diffuse Noxious Inhibitory Controls

In the dorsal horn of the spinal cord and the trigeminal nucleus caudalis of the rat, convergent neurons are under the influence of what we have termed DNIC (Le Bars et al., 1979a; Dickenson et al., 1980a). The existence of such controls is demonstrated by the fact that the activities of convergent neurons are strongly inhibited by various noxious stimuli applied to widespread areas of the body unrelated to the excitatory receptive field of the neuron itself. These inhibitory effects affect all activities of convergent neurons, whether induced by noxious or non-noxious stimulation, and are specific features of such units, since other neurons such as noxious only, non-noxious, proprioceptive or cold responsive cells are not affected by DNIC (Le Bars et al., 1979b; Dickenson et al., 1980a).

II.1. Spinal level

The inhibitions, observed on neurons at the lumbar level, can be induced from widespread areas: the tail, hind paw contralateral to excitatory receptive field, forepaws, ears, muzzle and the viscerae. By contrast, innocuous stimuli are ineffective when applied to these same areas. These inhibitions of convergent neurons can be produced by a variety of noxious stimuli: (a) pinch applied by forceps produced strong inhibitory effects – on the other hand, light tactile stimuli and moderate pressure were ineffective; (b) intraperitoneal injection of bradykinin, known to be a potent noxious stimulation in man (Lim et al., 1967), was equally effective in inducing these inhibitions; (c) noxious heat applied to the tail by means of hot water at temperatures above noxious threshold in man also produced these inhibitions. The degree of inhibition increased with the level of noxious heat; and (d) electrical stimulation of the tail was equally effective using the same parameters of stimulation as those which produce vocalization in the freely moving rat. Augmentation of the current above this level produced an increased degree of inhibition of the convergent neurons.

In the majority of cases, long lasting post-effects directly related to the duration of conditioning painful stimulus were observed.

It seems that clear inhibitory effects require a certain degree of recruitment of peripheral nociceptors. For example, noxious radiant heat applied to a restricted area of the tail (a few mm^2) was almost ineffective, whereas noxious heat applied over several cm^2 by means of hot water produced powerful inhibitory effects. The strength of the inhibitory effects of bradykinin could well be due to the degree of spatial summation induced by the stimulus since the intraperitoneal injection will presumably act on a large pool of visceral nociceptors. The efficacy of pinch, applied to a relatively large area of the periphery, in inducing the inhibitions would seem again to relate to an effect of spatial summation. Furthermore, the greater degree of inhibition produced by pinch applied to the tail or muzzle than that produced from the paws or ears may result from the higher degree of central representation of the former areas.

In addition to the influence of spatial summation, there seems to be a major role of temporal summation in these inhibitory effects, as demonstrated by the electrical stimulation of the tail. Indeed, when using a 500 msec duration train of shocks (square pulses of 1 msec duration, 50 Hz), potent inhibitory effects were observed whereas shorter trains of single shocks were not so clearly effective. It seems interesting to note that, using similar current values in the freely moving animal, a 500 msec train produces easily reproducible vocalization, whereas shorter stimuli result in either no vocalization or extremely variable effects.

The types of convergent neuronal activity inhibited include both spontaneous and evoked activities, the latter being induced by either noxious or non-noxious stimuli.

(a) *Spontaneous activity.*

In our experimental conditions, the presence of a reliable spontaneous activity of convergent units is rarely encountered and, when present, is less than 10 spikes/sec. When tested, noxious stimuli induce a large reduction (70–80%) in this type of activity. By way of example, strong noxious pinch applied to the tail or the muzzle produces an almost instantaneous blockade of firing rate followed by long lasting post-effects which can outlast by 3–4 times the period of stimulation.

(b) *Responses to natural stimulation.*

(i) *Responses to radiant heat.* Convergent neurons respond to the application of noxious radiant heat to the center of their receptive field; in most cases, there is a good correlation between stimulus intensity and neuronal discharge. For all intensities of thermal stimuli tested (in the 42–50°C range), the responses are almost totally suppressed by the concomitant application of various noxious stimuli either mechanical, thermal or chemical in nature, to remote body areas. This is illustrated in Figure 1.

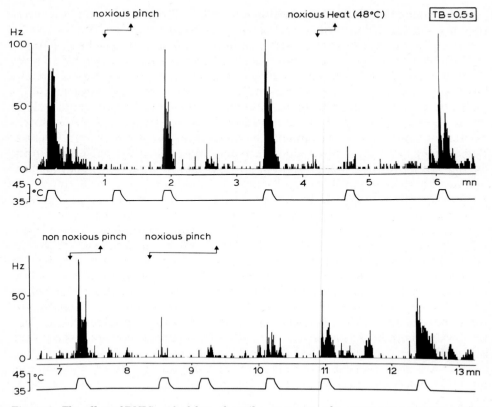

Figure 1. The effect of DNIC evoked from the tail on responses of a convergent neuron to noxious radiant heat (as depicted under the time scale) applied on its receptive field located on the ipsilateral hindpaw extremity. Whereas noxious pinch and noxious heat produce complete inhibition of the response, non-noxious pinch is without effect. Note the pronounced post-effect following the sustained final period of pinch. (From Le Bars et al., 1979a, with permission.)

(ii) *Responses to sustained noxious pinch.* The application of a sustained noxious pinch to the receptive field of convergent neurons induces a steady high level of firing following a short phasic adapting period (usually 10–20 sec). Tested upon the tonic discharge, DNIC induced inhibitions very similar to those observed against the spontaneous activity, both in terms of magnitude and duration (with long lasting post-effects).

(iii) *Responses to light mechanical stimulation.* In all cases, convergent neurons respond to natural tactile stimulation such as stroking, hair movement or light pressure; in most cases, a high level of firing can be achieved by the repetitive application of such stimuli. As shown in Figure 2, these kinds of responses were also highly sensitive to DNIC (percentage of inhibition ranging from 50 to 70%).

(c) *Responses to electrical transcutaneous stimulation* (see Fig. 4)

Transcutaneous electrical stimulation applied to the center of the excitatory receptive field of convergent neurons induced clear Aαβ and C fiber responses, and occasionally Aδ fiber responses. These responses have been shown to be similar to those induced by direct nerve stimulation (Menétrey et al., 1977).

Responses to C fiber input. Intense transcutaneous electrical stimulation produced a C fiber response with a mean threshold of 3–4 mA for a 2msec duration pulse. Increasing the current to a suprathreshold level produced an easily reproducible maximal C fiber response against which DNIC was tested. In the majority of neurons this response consisted of several bands, each containing a train of spikes. The mean latency of the maximal firing due to C fibers was around 250 msec, indicating a mean peripheral conduction velocity of about 0.6 m/sec.

These responses due to C fiber input were powerfully depressed by DNIC. By way of example, strong pinch of the tail or muzzle resulted in an almost complete blockade of these responses (mean inhibition 88% and 85%, respectively) which was significantly greater than those produced by similar pinches applied to the contralateral hindpaw (70%), one forepaw (70%) or one ear (62%).

Other conditioning noxious stimuli such as noxious (52°C) heat applied to the tail (see the control sequence of Fig. 7) or i.p. administration of bradykinin – a potent stimulant of visceral nociceptors – also depressed (70% and 84% respectively) responses due to C fiber activation.

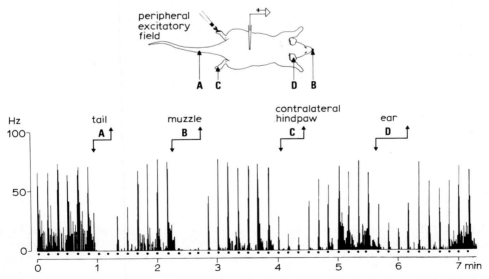

Figure 2. The effects of DNIC evoked from various parts of the body by noxious pinch (period of pinch arrowed) on the responses of a convergent neuron to regular light stroking (indicated by black circles) applied each 10 sec.

386

Responses to Aαβ input. All convergent units received Aαβ fiber input in addition to the C-fiber input. The effect of DNIC was tested against the Aαβ fiber responses in two ways. The first was to qualitatively examine the effect of the noxious stimulation with the supramaximal Aαβ fiber response concurrent with the C fiber response. With this extreme suprathreshold stimulation of Aαβ fibers, inhibitory effects were seen in only 45% of the neurons (see the control sequence of Fig. 7 for an example). Because of the supramaximal nature of this stimulation, neurons were also tested at Aαβ threshold current producing 1–4 spikes per stimulus (Fig. 3). In most cases, pinching the tail, the contralateral hind paw, the ear or the muzzle, produced 60–80% inhibitions. Augmentation of the voltage to 3 or 4 times suprathreshold reduced the effect of noxious mechanical stimulation of the tail to a mere mean 19% inhibition. This suggests that, in some cases, by increasing stimulation parameters above thresholds for the Aαβ fiber response, the effect of DNIC may be overridden.

The apparent differential effects of DNIC upon Aαβ fiber inputs is probably due to the characteristic of the response of convergent neurons to brief electrical stimulation; indeed the sharp and short excitatory post-synaptic potentials

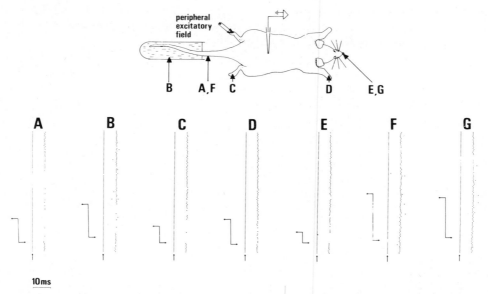

Figure 3. Dot display analysis (each dot represents one spike; read from bottom to top) of the threshold short latency responses of a convergent neuron elicited by transcutaneous peripheral electrical stimulation applied to the ipsilateral hindpaw receptive field (shock artefacts marked by the vertical arrows). DNIC are triggered during the horizontal double arrows. A, noxious pinch (tail); B, noxious heat 49°C (tail); C, noxious pinch (contralateral hind paw); D, noxious pinch (contralateral forepaw); E, noxious pinch (muzzle). The application of air jet was ineffective whether applied on the tail (F) or the muzzle (G).

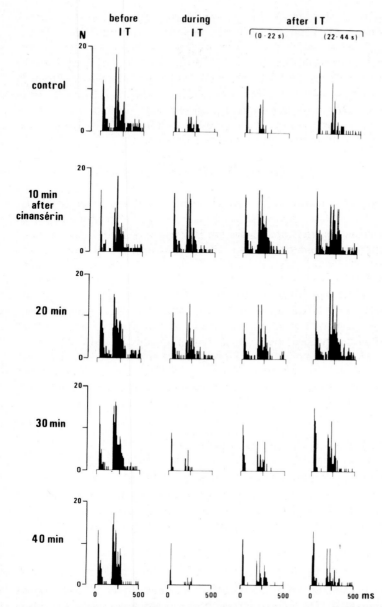

Figure 7. Example of the effect of cinanserin (4 mg/kg; i.v.) upon DNIC. Post-stimulus histograms (summation of 15 responses, 5 msec bin width) for intense electrical transcutaneous stimulation (0.6 Hz, 4.5 mA, 2 msec duration) of excitatory field located on the ipsilateral hindpaw extremity. A short latency response to activation of Aαβ fibers, followed by a longer latency response subsequent to C fiber activation, are seen. Both are inhibited during and after (0–22 sec; 22–44 sec) immersion of the tail (IT) in 52°C hot water. Note the lifting of the powerful inhibitory effects of IT and of the subsequent post effects by cinanserin and the recovery of the responses at 30–40 min.

though this structure is apparently of pre-eminent importance, we cannot exclude an interaction with other supraspinal structures such as the PAG. (2) A spinal site of naloxone action is supported by the high density of en-kephalinergic terminals (Hökfelt et al., 1977; Simantov et al., 1977) and opiate receptors (Atweh and Kuhar, 1977) in the substantia gelatinosa of Rolando (SGR), one of the principal terminal sites of projection from the NRM (Oliveras et al., 1977). In any case, as it is generally agreed that naloxone is a pure opiate antagonist – at least at low doses (see Goldstein, 1979) – these data strongly suggest a participation of endogenous opiates in DNIC.

III.5. Evidence for a post-synaptic inhibitory mechanism

In order to approach the question of the final mechanisms underlying DNIC, we have studied their effects upon the responses of convergent neurons to glutamate iontophoretic application. As shown in Figure 8, DNIC strongly de-pressed the glutamate-induced excitation. Since glutamate is known to di-rectly excite the neuronal membrane (Curtis and Watkins, 1960; Zieglgänsberger and Puil, 1973), hyperpolarization of convergent neurons is probably one of the ultimate mechanisms for DNIC. Here again, the paral-lelism between DNIC- and NRM-mediated inhibitions has to be emphasized, since inhibitory post-synaptic potentials evoked by stimulation of this nucleus have been recorded in convergent neurons at the origin of the spino-thalamic tract in the monkey (Giesler et al., 1981). However, we cannot exclude the par-ticipation of other complementary mechanisms in DNIC, since signs of pre-synaptic inhibitory mechanisms have been reported after NRM stimulation (Proudfit and Anderson, 1974; Lovick et al., 1978; Martin et al., 1979).

IV. Clinical and Theoretical Implications

In our electrophysiological experiments, all types of dorsal horn convergent neurons responses could be inhibited by noxious conditioning stimuli applied to other parts of the body. These results give rise to several situations in which one could speculate on the role of convergent neurons in nociception.

IV.1. Clinical correlates

We have emphasized the fact that DNIC affect the responses of convergent neurons to noxious stimuli. By way of an example, the responses of a conver-gent neuron to C fiber input (see Fig. 4) or to radiant heat application (see Fig. 1), both presumably capable of triggering a pain sensation, are abolished by strong noxious stimulation applied to parts of the body remote from the ex-citatory receptive field of the neuron. In other words, when two simultaneous noxious stimuli are applied to two distant parts of the body, the pool of convergent dorsal horn units related to the lesser stimulus is inhibited. If indeed convergent neurons play an important role in the transmission of nociceptive messages, one could therefore postulate in terms of pain sensation, that the perception resulting from the concomitant application of two distinct noxious stimuli would depend upon the balance between the two noxious inputs to the brain, which would result in attenuation of the pain emanating from the weaker stimulus.

In this respect, we have proposed (Le Bars et al., 1979b) that DNIC may well

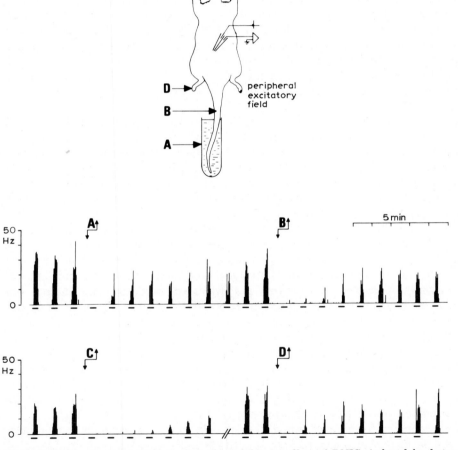

Figure 8. Ratemeter record illustrating the inhibitory effect of DNIC, induced by hot water applied to the tail (A), or pinch of the tail (B), nose (C) and contralateral hindpaw (D), on the excitatory responses of a convergent neuron induced by iontophoretic glutamate applied once every minute. The pulses of glutamate (25 nA) are indicated by the horizontal bars below the record.

form the neural basis of the pain-relieving effects of counterirritation where a peripheral nociceptive stimulus is used against pain originating elsewhere (Duncker, 1937; Hardy et al., 1940; Gammon and Starr, 1941; Parsons and Goetzl, 1945; Berlin et al., 1958). In the same way, painful cutaneous electrical stimulation has been shown to reduce chronic somatic pain (Melzack, 1975). Further clinical evidence for the existence of a pain inhibiting system of noxious peripheral origin is the observation that organic pain raises pain thresholds in other areas of the body (Hazouri and Mueller, 1950; Merskey and Evans, 1975).

Whether certain techniques of acupuncture inducing analgesia are equivalent to the counterirritation phenomenon is not clear, but it seems likely that, at least in some cases, the two methods share common characteristics. This has been suggested by Levine et al. (1976) and Melzack et al. (1977). In fact, as pointed out by Eriksson and Sjölund (1976), there are clinical indications that there seems to be an increased efficacy of electroacupuncture with parameters producing a feeling of pain at the stimulation site compared with less intense stimulation. Mann (1974) has also concluded that, for effective analgesia, the painful sensation resulting from the stimulation point should be the maximum that the patient can tolerate.

From the electrophysiological standpoint, a series of experiments in animals (Chiang et al., 1975; Shen et al., 1975; Du and Chao, 1976) using electroacupuncture versus viscero-somatic reflex discharges strongly supports the idea of the ascending–descending nature of mechanisms subserving this kind of analgesia. Inhibitions disappeared in spinal preparations, but remained after decerebration, suggesting that the brain stem is a main link in these phenomena. More precisely, a lesion of the median region of the medulla, mainly of the NRM, produced a strong reduction of the inhibitory effects which, in addition, according to sectioning experiments, required the ventrolateral and the dorsolateral funiculus as, respectively, the ascending and descending pathways. The results strongly suggest that both ascending pain pathways and descending inhibitory pathways are involved. The analogy between some forms of electroacupuncture and DNIC is further supported by the fact that, in the spinal trigeminal nuclei, convergent units are inhibited by electroacupuncture whereas noxious only units are unaffected (Department of Physiology, Kirin Medical College, Changchun, 1977). Interestingly there is evidence in man for an involvement of endogenous opiates in some forms of acupuncture analgesia (Chapman and Benedetti, 1977; Mayer et al., 1977; Jiang et al., 1978; Boureau et al., 1979; Sjölund and Eriksson, 1979), and we have reported that DNIC is naloxone-sensitive (Le Bars et al., 1981b).

In summary, a number of pain-relieving stimuli share common characteristics: the painful or unpleasant nature of the stimulus, widespread analgesic effects, association with long lasting post-effects, requirement of ascending–descending pathways, and the possible involvement of endogenous opiates. To explain some of these clinical effects. Melzack (1971) has suggested the existence of a "central biasing mechanism", including a spinal–supraspinal loop which would be activated by small fiber inputs from the periphery and would inhibit the sensation of pain from other areas. DNIC may well fit at least some of the requirements of this system.

IV.2. Behavioral correlates

In order to investigate in detail the counterirritation phenomenon, we have developed a behavioral model in the rat by the concomitant application of two noxious stimuli used in classical pharmacological testing (Kraus et al., 1981). It was found that the threshold for vocalization induced by electric shocks to the tail was increased by the intraperitoneal injection of the algogenic agent phenylbenzoquinone (PBQ). This is in keeping with other behavioral experiments showing that hypertonic saline injected intraperitoneally (Komisaruk and Wallman, 1977; Hayes et al., 1978), sustained pinch applied to the paws or tail (Colpaert et al., 1978), and electrical stimulation of the tail at currents sufficient to produce vocalization (Buckett, 1979, 1981), also induce analgesic effects when the test for analgesia is applied to other areas of the body. In the cat, stimulation of the tooth pulp at an intensity which is obviously painful is able to greatly increase the threshold of escape behavior induced by foot shock (Anderson et al., 1976). We consider that our paradigm using PBQ offers a good experimental model for these phenomena for the following reasons: (1) the deep visceral pain may resemble that seen in some clinical situations, and is not associated with the dramatic behavioral reactions seen during the stress-inducing footshock which has often been used in other studies, and (2) the behavioral tests can be effected simultaneously with the painful stimulus, thus allowing determination of the time-course of drug effects and, unlike tests requiring escape reactions by the animals, motor capacity does not bias the results.

We found (Kraus et al., 1981) that the hypoalgesia induced by visceral pain is dose-dependently antagonized by low doses of naloxone ($\leqslant 0.2$ mg/kg). This suggests the involvement of endogenous opiates and is in keeping with reports of naloxone-reversible hypoalgesia following brief periods of tail-shock to the mouse (Buckett, 1979). In the rat, the naloxone reversibility of footshock-induced hypoalgesia in the tail-flick test seems to depend on experimental situations, such as the area where the conditioning stimuli are applied (Watkins et al., 1981) or their temporal characteristic (Lewis et al., 1980). In any case, many of these data suggest the possible involvement of endogenous opiates in some hypoalgesia phenomena triggered by peripheral noxious inputs; however, they must be interpreted with caution, especially in the light of the fact that, in man, stress itself induces a naloxone-reversible depression of pain reflexes (Willer and Albe-Fessard, 1980; Willer et al., 1981).

The participation of 5-HT mechanisms in the counterirritation phenomenon has been investigated using the model described above. It was found that pretreatment with 5-HTP strongly potentiated, in a dose-dependent fashion over the range 5.5–50 mg/kg (i.p.), the PBQ-induced rise in threshold (Kraus et al., 1982), while intraperitoneal injection of PBQ in non-pretreated rats results in a mean threshold increase of 30–40% (with an upper limit of 100% rarely, if ever, being exceeded). Following pretreatment with 50 mg/kg 5-HTP, there was a mean increase of 130% with extremely dramatic results (threshold increase 400–500%) in several animals. The specificity of this effect was confirmed by its suppression by the 5-HT receptor blocker cinanserin.

Along with results of other investigators, these observations provide support for the notion of a linkage between the 5-HT and enkephalinergic systems in the modulation of pain. Shimizu et al. (1981) showed a potentiation of transcutaneous electrical analgesia by 5-HTP, this potentiation being antagonized both by methysergide and by naloxone. Similarly, Buckett (1981) has shown that these same blocking agents antagonize peripheral stimulation-produced analgesia as measured in the hot-plate test.

IV.3. Convergent neurons and nociception

On the basis of current knowledge, convergent neurons seem to play a major role in the transmission of painful messages. They are activated by a variety of painful stimuli from cutaneous, muscular and visceral origins. They are strongly excited by pain-producing chemicals and project in some ascending pathways such as the spino-thalamic, spino-reticular and spino-cervical tracts (see Section I). Further indirect evidence for an important involvement of convergent neurons in the transmission of nociceptive information is provided by the possible correlations between the clinical and behavioral observations we have reported above and DNIC, with their selectivity of action upon this kind of neuron (noxious-only neurons recorded in lamina I were not found to be under DNIC).

However, the response characteristics of convergent neurons present some paradoxical points. One is that these neurons can exhibit similar or greater levels of activity in response to innocuous peripheral stimulation than their responses to noxious stimulation. This is illustrated in Figure 9, where it is shown that rapid repetition of light mechanical stimuli can result in an equal or even greater level of firing than, for example, that produced by noxious radiant heat. Two series of experiments were carried out, one in anesthetized intact rats and the other in unanesthetized spinal rats, in which the application of radiant heat (49°C) to the excitatory receptive fields of convergent cells induced a firing rate which could be exceeded in most cases by sufficiently rapid repetitive brushing of the same area. The former stimulus was obviously painful when applied to the experimenter's skin, whereas the latter was not. Therefore, in the intact animal, a high rate of impulses can reach supraspinal structures via convergent units when repetitive innocuous peripheral stimuli are applied. On the basis of these observations, and if the spinal mechanisms of

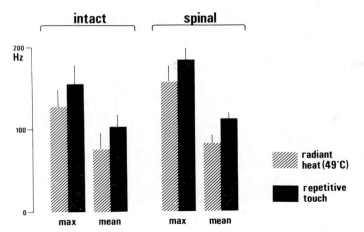

Figure 9. Comparison of the responses of convergent neurons induced by noxious radiant heat (49°C) and by repetitive light touch, both applied on their receptive field. Note that in either anesthetized intact rats (n = 14) or unaneshetized spinal rats (n = 16), both the maximal or the mean firing rate were of the same order.

nociception are interpreted only in terms of a gain system modulated by spinal and supraspinal inhibitory processes, it is difficult to imagine how the excitatory responses or dorsal horn convergent neurons can be involved in a specific pain signalling message. We have proposed (Le Bars et al., 1979b) that DNIC might be interpreted as an additional filter system allowing the extraction of nociceptive messages emanating from convergent neurons. Indeed, in the freely moving animal, one can envisage that the activity of the whole population of spinal and trigeminal convergent units due to the continual random activation of non-noxious receptors (e.g. hair and touch receptors) would not be negligible. This basic "somatosensory noise"* transmitted to higher centers would hardly aid the recognition of a meaningful painful signal, but DNIC might provide the means by which a specific pain signal could emerge from such a non-specific system.

We have previously mentioned that DNIC affect all activities of convergent units, including both spontaneous firing and activity evoked by non-noxious stimuli (see Fig. 2). During an intense nociceptive stimulus, both the noxious only and convergent units send a positive excitatory signal towards the higher centers. Concurrently, this signal will activate the DNIC system, which inhibits all those spinal and trigeminal convergent neurons not activated by the initial noxious stimulus, thus resulting in a considerable reduction of the

---

* The term "noise" should be understood with respect to pain sensation. We refer to somatosensory activity which does not convey nociceptive information; this does not exclude any other functional significance of such activity.

A

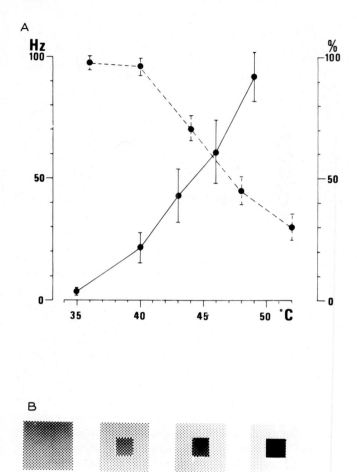

B

Figure 10. Complementary action of excitatory and inhibitory events in the encoding of noxious stimuli by convergent neurons. In A, solid line, left ordinate (n = 14) shows the relationship between radiant heat applied to their excitatory receptive fields located on the ipsilateral hindpaw extremity and mean firing rate. Dotted line, right ordinate (n = 20) shows the inhibitory effects induced by the application of various temperatures to the tail upon neuronal responses to C fiber inputs elicited by the electrical stimulation of their excitatory receptive fields located on the ipsilateral hindpaw extremity. Results are expressed as the mean of the percentage of pre-conditioning values calculated for each individual unit. B, hypothetical interpretation of experiments illustrated in A. In the absence of noxious stimuli, the global activity of both spinal and trigeminal convergent neurons of a freely moving animal would be of a reasonably high order, sending a kind of "noise" towards the brain (left square). The application of increasing noxious (thermal) stimuli on a restricted somatic area would result in an increase of the activity of the corresponding segmental pool of neurons and in a DNIC-mediated progressive decrease of the "noise" due to the random activity of the remaining convergent neuronal population (from left to right). Thus the complementary action of both excitatory and inhibitory events would produce a contrasted picture sent to the brain.

Giesler, G.J., Jr., Gerhart, K.D., Yezierski, R.P., Wilcox, T.K. and Willis, W.D. (1981) Postsynaptic inhibition of primate spinothalamic neurons by stimulation in nucleus raphé magnus, *Brain Res.*, 204: 184-188.

Goldstein, A. (1979) Endorphins and pain: a critical review. In R.F. Beers, Jr. and E.G. Bassett (Eds.), *Mechanisms of Pain and Analgesic Compounds*, Raven Press, New York, pp. 249-262.

Griersmith, B.T., Duggan, A.W. and North R.A. (1981) Methysergide and supraspinal inhibition of the spinal transmission of nociceptive information in the anaesthetized cat, *Brain Res.*, 204: 147-158.

Guilbaud, G., Besson, J.M., Oliveras, J.L. and Liebeskind, J.C. (1973) Suppression by LSD of the inhibitory effects exerted by dorsal raphé stimulation on certain spinal cord interneurons in the cat, *Brain Res.*, 61: 417-422.

Gybels, J., Handwerker, H.O. and Van Hees, J. (1979) A comparison between the discharges of human nociceptive nerve fibres and the subject's rating of his sensations, *J. Physiol. (Lond.)*, 292: 193-206.

Hardy, J.D., Wolff, H.G. and Goodell, H. (1940) Studies on pain. A new method for measuring pain threshold: observations on spatial summation of pain, *J. clin. Invest.*, 19: 649-657.

Hardy, J.D., Goodell, H. and Wolff, H.G. (1951) The influence of skin temperature upon the pain threshold as evoked by thermal radiation, *Science*, 114: 149-150.

Hayes, R.L., Bennett, G.J., Newton, P.G. and Mayer, D.J. (1978) Behavioral and physiological studies of non-narcotic analgesia in the rat elicited by certain environmental stimuli, *Brain Res.*, 155: 69-90.

Hazouri, L.A. and Mueller, A.D. (1950) Pain threshold studies on paraplegic patients, *Arch. Neurol. Psychiat.*, 64: 607-613.

Hökfelt, T., Ljungdahl, A., Terenius, L., Elde, R. and Nilsson, G. (1977), Immunohistochemical analysis of peptide pathways possibly related to pain and analgesia: enkephalin and substance P, *Proc nat. Acad. Sci. U.S.A.*, 74: 3081-3085.

Iggo, A. (1974) Activation of cutaneous nociceptors and their actions on dorsal horn neurons. In *Advances in Neurology, Vol. 4, Pain*, Raven Press, New York, pp. 1-9.

Iggo, A. and Ogawa, H. (1971) Primate cutaneous thermal nociceptors, *J. Physiol. (Lond.)*, 216: 77-78.

Jiang, Z., Ye, Q., Shen, Y., Zhu, F., Tang, S., Liang, N. and Zeng, X. (1978) Effects of naloxone on experimental acupuncture analgesia evaluated by sensory decision theory, *Acta zool. sin.*, 14: 1-10.

Jordan, L.M., Kenshalo, D.R., Martin, R.F., Haber, L.H. and Willis, W.D. (1979) Two populations of spinothalamic tract neurons with opposite responses to 5-hydroxytryptamine, *Brain Res.*, 164: 342-346.

Komisaruk, B.R. and Wallman, J. (1977) Antinociceptive effects of vaginal stimulation in rats: neurophysiological and behavioural studies, *Brain Res.*, 137: 85-107.

Kraus, E., Le Bars, D. and Besson, J.M. (1981) Behavioral confirmation of "Diffuse Noxious Inhibitory Controls" (DNIC) and evidence for a role of endogenous opiates, *Brain Res.*, 206: 495-499.

Kraus, E., Besson, J.M. and Le Bars, D. (1982) Behavioural model for Diffuse Noxious Inhibitory Controls (DNIC): potentiation by 5-hydroxytryptophan, *Brain Res.*, in press.

Kumazawa, T. and Perl, E.R. (1977) Primate cutaneous sensory units with unmyelinated (C) afferent fibers, *J. Neurophysiol.*, 40: 1325-1339.

Lamotte, R.H. and Campbell, J.N. (1978) Comparison of responses of warm and nociceptive C-fiber afferents in monkey with human judgments of thermal pain, *J. Neurophysiol.*, 41: 509-528.

Le Bars, D., Dickenson, A.H. and Besson, J.M. (1979a) Diffuse Noxious Inhibitory Controls (DNIC) – I. Effects on dorsal horn convergent neurones in the rat, *Pain*, 6: 283-304.

Le Bars, D., Dickenson, A.H. and Besson, J.M. (1979b) Diffuse Noxious Inhibitory Controls (DNIC) – Lack of effect on non-convergent neurones, supraspinal involvement and theoretical implications, *Pain*, 6: 305-327.

408

Le Bars, D., Rivot, J.P., Dickenson, A.H., Chaouch, A. et Besson, J.M. (1980) Rôle de la sérotonine dans les contrôles inhibiteurs diffus induits par des stimulations nociceptives, *C.R. Acad. Sci. (Paris)*, 290: 379-382.

Le Bars, D., Chitour, D., Kraus, E., Clot, A.M., Dickenson, A.H. and Besson, J.M. (1981a) The effect of systemic morphine upon Diffuse Noxious Inhibitory Controls (DNIC) in the rat: evidence for a lifting of certain descending inhibitory controls of dorsal horn convergent neurons, *Brain Res.*, 215: 257-274.

Le Bars, D., Chitour, D., Kraus, E., Dickenson, A.H. and Besson, J.M. (1981b) Effect of naloxone upon Diffuse Noxious Inhibitory Controls (DNIC) in the rat, *Brain Res.*, 204: 387-402.

Le Bars, D., Dickenson, A.H., Rivot, J.P., Chitour, D., Chaouch, A., Kraus, E. and Besson, J.M. (1981c) Les systèmes sérotoninergiques bulbospinaux jouent-ils un rôle dans la détection des messages nociceptifs? *J. Physiol. (Paris)*, 77: 463-471.

Le Bars, D., Chitour, D. and Clot, A.M. (1982a) The encoding of thermal stimuli by Diffuse Noxious Inhibitory Controls (DNIC), *Brain Res.*, in press.

Le Bars, D., Dickenson, A.H. and Besson, J.M. (1982b) Opiate analgesia and descending control systems. In J.J. Bonica et al. (Eds.), *Advances in Pain Research and Therapy, Vol. 5*, Raven Press, New York, in press.

Levine, J.D., Gormley, J. and Fields, H.L. (1976) Observations on the analgesic effects of needle puncture (acupuncture), *Pain*, 2: 149-159.

Lewis, J.W., Cannon, J.T. and Liebeskind, J.C. (1980) Opioid and non opioid mechanisms of stress analgesia, *Science*, 208: 623-625.

Liebeskind, J.C., Giesler, G., Jr. and Urca, G. (1976) Evidence pertaining to an endogenous mechanism of pain inhibition in the central nervous system. In Y. Zotterman (Ed.), *Sensory Functions of the Skin*, Pergamon Press, Oxford, pp. 561-573.

Lim, R.K.S., Miller, D.G., Guzman, F., Rodgers, D.W., Rodgers, R.W., Wang, S.K., Chao, P.Y. and Shih, T.Y. (1967) Pain and analgesia evaluated by the intraperitoneal bradykinin evoked pain method in man, *Clin. Pharmacol. Ther.*, 8: 521-542.

Lovick, T.A., West, D.C. and Wolstencroft, J.H. (1978) A presynaptic action of the raphé on tooth pulp fibre terminals: is this mediated by an opioid peptide? In J.M. Van Ree and L. Terenius (Ed.), *Characteristics and Functions of Opioids*, Elsevier/North-Holland, Amsterdam, pp. 175-177.

McCreery, D. and Bloedel, J.R. (1976) Effect of trigeminal stimulation on the excitability of cat spinothalamic neurons, *Brain Res.*, 117: 136-140.

Magnusson, T. (1973) Effect of chronic transection on dopamine, noradrenaline and 5-hydroxytryptamine in the rat spinal cord. *Naunyn-Schmiedeberg's Arch. Pharmacol.*, 278: 13-22.

Mann, F. (1974) Acupuncture analgesia, report of 100 experiments, *Brit. J. Anaesth.*, 46: 361-364.

Martin, R.F., Haber, L.H. and Willis, W.D. (1979) Primary afferent depolarization of identified cutaneous fibers following stimulation in medial brain stem, *J. Neurophysiol.*, 42: 779-790.

Mayer, D.J. (1979) Endogenous analgesia systems: neuronal and behavioral mechanisms. In J.J. Bonica, J.C. Liebeskind and D. Albe-Fessard (Eds.), *Advances in Pain Research and Therapy, Vol. 2*, Raven Press, New York, pp. 385-410.

Mayer, D.J. and Price, D.D. (1976) Central nervous system mechanisms of analgesia, *Pain*, 2: 379-404.

Mayer, D.D., Price, D.D. and Rafii, A. (1977) Antagonism of acupuncture analgesia by the narcotic antagonist naloxone, *Brain Res.*, 121: 368-372.

Melzack, R. (1971) Phantom limb pain: implications for treatment on pathologic pain, *Anesthesiology*, 35: 409-419.

Melzack, R. (1975) Prolonged relief of pain by brief, intense transcutaneous somatic stimulation, *Pain*, 1: 357-373.

Melzack, R. and Wall, P.D. (1965) Pain mechanism: a new theory, *Science*, 150: 971-979.

Melzack, R., Stillwell, D.M. and Fox, E.J. (1977) Trigger points and acupuncture points for pain: correlations and implications, *Pain*, 3: 3-24.

Mendell, L.M. (1966) Physiological properties of unmyelinated fibers projections to the spinal cord, *Exp. Neurol.*, 16: 316-332.

Menétrey, D., Giesler, G.J., Jr. and Besson, J.M. (1977) An analysis of responses properties of spinal cord dorsal horn neurones to non noxious and noxious stimuli in the spinal rat, *Exp. Brain Res.*, 27: 15-33.

Merskey, H. and Evans, P.R. (1975) Variations in pain complaint threshold in psychiatric and neurological patients with pain, *Pain*, 1: 73-79.

Mokha, S.S., McMillan, J.A. and Iggo, A. (1981) Descending influences on spinal nociceptive neurons from locus coeruleus, *Pain*, Suppl. 1: S103.

Oliveras, J.L., Bourgoin, S., Hery, F., Besson, J.M. and Hamon, M. (1977) The topographical distribution of serotonergic terminals in the spinal cord of the cat: biomedical mapping by the combined use of microdissection and microassay procedures, *Brain Res.*, 138: 393-406.

Parsons, C.M. and Goetzl, F.R. (1945) Effect of induced pain on pain threshold, *Proc. Soc. exp. Biol. Med.*, 60: 327-329.

Price, D.D. and Dubner, R. (1977) Neurons that subserve the sensory-discriminative aspects of pain, *Pain*, 3: 307-338.

Price, D.D., Hull, C.D. and Buchwald, N.A. (1971) Intracellular responses of dorsal horn cells to cutaneous and sural nerve A and C fiber stimuli, *Exp. Neurol.*, 33: 291-309.

Proudfit, H.K. and Anderson, E.G. (1974) New long latency bulbospinal evoked potentials blocked by serotonin antagonists, *Brain Res.*, 65: 542-546.

Rivot, J.P., Chaouch, A. and Besson, J.M. (1979) The influence of naloxone on the C fiber response or dorsal horn neurons and their inhibitory control by raphé magnus stimulation, *Brain Res.*, 176: 355-364.

Rivot, J.P., Chaouch, A. and Besson, J.M. (1980) Nucleus raphé magnus modulation response of rat dorsal horn neurons to unmyelinated fibers input: partial involvement of serotonergic pathways, *J. Neurophysiol.*, 44: 1039-1057.

Ruda, M.A. and Gobel, S. (1980) Ultrastructural characterization of axonal endings in the substantia gelatinosa which take up [^{3}]serotonin, *Brain Res.*, 184: 57-83.

Ruda, M.A., Allen, B. and Gobel, S. (1981) Ultrastructural analysis of medial brain stem afferents to the superficial dorsal horn, *Brain Res.*, 205: 175-180.

Sar, M., Stumpf, W.E., Miller, R.J., Chang, K.J. and Cuatrecasas, P. (1978) Immunohistochemical localization of enkephalin in rat brain and spinal cord, *J. comp. Neurol.*, 182: 17-38.

Shen, E., Tsai, T.T. and Lan, C. (1975) Supraspinal participation in the inhibitory effect of acupuncture on viscero-somatic reflex discharges, *Chin. med. J.*, 1: 431-440.

Shimizu, T., Koja, T., Fujisaki, T., and Fukuda, T. (1981) Effects of methysergide and naloxone on analgesia induced by the peripheral electric stimulation in mice, *Brain Res.*, 208: 463-467.

Simantov, R., Kuhar, M.J., Uhl, G. and Snyder, S.H. (1977) Opioid peptide enkephalin: immunohistochemical mapping in rat central nervous system, *Proc. nat. Acad. Sci. U.S.A.*, 74: 2167-2171.

Sjölund, B.H. and Eriksson, M.B.F. (1979) The influence of naloxone on analgesia produced by peripheral conditioning stimulation, *Brain Res.*, 173: 295-301.

Stanton, E.S., Smolen, P.M., Nashold, B.S., Jr., Dreyer, D.A. and Davis, J.N. (1975) Segmental analysis of spinal cord monoamines after thoracic transection in the dog, *Brain Res.*, 89: 93-98.

Tyce, M.G. and Yaksh, T. (1981) Monoamine release from cat spinal cord by somatic stimuli: an intrinsic modulatory system, *J. Physiol. (Lond.)*, 314: 513-529.

Wagman, I.H. and Price, D.D. (1969) Responses of dorsal horn cells of *M. mulatta* to cutaneous and sural nerve A- and C-fiber stimulation, *J. Neurophysiol.*, 32: 803-817.

Wall, P.D. (1967) The laminar organization of dorsal horn cells and effects of descending impulses, *J. Physiol. (Lond.)*, 188: 403-423.

Watkins, L.R., Cobelli, D.A. and Mayer, D.J. (1981) Footshock induced analgesia (FSIA) and classical conditioned analgesia (CCA): differential activation of opiate and non-opiate systems, *Pain*, Suppl. 1: 318.

Weil-Fugazza, J., Godefroy, F., Chitour, D. and Le Bars, D. (1981) Synthèse de la sérontonine au niveau spinal chez le rat: modifications induites par stimulation somatique nociceptive associée ou non à l'administration de morphine, *C.R. Acad. Sci. (Paris)*, 293: 89-92.

Willer, J.C. and Albe-Fessard, D. (1980) Electrophysiological evidence for a release of endogenous opiates in stress-induced analgesia in man, *Brain Res.*, 198: 419-426.

Willer, J.C., Dehen H. and Cambier, J. (1981) Stress-induced analgesia in humans: endogenous opioids and naloxone-reversible depression of pain reflexes, *Science*, 212: 689-691.

Willis, W.D. and Coggeshall, R.E. (1978) *Sensory Mechanisms of the Spinal Cord*, Plenum Press, New York.

Young, W.S. and Kuhar, M.J. (1980) Serotonin receptor localization in rat brain by light microscopic autoradiography, *Europ. J. Pharmacol.*, 62: 237-239.

Zieglgänsberger, W. and Puil, E.A. (1973) Actions of glutamic acid on spinal neurones, *Exp. Brain Res.*, 17: 35-49.

Zimmermann, M. (1976) Neurophysiology of nociception. In R. Porter (Ed.), *International Review of Physiology, Neurophysiology II, Vol. 10*, University Park Press, Baltimore, MD, pp. 179-221.

Zimmermann, M. (1977) Encoding in dorsal horn interneurons receiving noxious and non noxious afferents, *J. Physiol. (Paris)*, 73: 221-240.

Brain Stem Control of Spinal Mechanisms
– B. Sjölund and A. Björklund, editors
© 1982 Elsevier Biomedical Press

18

Mechanisms of Medial Brain Stem Stimulation-Induced Inhibition in Spinothalamic Neurons

W.D. WILLIS

Marine Biomedical Institute, Departments of Anatomy and of Physiology and Biophysics, University of Texas Medical Branch, Galveston, Texas 77550-2772, U.S.A.

I. Introduction

There has been considerable interest in the descending control of spinal cord transmission of nociceptive information by pathways originating in the brain stem. In addition to the inherent interest of the topic of centrifugal control of sensory mechanisms, there is also the possibility that an increase in our understanding of such control systems may help explain current therapy or suggest ways to improve therapy for pain.

Many of the experimental studies concerned with the descending control pathways have utilized flexion reflexes or the responses of interneurons to assay the inhibitory actions of these pathways at a spinal cord level. Insofar as the flexion reflex reflects pain sensation (cf. Willer, 1977), this is a reasonable approach. However, it appears that there may be at least partially separate descending control systems for flexion reflexes and for pain sensation, since these can be altered independently in human subjects under certain circumstances (McGrath et al., 1981; Willer et al., 1979). For this reason, we believe that it is important to examine the descending control of sensory pathways that are likely to be involved in the transmission of nociceptive information to the brain. One pathway believed to play a crucial role in pain sensation, at least in humans and in subhuman primates, is the spinothalamic tract (Foerster and Gagel, 1932; Vierck and Luck, 1979; White and Sweet, 1955).

Our laboratory has been engaged in a systematic investigation of the primate spinothalamic tract. We identify the cells of origin of this pathway in the monkey (*Macaca fascicularis*) spinal cord by antidromic activation from the thalamus (Trevino et al., 1973). Usually, we study cells that project to the contralateral ventral posterior lateral nucleus, although we have also begun to study those that project to the intralaminar complex (Giesler et al., 1981b).

The recordings are generally made in the lumbosacral enlargement, although in some cases we have studied spinothalamic tract (STT) cells in the thoracic or sacral spinal cord. The animals are anesthetized (α-chloralose and supplemental pentobarbital) so that the neuraxis can be kept intact, allowing antidromic identification. Although the anesthesia may depress responses somewhat, the fact that we observe graded responses to graded noxious stimuli indicates that these cells can code nociceptive signals despite the presence of the anesthetic (Chung et al., 1979; Foreman et al., 1979; Kenshalo et al., 1979; Milne et al., 1981; Willis et al., 1975). Descending control systems are activated by electrical stimulation within the brain at various sites known from behavioral studies to reduce the flexion reflex responses to noxious stimuli or from clinical studies to counteract pain in humans.

II. Inhibition of Spinothalamic Tract Cells by Stimulation in Nucleus Raphe Magnus

II.1. Anatomical studies

A brain stem nucleus that is believed to play an important role in the descending control of nociceptive transmission in the spinal cord is the nucleus raphe magnus (NRM). Stimulation in the NRM causes "analgesia" in behavioral tests using the flexion reflex (Oliveras et al., 1975, 1977, 1978, 1979). Furthermore, stimulation in the NRM causes inhibition of the nociceptive responses of dorsal horn interneurons by way of a pathway that descends in the dorsal part of the lateral funiculus (Fields et al., 1977). These recent observations are consistent with earlier work by Lundberg and his associates and others on the pathways descending from the medial brain stem that produce inhibition of the flexion reflex pathways (Eccles and Lundberg, 1959; Engberg et al., 1978a, b, c, d; Holmqvist and Lundberg, 1959, 1961; Job, 1953; Sherrington and Sowton, 1915).

The NRM is one of several medullary raphe nuclei. The others include the raphe pallidus and obscurus nuclei (Taber et al., 1960). Figure 1A shows the disposition of these nuclei in the medulla of a cat. The cells of the medullary raphe that project to the spinal cord were labeled retrogradely by horseradish peroxidase injected into the spinal cord at the L6 segmental level (Martin et al., 1978). The dots represent individual labeled cells that were observed in three sagittal histologic sections separated by 50 μm on each side of the midline and plotted on a drawing of a sagittal section taken near the midline. The raphe obscurus nucleus is seen dorsally, and projects caudally from a dense population of neurons in the mid-medulla; the raphe pallidus nucleus is a narrow band of neurons ventral to the raphe obscurus nucleus; and the NRM extends rostrally into the pons.

A similar technique was used to demonstrate the nuclei of the medullary raphe in the monkey, as shown in Figure 1C. Here, the raphespinal cells labeled retrogradely by horseradish peroxidase injected into the lumbar enlargement are plotted on three drawings of sagittal sections taken at the midline (center) and on either side of the midline (above and below). Labeled cells are concentrated in areas corresponding to the NRM and the nucleus raphe obscurus of the cat, but there does not seem to be a prominent raphe pallidus nucleus in the monkey. The raphe pallidus nucleus may be represented by the most ventrally placed cells, but there is no extension of this cell group caudally into the lower medulla.

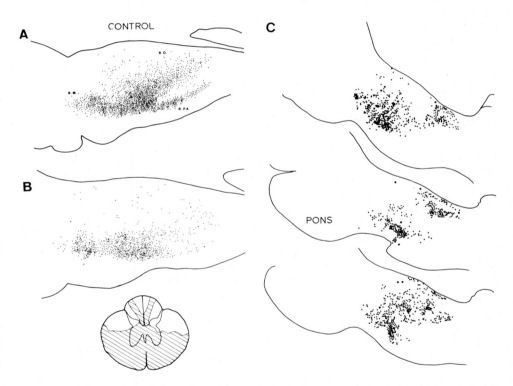

Figure 1. Cells of origin of the raphe-spinal tracts. In A, the neurons of medullary raphe nuclei in the cat that were labeled retrogradely by horseradish peroxidase (HRP) injected into the L6 spinal segment are plotted on a drawing of a sagittal section at the midline of the lower brain stem. The nuclei containing labeled cells include the raphe magnus (R.M.), raphe obscurus (R.O.) and raphe pallidus (R.PA.). All of the labeled cells on three 50 μm alternate sections on either side of the midline are included. In B, the raphe neurons that are labeled following a similar injection of HRP, but after interruption of the ventral half of the cord at T13–L1; the drawing of the cord section shows the extent of the lesion. (A and B are from Martin et al., 1978, with permission.) In C, the distribution of labeled cells in the medullary raphe nuclei of the monkey following an HRP injection into the lumbar enlargement. (From unpublished data of Martin and Willis.)

414

Raphe neurons that project into the spinal cord through the dorsal part of the lateral funiculus have been identified by anterograde or retrograde labeling by several groups (Basbaum et al., 1978; Basbaum and Fields, 1979; Martin et al., 1978; Tohyama et al., 1979a, b; Watkins et al., 1980). In the cat, we have demonstrated these cells by first sectioning the ventral pathways of the cord and then injecting horseradish peroxidase below the level of the lesion (Martin et al., 1978). The labeled cells are located chiefly in the NRM (Fig. 1B).

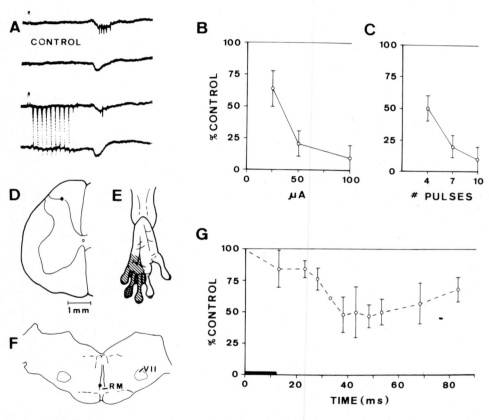

Figure 2. Inhibition of a high threshold STT cell by stimulation in NRM. In A, two pairs of records. The upper trace in each set is an extracellular recording of the burst discharge of an STT cell in response to electrical stimulation of the skin. The lower trace is the cord dorsum potential. The bottom set of records shows the inhibitory effect of stimulation of the NRM. B, the relationship between the amount of inhibition (the number of spikes is expressed as a percentage of control) produced by stimulation of the NRM with different intensities. C, the relationship between the amount of inhibition and the number of stimulus pulses. The location of the cell is shown in D, of the receptive field in E, and of the stimulus site in F. The time course of the inhibition is plotted in G. (From Willis et al., 1977, with permission.)

II.2. Physiological studies

Stimulation in the NRM of the monkey produces a powerful inhibition of STT cells (Beall et al., 1976; Gerhart et al., 1981; Willis et al., 1977; Yezierski et al., 1982). This inhibition can be shown either by testing with the responses of STT cells to electrical stimulation or to natural stimulation of the receptive field. A similar inhibition has been demonstrated for STT cells in the cat (McCreery and Bloedel, 1975; McCreery et al., 1979).

Inhibition of responses to electrical stimulation of afferent fibers. Figure 2A (top) shows the burst discharge of an STT cell in response to electrical stimulation of the skin in the cell's receptive field (Willis et al., 1977). Stimulation in the NRM using a brief train of shocks (10 pulses, 50 µA, 0.1 msec, 333 Hz) inhibited the response (bottom). The dependence of the inhibition upon stimulus strength (using the same number of stimulus pulses and the same conditioning–testing interval as in Fig. 2A) is shown by the graph in Figure 2B; the threshold for inhibition was less than 25 µA. The relationship between the number of stimulus pulses and the amount of inhibition is shown in Figure 2C (stimulus intensity fixed at 100 µA); evidently, temporal summation is important in the inhibitory pathway. The time course of the inhibition is shown in Figure 2G. The inhibition began within 13 msec of the start of the stimulus train, indicating that the fastest axons in the inhibitory pathway are myelinated. The location of the neuron was reconstructed to be in or near lamina I (Fig. 2D). The receptive field of the cell is shown in Figure 2E and the location of the stimulus site in the NRM in Figure 2F. The STT cell was classified as a high threshold cell, because it was excited by strong mechanical stimuli but not by gentle mechanical stimuli applied within the receptive field.

STT cells are often excited both by weak and by strong mechanical stimuli (Chung et al., 1979; Willis et al., 1974). Such cells are termed "wide dynamic range" cells (Mendell, 1966). When electrical shocks are applied to a nerve supplying the cutaneous receptive field, wide dynamic range STT cells can be activated by several different afferent fiber groups, including Aαβ, Aδ and C fibers (Beall et al., 1977; Chung et al., 1979; Foreman et al., 1975). We have found that stimulation in the NRM preferentially inhibits the responses of STT cells to Aδ and C fibers. Figure 3 illustrates a case of a preferential inhibition of the excitation of an STT cell by Aδ fibers, as contrasted with the response to Aαβ fibers. The records in Figure 3A–D show the responses of a wide dynamic range STT cell (upper two traces in each set of records on fast and slow sweeps) and the cord dorsum potentials (lower trace) evoked by stimulation of the sural nerve at a strength sufficient to activate most of the myelinated afferent fibers. The control record in Figure 3A shows that the cell responded with two separate burst discharges to the afferent volley. The early burst has been shown in previous work to be due to the Aαβ fibers and the second burst to the Aδ fibers (Beall et al., 1977). When the NRM was stimulated before the sural nerve at the conditioning–testing intervals indicated (NRM stimulus parameters: 7

pulses, 200 µA, 333 Hz), both responses of the STT cell were inhibited (Fig. 3B–D). However, the response to the Aδ volley was inhibited to a greater degree than was the response to the Aαβ volley. The time course of the inhibition of the early and late burst discharges is shown in Figure 3E. The site of stimulation is shown in Figure 3F.

Similarly, the responses of STT cells to C fiber volleys are inhibited to a greater extent than are the responses to A fiber volleys (Gerhart et al., 1981). For example, in Figure 4A and C, the responses of a wide dynamic range STT cell to single afferent volleys in the A fibers or the A plus C fibers of the sural nerve are shown. The C fiber compound action potential was monitored by re-

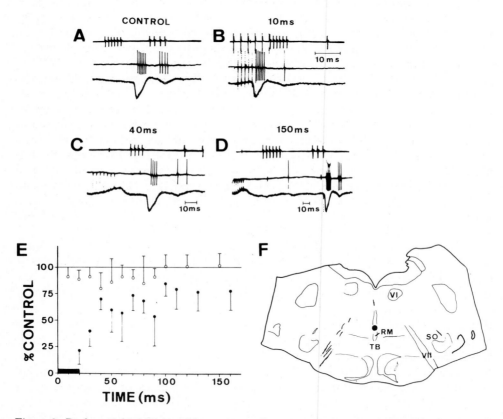

Figure 3. Preferential inhibition of the response of a wide dynamic range STT cell to a volley in A fibers. The records in A–D include recordings of the early and late burst discharges of an STT cell due to Aαβ and Aδ fibers, respectively, at a fast (upper) and slower (middle) sweep, along with the cord dorsum potentials (lower) record. The afferent volleys were evoked by electrical stimulation of the sural nerve. The NRM was stimulated in B–D before the sural nerve at the conditioning–test intervals indicated. A plot of the time course of the inhibition of the early (open circles) and late (filled circles) discharges is shown in E. The location of the stimulus point is in F. (From Willis et al., 1977, with permission.)

cording from a region of the sural nerve proximal to the stimulating electrodes and is shown in the inset in Figure 4C. When the NRM was stimulated (500 msec trains; 150 μA, 333 Hz) at the location indicated in Figure 4E, the responses to both the A and the C fiber volleys were inhibited, as shown in Figure 4B and D. The response to the A fiber volley was not inhibited as pro-

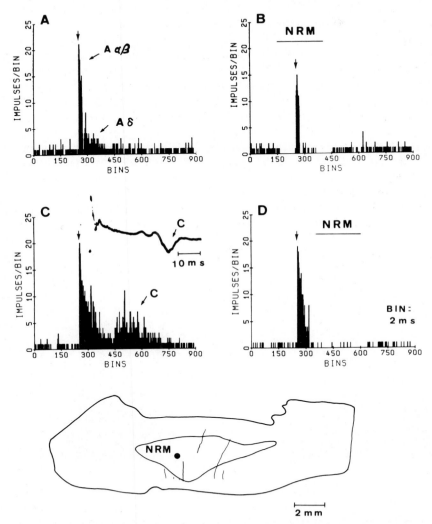

Figure 4. Preferential inhibition of the response of a wide dynamic range STT cell to a volley in C fibers. The poststimulus–time histogram in A shows the response of an STT cell to stimulation of the A fibers in the sural nerve, while that in C shows the response to the A and C fibers. The C fiber compound action potential is shown in the inset. B and D, the inhibitory effect of stimulation in the NRM on the responses to A and C fibers, respectively. The stimulus location is in E. (From Gerhart et al., 1981, with permission.)

418

foundly as that to the C fiber volley. It should be noted that much of the inhibition of the response to the A fiber volley can be attributed to a selective inhibition of the response to the Aδ component.

The inhibition of STT cells by stimulation within the NRM using brief stimulus trains is blocked when the dorsal parts of the lateral funiculi are sectioned (Willis et al., 1977). This observation suggests that the inhibition depends upon axons descending within the dorsolateral funiculi.

Inhibition of responses to natural stimulation of receptive field. Stimulation in the NRM produces a powerful inhibition not only of the responses of STT cells to afferent volleys evoked by electrical stimulation of peripheral nerves, but also of activity elicited by more natural forms of stimulation of the cutaneous receptive fields of these neurons (Gerhart et al., 1981; Willis et al., 1977; Yezierski et al., 1982). For example, in Figure 5A are shown the responses of a wide dynamic range STT cell to brushing and to pinching the skin. The cell also had a substantial background discharge. At the times indicated by the dots, a train of stimuli (2 sec train, 100 μA, 333 Hz) was delivered within the NRM. The background discharges and the responses to innocuous and noxious mechanical stimuli were all inhibited nearly to baseline by each stimulus train. In Figure 5B, another STT cell with very little background discharge is shown to respond to a noxious heat pulse lasting 120 sec (skin temperature

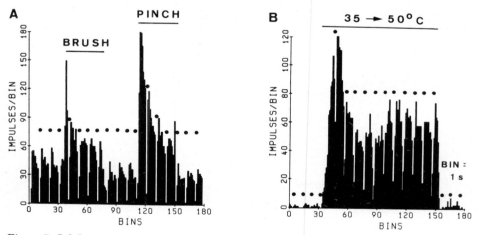

Figure 5. Inhibition of the responses of STT cells to natural forms of cutaneous stimulation. The activity of the cells is shown by single-pass peristimulus histograms. The cell in A had a substantial background discharge, and its activity was increased by brushing or by pinching the receptive field at the times indicated by the horizontal bars. The NRM was stimulated repetitively for 2 sec every 10 sec; the times of NRM stimulation are indicated by the dots. For B, records were made from another STT cell that had only a low level of background activity. The cell responded vigorously when the skin temperature was raised from 35 to 50°C during the time indicated by the horizontal bar. Again, the NRM was stimulated every 10 sec. (From Gerhart et al., 1981, with permission.)

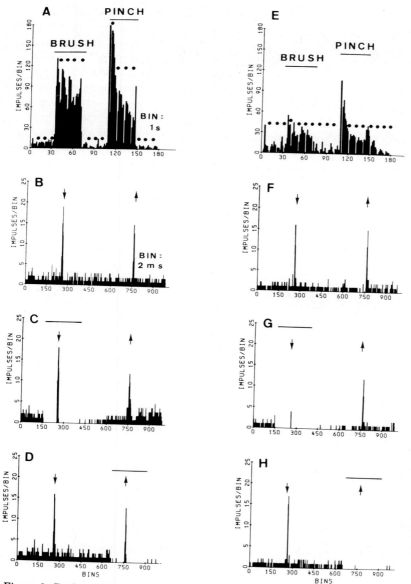

Figure 6. Preferential inhibition of the response to noxious stimulation by NRM stimulation. The activity of one STT cell is shown in A–D and of another STT cell in E–H. The single pass post-stimulus–time histograms in A and E show the effects of stimulating the NRM every 10 sec on the background activity, and the responses of these cells to brushing and pinching the receptive field on the skin. In B and F are the responses of the two cells to innocuous indentation of the skin during the time between the arrows. The poststimulus–time histograms represent the sum of the activity for 10 trials. In C–D and G–H, the effects of NRM stimulation on the transient responses of the cells are shown. (From Gerhart et al., 1981, with permission.)

420

raised from 35 to 50°C). Again, at the times indicated by the dots, stimulation in the NRM (same stimulus parameters as in A) caused a potent inhibition.

Despite the selectivity of NRM inhibition of the responses of STT cells to afferent volleys in fine afferent fibers when electrical stimulation of peripheral nerves was used, the NRM inhibition was only rarely selective in inhibiting responses to innocuous versus noxious stimulation of the receptive field. This observation was true for 34 of 38 STT cells in which this issue was tested (e.g. the cell in Fig. 5A). However, occasionally STT cells are found that show a preferential inhibition of the response to noxious stimulation. For example, Figure 6 shows the responses of two different STT cells recorded in a single experiment. The cell whose responses are seen in Figure 6A–D showed a differen-

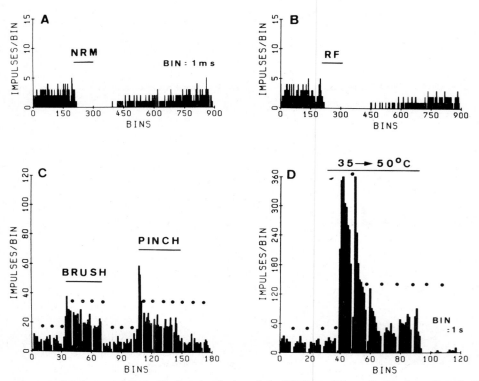

Figure 7. Inhibition of STT cells by stimulation of the NRM or of the reticular formation. In the poststimulus–time histograms in A and B, the activity of an STT cell was summed over 10 trials. The discharge rate of the cell was enhanced by pinching the skin in the receptive field. The periods during which the NRM or the reticular formation were stimulated are indicated by the horizontal bars. C and D, single pass peristimulus–time histograms showing the responses of two different STT cells to brushing, pinching and noxious heating of the skin. The reticular formation was stimulated every 10 sec at the times indicated by the dots. (From Gerhart et al., 1981, with permission.)

tial inhibition, while the cell illustrated in Figure 6E–H did not. In Figure 6A, stimulus trains were delivered at a point in the NRM at the times indicated by the dots (2 sec trains, 200 μA, 0.1 msec pulses, 333 Hz). The response to brushing was only slightly affected by the NRM stimulation, whereas the response to pinching the skin was powerfully inhibited. In Figure 6B–D, the skin was indented in an innocuous fashion, using a servo controlled mechanical stimulator. The control record in Figure 6B shows that the indentation (0.5 mm from a static indentation of 0.5 mm; 1 sec indentation repeated at 5 sec intervals) caused a rapidly adapting response at the onset (downward arrow) and at the termination (upward arrow) of the stimulus. In Figure 6C and D, the NRM was stimulated at the times indicated by the horizontal bars (500 msec trains, 150 μA, 0.1 msec pulses, 333 Hz). Although the NRM stimulation resulted in a reduction in the background discharges of the cell, there was little, if any, change in the responses to skin indentation. By contrast, stimulation in the NRM, using the same parameters, had quite a different effect on another cell examined in the same experiment. In Figure 6E, it is seen that NRM stimulation effectively inhibited the responses of this STT cell to brushing and to pinching, and Figure 6F–H show that NRM stimulation caused an inhibtion of the transient responses to indentation of the skin.

The time course of the inhibitory action of NRM stimulation is shown in Figure 7A. The period of stimulation is indicated by the horizontal bar (100 msec train, 150 μA, 0.1 msec, 333 Hz). The activity of the cell was enhanced by pinching the skin while the histogram was compiled. The activity of this STT cell was completely inhibited during, and for about 100 msec after, stimulation, and the activity did not return to baseline for another several hundred milliseconds.

II.3. Mechanism of nucleus raphe magnus inhibition

It is known that stimulation in the medial brain stem, including the NRM, can result in a depolarization of primary afferent terminals in the spinal cord (Carpenter et al., 1966; Proudfit and Anderson, 1974; Proudfit et al., 1980). In an effort to determine if there might be a preferential depolarization of the terminals of nociceptive afferent fibers, we examined changes in the excitability of single identified cutaneous myelinated afferents produced by stimulation in the NRM (Martin et al., 1979), using the excitability testing technique described by Wall (1958). The afferent fibers were impaled with a glass micropipette, and their receptive fields were mapped. The central processes of the afferent fibers were stimulated by an electrode placed within the dorsal horn. The stimulus strength was adjusted so that the afferent was discharged in only a few of several repeated trials. The number of times the afferent discharged in ten trials was defined as the "firing index". Then the NRM was stimulated to see if the descending volleys changed the firing index. As shown in Figure 8I, NRM stimulation in the cat at different stimulus intensities could produce a graded increase in the firing index of an Aδ nociceptor. However, comparable stimulation also resulted in increased firing indices in afferents supplying Aδ mechanoreceptors (presumably supplying down hairs) and Aαβ mechanoreceptors of various classes (Fig. 8II; Table I). Similar results were found in monkeys. Thus there does not seem to be a restriction of the ability of NRM stimulation to produce primary afferent depolarization to a particular class of afferent fiber. However, we cannot rule out quantitative differences. Others have found that NRM stimulation also affects the excitability of the central proces-

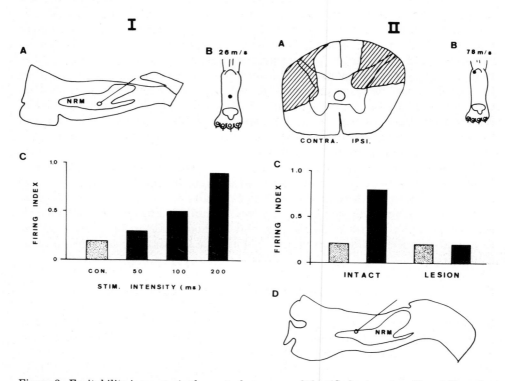

Figure 8. Excitability increases in the central processes of identified cutaneous afferent fibers due to stimulation in the NRM in the cat. In I, the effect of NRM stimulation on the excitability of the central process of an Aδ nociceptor is shown. The stimulus location in the NRM is shown in IA, and the location of the receptive field and the conduction velocity of the afferent in IB. Firing indices were determined from the ratio of successful to total attempts to backfire the afferent by an electrode placed in the dorsal horn. C, the control firing index (stippled bar), with the firing indices, when the NRM was stimulated 70 msec prior to the test stimulus (black bars). The NRM stimulus strength was varied from 50 to 200 μA (other parameters: 50 msec train, 333 Hz). In II, the NRM action is shown to be blocked following interruption of the dorsolateral funiculi. The lesions are drawn in IIA, and the receptive field location and conduction velocity of a hair follicle afferent are in IIB. The increase in firing index produced by NRM stimulation is shown at the left in IIC, and the ineffectiveness of the same stimulus after the lesions at the right in IIC. The NRM stimulus site is in IID. (From Martin et al., 1979, with permission.)

ses of C fibers (Hentall and Fields, 1979); however, in this case the excitability is reduced.

The increases in the firing indices of primary afferent fibers resulting from stimulation in the NRM depend upon axons descending in the dorsolateral funiculi, since these increases do not occur after lesions interrupting the dorsolateral funiculi (Fig. 8II).

Since it is known that stimulation in the medial brain stem can evoke inhibitory postsynaptic potentials (IPSPs) in dorsal horn interneurons (Engberg et al., 1968d), it is reasonable to suppose that a similar action may occur with respect to STT cells. We have recorded intracellularly from STT cells and have observed that NRM stimulation can indeed produce IPSPs (Fig. 9) in these cells (Giesler et al., 1981a). The STT cell was identified by antidromic activation, as shown in Figure 9A. There was a considerable background discharge soon after impalement (Fig. 9B), possibly due to membrane damage. Repetitive stimulation in the NRM silenced this background discharge (Fig. 9C; stimulus parameters: 100 msec train, 200 µA). The spike generating mechanism then failed, and the IPSP shown in Figure 9D could be seen at high amplifier gain

TABLE I

TYPES AND NUMBERS OF MYELINATED CUTANEOUS AFFERENTS OF SURAL NERVE

Statistically significant (two-tailed t-test) excitability increase produced by stimulation in or near the nucleus raphe magnus (NRM) or within the nucleus reticular gigantocellularis (NGc). PAD, primary afferent depolarization.

Afferent Type	PAD Following Stimulation of:			
	NRM		NGc	
	No.	%	No.	%
Aαβ				
Hair	27/32	84	4/4	100
Field	9/9	100	2/2	100
Slowly adapting				
Type I	5/5	100	1/1	100
Type II	1/1	100	1/1	100
Unclassified	4/4	100	2/2	100
Unidentified	55/60	92	9/9	100
Total	101/111	91	18/18	100
Aδ				
Hair	4/10	40		
Nociceptor	7/11	64	5/5	100
Unidentified	0/4		1/3	33
Total	11/25	44	6/8	75

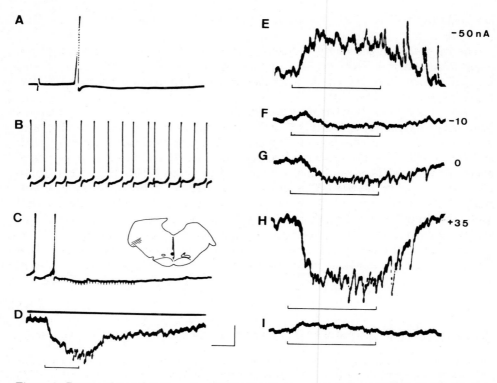

Figure 9. Postsynaptic inhibition of an STT cell following stimulation of NRM. The antidromic spike of an STT cell is seen in A. The background activity of the cell shortly after impalement is shown in B, and the inhibition of this activity by stimulation in the NRM is shown in C. After the spike generator failed, the hyperpolarization seen in D was recorded. The hyperpolarizing potential was shown to be an inhibitory postsynaptic potential by passing hyperpolarizing and depolarizing currents through the microelectrode (E–H). The extracellular field potential produced by NRM stimulation is in I. Calibrations at center under: 20 mV, 2 msec for A; 20 mV, 20 msec for B–C; 2 mV, 50 msec for D; 2 mV, 20 msec for E–I. (From Giesler et al., 1981a, with permission.)

when the NRM was stimulated (same parameters). The IPSP amplitude could be increased or the sign reversed when current was passed through the recording microelectrode in the appropriate direction (Fig. 9E–H). The anion in the electrode used in this experiment was acetate. In another experiment, the IPSP evoked in an STT cell by NRM stimulation was reversed after recording for some time with a KCl-filled microelectrode, and so we suppose that the IPSPs in STT cells may involve an increase in chloride conductance. However, more experiments are needed to demonstrate this conclusively.

These studies suggest that the mechanism of inhibition of STT cells following stimulation in the NRM may be complex, involving both pre- and postsynaptic events.

II.4. Pharmacological studies

The raphe nuclei are rich in serotonin-containing neurons (Dahlström and Fuxe, 1965), and it is thought that most, if not all, of the serotonin-containing axonal terminals in the spinal cord originate from the raphe nuclei and from serotonin-containing neurons in the reticular formation adjacent to the raphe nuclei (Bowker et al., 1981). Some serotonergic connections in the spinal cord are presumably also made by the recently discovered serotonin-containing neurons intrinsic to the spinal cord (Johns et al., 1981; Ritchie and Leonard, 1982). Drugs that affect serotonergic transmission are known to alter the inhibitory actions resulting from stimulation in the medial brain stem (Engberg et al., 1968a, b; Proudfit and Anderson, 1974; Proudfit et al., 1980; Rivot et al., 1980). For this reason, we have made an effort to see if serotonin might play a role in the inhibition of STT cells by NRM stimulation.

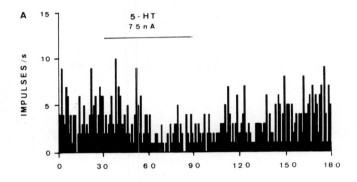

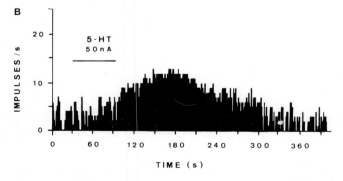

Figure 10. Depression or excitation of two different types of STT cells by iontophoretic application of serotonin. The single pass poststimulus–time histograms show the effect of serotonin released with the iontophoretic current strengths indicated during the times shown by the horizontal bars on the background activity of two different STT cells. The cell in A was classified as wide dynamic range, whereas that in B was classified as deep. (From Jordan et al., 1979, with permission.)

We found that the activity of nociceptive STT cells is depressed following iontophoretic release of serotonin in the vicinity of the cell body (Jordan et al., 1978, 1979). This is illustrated in Figure 10A. The cell was a wide dynamic range neuron, and the response to serotonin release outlasted the time of application (75 nA) by more than a minute. Serotonin sometimes excited STT cells, as in Figure 10B; however, cells that were excited generally had predominantly deep receptive fields and so presumably play a rather different sensory role than do the nociceptive STT cells. In iontophoresis experiments using extracellular recordings, it is difficult to know if the site of action of a drug is directly on the postsynaptic membrane. One way to test this is to activate the cell being studied by iontophoretic application of an excitatory amino acid, such as glutamate ions, which are thought to act selectively on receptors on the postsynaptic cell. When this is done, serotonin can be shown to interfere with

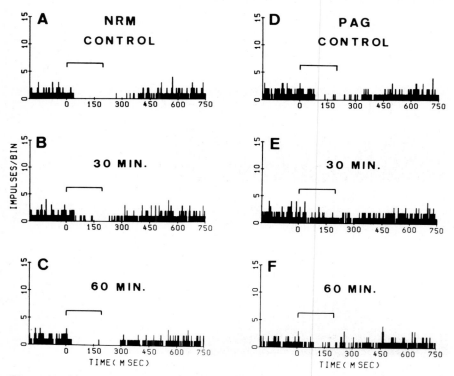

Figure 11. Antagonism of NRM and PAG inhibition of a high threshold STT cell by a serotonin receptor blocker. The peristimulus–time histograms represent the summed activity of ten trials. The discharge rate of the cell was enhanced by pinching the skin during each period of stimulation. The control levels of inhibition following stimulation in NRM or in the PAG are shown in A and D. Methysergide (2 mg/kg) was then administered intravenously. The NRM inhibition was partially, and the PAG inhibition substantially, blocked at 30 min after drug injection (B and E). There was some recovery by an hour after the drug (C and F). (From Yezierski et al., 1982, with permission.)

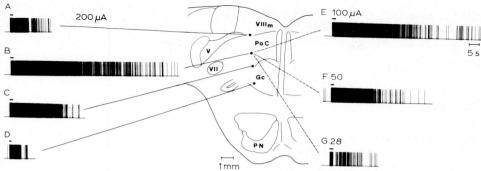

Figure 14. Excitation of an STT cell projecting to the intralaminar region of the thalamus by stimulation in the reticular formation of the pons. The window discriminator pulses in A–D show the excitatory effects of 2 sec stimulus trains applied at the points indicated along an electrode track through the pontine reticular formation. E–G, the effects of stimulation at the point indicated at progressively lower stimulus intensities. Abbreviations: PoC, nucleus reticularis pontis caudalis; Gc, nucleus reticularis gigantocellularis. (From Giesler et al., 1981b, with permission.)

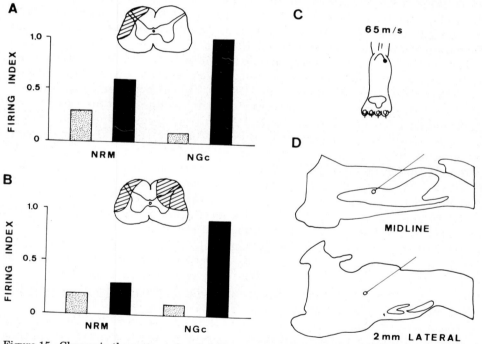

Figure 15. Change in the pattern of excitability changes produced by stimulation in the NRM and reticular formation in a primary afferent fiber following lesions of the dorsolateral funiculi. The central process of a hair follicle afferent was stimulated antidromically to test for excitability changes. The receptive field location and conduction velocity of the afferent are indicated in C. Changes in the firing index produced by stimulation in the NRM or the reticular formation after interruption of one dorsolateral funiculus are seen in A and, after both dorsolateral funiculi were interrupted, in B. The stimulus sites are shown in D. (From Martin et al., 1979, with permission.)

did not interfere with the action of reticular formation stimulation. We have not yet attempted to record intracellularly from STT cells during reticular formation stimulation to see if there is a postsynaptic inhibition in addition to a presynaptic action.

IV. Discussion

These experiments demonstrate that spinothalamic tract cells in the primate, like dorsal horn interneurons in several species, are subject to a powerful descending inhibitory control that can be triggered by stimulation in the medial part of the medulla. In our experience, stimulation in the NRM almost invariably produces an inhibition of STT cells projecting to the ventral posterior lateral nucleus of the thalamus (Beall et al., 1976; Gerhart et al., 1981; Willis et al., 1977; Yezierski et al., 1982). Similarly, stimulation in the medullary reticular formation generally results in inhibition of STT cells, although in some cases there is instead, or in addition, an excitation of these neurons (Gerhart et al., 1981; Haber et al., 1978, 1980). On the other hand, STT cells that project to the intralaminar region of the thalamus are excited by reticular formation stimulation (Giesler et al., 1981b).

The descending pathways responsible for the effects of NRM stimulation are in the dorsolateral funiculi and presumably correspond to Lundberg's dorsal reticulospinal system (Engberg et al., 1968b). This provides an important correlation with studies on the pathways mediating analgesia. It has been shown that analgesia from stimulation of the PAG or from systemic injections of morphine is eliminated following interruption of the dorsolateral funiculi (Basbaum et al., 1977). Similarly, lesions of the NRM reduce morphine analgesia (Proudfit and Anderson, 1975). There are projections from the PAG to the NRM and adjacent reticular formation (Abols and Basbaum, 1981; Gallagher and Pert, 1978; Ruda, 1975; Pierce et al., 1976; Shah and Dostrovsky, 1980), and stimulation in the PAG causes the excitation of neurons in the NRM (Behbehani and Fields, 1979; Behbehani and Pomeroy, 1978; Fields and Anderson, 1978; Lovick et al., 1978; Oleson et al., 1978) and reticular formation (Mohrland and Gebhart, 1980). These observations support the hypothesis proposed by Basbaum and Fields (1978) that analgesia produced by stimulation in the PAG depends upon a brain stem relay in the NRM and possibly the adjacent reticular formation.

However, our observations of an inhibition of many STT cells following stimulation in the reticular formation supports the suggestions of others that there are alternative pathways that may contribute to analgesia in addition to the raphe-spinal pathway. At least part of the inhibitory effect of stimulation in the reticular formation involves axons that descend in ventral pathways. Stimulation within the nucleus gigantocellularis does not produce analgesia; instead, such stimulation triggers aversive responses (Casey, 1971). It can be suggested that this may be in part due to the activation of some STT cells, including the component of the STT that projects to the intralaminar nuclei of the thalamus (Giesler et al., 1981b; Haber et al., 1978, 1980). In addition, of course, the ascending connections of the reticular formation would be anticipated to contribute to the aversive responses of such stimulation (Pompeiano, 1973).

We suspect that at least a part of the inhibitory action of the NRM on STT cells depends upon release of serotonin from raphe-spinal terminals in the dorsal horn. However, further evidence for this is needed. Of particular interest would be evidence from administration of receptor blockers specific for inhibitory serotonin receptors in the central nervous system. In addition, it will be important to determine what other transmitters might be released following stimulation of the NRM. The observation of release of norepinephrine in cats following NRM stimulation (Hammond et al., 1981) is of particular interest, since it is known that norepinephrine, as well as serotonin, causes analgesia when applied intrathecally to the spinal cord (Yaksh, 1979; Yaksh and Wilson, 1979), and that these monoamines produce a selective depression of the nociceptive responses of dorsal horn neurons when administered iontophoretically (Headley et al., 1978).

Future studies need to address such questions as the normal physiological role of the "analgesia" systems and how these systems can best be activated. A better understanding of the descending control systems may allow a better use of their powerful inhibitory actions to reduce nociceptive transmission in the spinal cord.

Acknowledgements

The experiments described were performed in collaboration with the following individuals: A.E. Applebaum, J.E. Beall, A.B. Chatt, J.M. Chung, K.D. Gerhart, G.J. Giesler, L.H. Haber, L.M. Jordan, D.R. Kenshalo, Jr., R.F. Martin, T.K. Wilcox, and R.P. Yezierski. The author thanks Helen Willcockson, Gail Silver and Bart Moore for their expert technical assistance, and Phyllis Waldrop for typing the manuscript. The work was supported by NIH Postdoctoral Fellowships NS 05087, NS 06071 and NS 06193, and by Research Grants NS 09743 and NS 11255 from the National Institutes of Health and a grant from the Moody Foundation. Dr. Jordan's participation was supported by the Canadian M.R.C.

References

Abols, I.A. and Basbaum, A.I. (1981) Afferent connections of the rostral medulla of the cat: a neural substrate for midbrain-medullary interactions in the modulation of pain, *J. comp. Neurol.*, 201: 285-297.

Basbaum, A.I. and Fields, H.L. (1978) Endogenous pain control mechanisms: review and hypothesis, *Ann. Neurol.*, 4: 451-462.

Basbaum, A.I. and Fields, H.L. (1979) The origin of descending pathways in the dorsolateral funiculus of the spinal cord of the cat and rat: further studies on the anatomy of pain modulation, *J. comp. Neurol.*, 187: 513-532.

Basbaum, A.I., Marley, N.J.E., O'Keefe, J.O. and Clanton, C.H. (1977) Reversal of morphine and stimulus-produced analgesia by subtotal spinal cord lesions, *Pain*, 3: 43-56.

Basbaum, A.I., Clanton, C.H. and Fields, H.L. (1978) Three bulbospinal pathways from the rostral medulla of the cat: an autoradiographic study of pain modulating systems, *J. comp. Neurol.*, 178: 209-224.

Beall, J.E., Martin, R.F., Applebaum, A.E. and Willis, W.D. (1976) Inhibition of primate spinothalamic tract neurons by stimulation in the region of the nucleus raphe magnus, *Brain Res.*, 114: 328-333.

Beall, J.E., Applebaum, A.E., Foreman, R.D. and Willis, W.D. (1977) Spinal cord potentials evoked by cutaneous afferents in the monkey, *J. Neurophysiol.*, 40: 199-211.

Behbehani, M.M. and Fields, H.L. (1979) Evidence that an excitatory connection between the periaqueductal gray and nucleus raphe magnus mediates stimulation produced analgesia, *Brain Res.*, 170: 85-93.

Behbehani, M.M. and Pomeroy, S.L. (1978) Effect of morphine injected in periaqueductal gray on the activity of single units in nucleus raphe magnus of the rat, *Brain Res.*, 149: 266-269.

Bourgoin, S., Oliveras, J.L., Bruxelle, J., Hamon, M. and Besson, J.M. (1980) Electrical stimulation of the nucleus raphe magnus in the rat. Effects on 5-HT metabolism in the spinal cord, *Brain Res.*, 194: 377-389.

Bowker, R.M., Westlund, K.N. and Coulter, J.D. (1982) Origins of serotonergic projections to the spinal cord in rat: an immunocytochemical-retrograde transport study, *Brain Res.*, in press.

Briggs, I. (1977) Excitatory responses of neurons in rat bulbar reticular formation to bulbar raphe stimulation and to iontophoretically applied 5-hydroxytryptamine, and their blockade by LSD 25, *J. Physiol. (Lond.)*, 265: 327-340.

Carpenter, D., Engberg, I. and Lundberg, A. (1966) Primary afferent depolarization evoked from the brain stem and the cerebellum, *Arch. ital. Biol.*, 104: 73-85.

Carstens, E., Fraunhoffer, M. and Zimmermann, M. (1981) Serotonergic mediation of descending inhibition from midbrain periaqueductal gray, but not reticular formation, of spinal nociceptive transmission in the cat, *Pain*, 10: 149-167.

Casey, K.L.(1971) Escape elicited by bulboreticular stimulation in the cat, *Int. J. Neurosci.*, 2: 29-34.

Chan-Palay, V. (1979) Combined immunocytochemistry and autoradiography after in vivo injections of monoclonal antibody to substance P and ^{3}H-serotonin: co-existence of two putative transmitters in single raphe cells and fiber plexuses, *Anat. Embryol.*, 156: 241-254.

Chung, J.M., Kenshalo, D.R., Jr., Gerhart, K.D. and Willis, W.D. (1979) Excitation of primate spinothalamic neurons by cutaneous C-fiber volleys, *J. Neurophysiol.*, 42: 1354-1369.

Dahlström, A. and Fuxe, K. (1965) Evidence for the existence of monoamine neurons in the central nervous system, *Acta physiol. scand.*, 64, Suppl. 247: 1-36.

Eccles, R.M. and Lundberg, A. (1959b) Supraspinal control of interneurons mediating spinal reflexes, *J. Physiol. (Lond.)*, 147: 565-584.

Engberg, I., Lundberg, A. and Ryall, R.W. (1968a) The effect of reserpine on transmission in the spinal cord, *Acta physiol. scand.*, 72: 115-122.

Engberg, I., Lundberg, A. and Ryall, R.W. (1968b) Is the tonic decerebrate inhibition of reflex paths mediated by monoaminergic pathways?, *Acta physiol. scand.*, 72: 123-133.

Engberg, I., Lundberg, A. and Ryall, R.W. (1968c) Reticulospinal inhibition of transmission in reflex pathways, *J. Physiol. (Lond.)*, 194: 201-223.

Engberg, I., Lundberg, A. and Ryall, R.W. (1968d) Reticulospinal inhibition of interneurons, *J. Physiol. (Lond.)*, 194: 225-236.

Fields, H.L. and Anderson, S.D. (1978) Evidence that raphe-spinal neurons mediate opiate and midbrain stimulation-produced analgesia, *Pain*, 5: 333-349.

Fields, H.L., Basbaum, A.I., Clanton, C.H. and Anderson, S.D. (1977) Nucleus raphe magnus inhibition of spinal cord dorsal horn neurons, *Brain Res.*, 126: 441-453.

Foerster, O. and Gagel, O. (1932) Die Vorderseitenstrangdurchschneidung beim Menschen. Eine klinisch-patho-physiologischanatomische Studie, *Z. ges. Neurol. Psychiat.*, 138: 1-92.

Foreman, R.D., Applebaum, A.E., Beall, J.E., Trevino, D.L. and Willis, W.D. (1975) Responses of primate spinothalamic tract neurons to electrical stimulation of hindlimb peripheral nerves, *J. Neurophysiol.*, 38: 132-145.

Foreman, R.D., Schmidt, R.F. and Willis, W.D. (1979) Effects of mechanical and chemical stimulation of fine muscle afferents upon primate spinothalamic tract cells, *J. Physiol. (Lond.)*, 286: 215-231.

Gallager, D.W. and Pert, A. (1978) Afferents to brain stem nuclei (brain stem raphe, nucleus reticularis pontis caudalis and gigantocellularis) in the rat as demonstrated by microiontophoretically applied horseradish peroxidase, *Brain Res.*, 144: 257-275.

Gerhart, K.D., Wilcox, T.K., Chung, J.M. and Willis, W.D. (1981) Inhibition of nociceptive and nonnociceptive responses of primate spinothalamic cells by stimulation in medial brain stem, *J. Neurophysiol.*, 45: 121-136.

Giesler, G.J., Gerhart, K.D., Yezierski, R.P., Wilcox, T.K. and Willis, W.D. (1981a) Postsynaptic inhibition of primate spinothalamic neurons by stimulation in nucleus raphe magnus, *Brain Res.*, 204: 184-188.

Giesler, G.J., Jr., Yezierski, R.P., Gerhart, K.D. and Willis, W.D. (1981b) Spinothalamic tract neurons that project to medial and/or lateral thalamic nuclei: evidence for a physiologically novel population of spinal cord neurons, *J. Neurophysiol.*, 46: 1285-1307.

Haber, L.H., Martin, R.F., Chatt, A.B. and Willis, W.D. (1978) Effects of stimulation in nucleus reticularis gigantocellularis on the activity of spinothalamic tract neurons in the monkey, *Brain Res.*, 153: 163-168.

Haber, L.H., Martin, R.F., Chung, J.M. and Willis, W.D. (1980) Inhibition and excitation of primate spinothalamic tract neurons by stimulation in region of nucleus reticularis gigantocellularis, *J. Neurophysiol.*, 43: 1578-1593.

Haigler, H.J. and Aghajanian, G.K. (1974) Peripheral serotonin antagonists: failure to antagonize serotonin in brain areas receiving a prominent serotonergic input, *J. Neural Transm.*, 35: 257-273.

Hammond, D.L., Tyce, G.M. and Yaksh, T.L. (1981) Release of serotonin and norepinephrine into superfusates of the rat spinal cord following electrical stimulation of the nucleus raphe magnus, *Soc. Neurosci., Abstr.*, 7: 532.

Headley, P.M., Duggan, A.W. and Griersmith, B.T. (1978) Selective reduction by noradrenaline and 5-hydroxytryptamine of nociceptive responses of cat dorsal horn neurons, *Brain Res.*, 145: 185-189.

Hentall, I.D. and Fields, H.L. (1979) Segmental and descending influences on intraspinal thresholds of single C-fibers, *J. Neurophysiol.*, 42: 1527-1537.

Hökfelt, T., Ljungdahl, A., Steinbusch, H., Verhofstad, A., Nilsson, G., Brodin, E., Pernow, B. and Goldstein, M. (1978) Immunohistochemical evidence of substance P-like immunoreactivity in some 5-hydroxytryptamine-containing neurons in the rat central nervous system, *Neuroscience*, 3: 517-538.

Holmqvist, B. and Lundberg, A. (1959) On the organization of the supraspinal inhibitory control of interneurons of various spinal reflex arcs, *Arch. ital. Biol.*, 97: 340-356.

Holmqvist, B. and Lundberg, A. (1961) Differential supraspinal control of synaptic actions evoked by volleys in the flexion reflex afferents in alpha motoneurons, *Acta physiol. scand.*, 54, Suppl. 186: 1-51.

Job, C. (1953) Über autogene Inhibition und Reflexumkehr bei spinalisierten und decerebrierten Katzen, *Pflüger's Arch.*, 256: 406-418.

Johns, D., De Lanerolle, N. and LaMotte, C. (1981) Localization of 5-HT in monkey spinal cord using light and EM immunohistochemistry, *Anat. Rec.*, 199: 129A.

Jordan, L.M., Kenshalo, D.R., Jr., Martin, R.F., Haber, L.H. and Willis, W.D. (1978) Depression of primate spinothalamic tract neurons by iontophoretic application of 5-hydroxytryptamine, *Pain*, 5: 135-142.

Jordan, L.M., Kenshalo, D.R., Jr., Martin, R.F., Haber, L.H. and Willis, W.D. (1979) Two populations of spinothalamic tract neurons with opposite responses to 5-hydroxytryptamine, *Brain Res.*, 164: 342-346.

Kenshalo, D.R., Jr., Leonard, R.B., Chung, J.M. and Willis, W.D. (1979) Responses of primate spinothalamic neurons to graded and to repeated noxious heat stimuli, *J. Neurophysiol.*, 42: 1370-1389.

Kuypers, H.G.J.M. and Maisky, V.A. (1977) Funicular trajectories of descending brain stem pathways in cat, *Brain Res.*, 136: 159-165.

Lovick, T.A., West, D.C. and Wolstencroft, J.H. (1978) Responses of raphespinal and other bulbar raphe neurons to stimulation of the periaqueductal gray in the cat, *Neurosci. Lett.*, 8: 45-49.

Martin, R.F., Jordan, L.M. and Willis, W.D. (1978) Differential projections of cat medullary raphe neurons demonstrated by retrograde labelling following spinal cord lesions, *J. comp. Neurol.*, 182: 77-88.

Martin, R.F., Haber, L.H. and Willis, W.D. (1979) Primary afferent depolarization of identified cutaneous fibers following stimulation in medial brain stem, *J. Neurophysiol.*, 42: 779-790.

McCreery, D.B. and Bloedel, J.R. (1975) Reduction of the responses of cat spinothalamic neurons to graded mechanical stimuli by electrical stimulation of the lower brain stem, *Brain Res.*, 97: 151-156.

McCreery, D.B., Bloedel, J.R. and Hames, E.G. (1979) Effects of stimulating in raphe nuclei and in reticular formation on response of spinothalamic neurons to mechanical stimuli, *J. Neurophysiol.*, 42: 166-182.

McGrath, P.A., Sharav, Y., Dubner, R. and Gracely, R.H. (1981) Masseter inhibitory periods and sensations evoked by electrical tooth pulp stimulation, *Pain*, 10: 1-17.

Mendell, L.M. (1966) Physiological properties of unmyelinated fiber projection to the spinal cord, *Exp. Neurol.*, 16: 316-332.

Milne, R.J., Foreman, R.D., Giesler, G.J. and Willis, W.D. (1982) Convergence of cutaneous and pelvic visceral nociceptive inputs onto primate spinothalamic neurons, *Pain*, in press.

Mohrland, J.S. and Gebhart, G.F. (1980) Effects of focal electrical stimulation and morphine microinjection in the periaqueductal gray of the rat mesencephalon on neuronal activity in the medullary reticular formation, *Brain Res.*, 201: 23-37.

Nyberg-Hansen, R. (1965) Sites and mode of termination of reticulospinal fibers in the cat, *J. comp. Neurol.*, 124: 71-100.

Oleson, T.D., Twombly, D.A. and Liebeskind, J.C. (1978) Effects of pain-attenuating brain stimulation and morphine on electrical activity in the raphe nuclei of the awake rat, *Pain*, 4: 211-230.

Oliveras, J.L., Redjemi, F., Guilbaud, G. and Besson, J.M. (1975) Analgesia induced by electrical stimulation of the inferior centralis nucleus of the raphe in the cat, *Pain*, 1: 139-145.

Oliveras, J.L., Hosobuchi, Y., Redjemi, F., Guilbaud, G. and Besson, J.M. (1977) Opiate antagonist, naloxone, strongly reduces analgesia induced by stimulation of a raphe nucleus (centralis inferior), *Brain Res.*, 120: 221-229.

Oliveras, J.L., Hosobuchi, G., Guilbaud, G. and Besson, J.M. (1978) Analgesic electrical stimulation of the feline nucleus raphe magnus: development of tolerance and its reversal by 5-HTP, *Brain Res.*, 146: 404-409.

Oliveras, J.L., Guilbaud, G. and Besson, J.M. (1979) A map of serotoninergic structures involved in stimulation producing analgesia in unrestrained freely moving cats, *Brain Res.*, 164: 317-322.

Peroutka, S.J. and Snyder, S.H. (1979) Multiple serotonin receptors: differential binding of (^{3}H)5-

hydroxytryptamine, (^{3}H)lysergic acid diethylamide and (^{3}H)spiroperidol, *Molec. Pharmacol.*, 16: 687-699.

Peroutka, S.J., Lebovitz, R.M. and Snyder, S.H. (1981) Two distinct central serotonin receptors with different physiological functions, *Science*, 212: 927-829.

Pierce, E.T., Foote, W.E. and Hobson, J.A. (1976) The efferent connection of the nucleus raphe dorsalis, *Brain Res.*, 107: 137-144.

Pompeiano, O. (1973) Reticular formation. In *Handbook of Sensory Physiology, Vol. 2, Simatosensory system.* Springer-Verlag, New York, pp. 381-488.

Proudfit, H.K. and Anderson, E.G. (1974) New long latency bulbospinal evoked potentials blocked by serotonin antagonists, *Brain Res.*, 65: 542-546.

Proudfit, H.K. and Anderson, E.G. (1975) Morphine analgesia: blockade by raphe magnus lesions, *Brain Res.*, 98: 612-618.

Proudfit, H.K., Larson, A.A. and Anderson, E.G. (1980) The role of GABA and serotonin in the mediation of raphe-evoked spinal cord dorsal root potentials, *Brain Res.*, 195: 149-165.

Ritchie, T.C. and Leonard, R.B. Immunocytochemical demonstration of serotonergic neurons, terminals and axons in the spinal cord of the stingray, *Dasyatis sabina*, submitted for publication.

Rivot, J.P., Chaouch, A. and Besson, J.M. (1980) Nucleus raphe magnus modulation of response of rat dorsal horn neurons to unmyelinated fiber inputs: partial involvement of serotonergic pathways, *J. Neurophysiol.*, 44: 1039-1057.

Ruda, M.A. (1975) *An Autoradiographic Study of the Efferent Projections of the Midbrain Central Gray in the Cat*, Univ. of Pennsylvania, Philadelphia.

Shah, Y. and Dostrovsky, J.O. (1980) Electrophysiological evidence for a projection of the periaqueductal gray matter to nucleus raphe magnus in cat and rat, *Brain Res.*, 193: 534-538.

Sherrington, C.S. and Sowton, S.C.M. (1915) Observations on reflex responses to single break-shocks, *J. Physiol. (Lond.)*, 49: 331-348.

Taber, E., Brodal, A. and Walbert, F. (1960) Raphe nuclei of the brainstem of cat. I. Cytoarchitecture, *J. comp. Neurol.*, 114: 161-188.

Tohyama, M., Sakai, K., Salvert, D., Touret, M. and Jouvet, M. (1979a) Spinal projections from the lower brain stem in the cat as demonstrated by the horseradish peroxidase technique. I. Origins of the reticulospinal tracts and their funicular trajectories, *Brain Res.*, 173: 383-403.

Tohyama, M., Sakai, T., Touret, M., Salvert, D. and Jouvet, M. (1979b) Spinal projections from the lower brain stem in the cat as demonstrated by the horseradish peroxidase technique. II. Projections from the dorsolateral pontine tegmentum and raphe nuclei, *Brain Res.*, 176: 215-231.

Trevino, D.L., Coulter, J.D. and Willis, W.D. (1973) Location of cells of origin of spinothalamic tract in lumbar enlargement of the monkey, *J. Neurophysiol.*, 36: 750-761.

Vierck, C.J. and Luck, M.M. (1979) Loss and recovery of reactivity to noxious stimuli in monkeys with primary spinothalamic cordotomies, followed by secondary and tertiary lesions of other cord sectors, *Brain*, 102: 233-248.

Wagman, I.H. and Price, D.D. (1969) Responses of dorsal horn neurons of *M. mulatta* to cutaneous and sural nerve A and C fiber stimuli, *J. Neurophysiol.*, 32: 803-817.

Wall, P.D. (1958) Excitability changes in afferent fiber terminations and their relation to slow potentials, *J. Physiol. (Lond.)*, 142: 1-21.

Watkins, L.R., Griffin, G., Leichnetz, G.R. and Mayer, D.J. (1980) The somatotopic organization of the nucleus raphe magnus and surrounding brain stem structures as revealed by HRP slow-release gels, *Brain Res.*, 181: 1-15.

White, J.C. and Sweet, W.H. (1955) *Pain. Its Mechanisms and Neurosurgical Control*, Charles C. Thomas, Springfield, Il.

Willer, J.C. (1977) Comparative study of perceived pain and nociceptive flexion reflex in man, *Pain*, 3: 69-80.

Willer, J.C., Boureau, F. and Albe-Fessard, D. (1979) Supraspinal influences on nociceptive flexion reflex and pain sensation in man, *Brain Res.*, 179: 61-68.

Willis, W.D., Trevino, D.L., Coulter, J.D. and Maunz, R.A. (1974) Responses of primate spinothalamic tract neurons to natural stimulation of hindlimb, *J. Neurophysiol.*, 37: 358-372.

Willis, W.D., Maunz, R.A., Foreman, R.D. and Coulter, J.D. (1975) Static and dynamic responses of spinothalamic tract neurons to mechanical stimuli, *J. Neurophysiol.*, 38: 587-600.

Willis, W.D., Haber, L.H. and Martin, R.F. (1977) Inhibition of spinothalamic tract cells and interneurons by brain stem stimulation in the monkey, *J. Neurophysiol.*, 40: 968-981.

Yaksh, T.L. (1979) Direct evidence that spinal serotonin and noradrenaline terminals mediate the spinal antinociceptive effects of morphine in the periaqueductal gray, *Brain Res.*, 160: 180-185.

Yaksh, T.L. ans Wilson, P.R. (1979) Spinal serotonin terminal system mediates antinociception, *J. Pharmacol. exp. Ther.*, 208: 446-453.

Yezierski, R.P., Wilcox, T.K. and Willis, W.D. (1982) The effects of serotonin antagonists on the inhibition of primate spinothalamic tract cells produced by stimulation in nucleus raphe magnus or the periaqueductal gray, *J. Pharmacol. exp. Ther.*, in press.

Brain Stem Control of Spinal Mechanisms
– B. Sjölund and A. Björklund, editors
© 1982 Elsevier Biomedical Press

19

Brain Stem Inhibition of the Spinal Transmission of Nociceptive Information – Pharmacological Studies of Tonic and Stimulation-Induced Inhibition

A.W. DUGGAN

Department of Pharmacology, John Curtin School of Medical Research, Australian National University, Canberra, ACT 2601, Australia

I. Introduction

There is now abundant evidence that there are mechanisms in the dorsal horn able to suppress the transmission of impulses in fine diameter primary afferents in a selective manner. Since many of these afferents convey information from peripheral noxious stimuli (Bessou and Perl, 1969), it is possible that important alterations in the perception of pain could result from inhibition at or near the initial synapses in the spinal cord and trigeminal nuclei. The present brief account examines some of the mechanisms by which brain stem areas activate inhibition in the spinal dorsal horn and, in particular, pharmacological experiments aimed at identification of the transmitters involved.

One problem in attempting to relate inhibition of dorsal horn neurons to alterations in pain perception is determining which neurons should be studied. When examined by extracellular recording techniques, many neurons in the upper dorsal horn of the cat are excited by both noxious and non-noxious cutaneous stimuli. When neurons have been antidromically identified as projecting to a particular supraspinal site, again many respond in this way. For example, spino-cervical and spino-thalamic neurons are commonly excited by hair deflection and by noxious heating of the skin (Cervero et al., 1977; Willis et al., 1974). Neurons excited only by noxious cutaneous stimuli have been described in lamina I (Christensen and Perl, 1970), but opinion is divided on whether such cells are abundant in lamina II where most unmyelinated primary afferents terminate (Kumazawa and Perl, 1978; Wall et al., 1979). With this uncertainty about the functional role of differing neurons there is clearly a dilemma in attempting to relate supraspinal inhibition of neuronal firing to analgesia. In the following account, therefore, emphasis is placed on the selective nature of some supraspinal inhibitions. Thus, with neurons of laminae IV and V responding to both noxious and non-noxious cutaneous stimuli, inhibition from some supraspinal areas can be shown to be non-selective, reducing all responses, whereas others reduce excitation only by noxious cutaneous stimuli. In this way the responses of a particular neuron studied can be regarded as a quantitative assay of the inhibition with the assumption that selective inhibition of nociceptive responses is that most likely to result in alterations in pain perception. Thus, these experiments do not investigate the mechanism of selective inhibition (which is unknown) but are suitable for describing the sites of origin and for pharmacological interference aimed at identifying transmitters involved.

Prior to discussing the pharmacology of descending inhibition, certain aspects of the physiology of such inhibition require comment.

II. Inhibition from Electrical Stimulation of Brain Stem Areas

Inhibition of dorsal horn neurons excited by noxious cutaneous stimuli has been shown for electrical stimulation near the periaqueductal gray (Oliveras et al., 1974; Duggan and Griersmith, 1979; Carstens et al., 1979, 1981; Jurna, 1980; Yezierski et al., 1982), locus coeruleus (Hodge et al., 1981), lateral midbrain reticular formation (Carstens et al., 1981), medullary raphé (Fields et al., 1977; Guilbaud et al., 1977; Willis et al., 1977; Duggan and Griersmith, 1979; Rivot et al., 1979; Yezierski et al., 1982) and medial reticular areas of the medulla (McCreery et al., 1979; Haber et al., 1980).

This list is so large that the significance of such inhibition to mechanisms of analgesia may well be questioned. In some of the studies cited, it was not shown whether the inhibition was selective for excitation by noxious stimuli alone or reduced responses to other cutaneous stimuli. With spino-thalamic neurons, inhibition from stimulation within the raphé nuclei and medial reticular formation was shown to be non-selective (Willis et al., 1977; Haber et al., 1980), a finding difficult at first sight to relate to analgesia. Moreover, Liebeskind et al. (1973) found that the brain stem areas producing inhibition of dorsal horn neurons in anesthetized cats were far more extensive than the sites producing analgesia in conscious cats. Thus, it appears that inhibition of neurons excited by noxious cutaneous stimuli may not be an adequate criterion that the area stimulated is normally concerned in the control of pain perception.

Recent studies on the effects of electrical stimulation in the midbrain of the barbiturate-anesthetized cat have suggested that inhibition produced from areas producing behavioral analgesia differs from that from more ventral areas. In these experiments electrical stimulation of the ventral periaqueductal gray (PAG) with pairs of electrodes sited across the midline reduced the excitation of laminae IV and V neurons by noxious cutaneous stimuli without effect on responses to non-noxious stimuli. Moving the stimulating electrodes ventrally to the midbrain tegmentum changed the inhibition to a non-selective one, all responses being reduced. The two sites also differed in their effects on peripheral circulation. Stimulation of areas producing selective inhibition increased cardiac output. Temperature probes showed that this was associated with an increase in muscle but not cutaneous circulation. In some instances a decrease in skin circulation was shown. It appears that stimulation in the PAG evokes an organized response. An inhibition of pain transmission together with an increased muscle perfusion could, for example, be appropriate in a potentially injurious environment where it is important that reflexes to impulses in nociceptive afferents should not impair motor performance. It is not known if this response is organized in the PAG or requires the participation of higher areas of the brain.

An important consideration in studying the pharmacology of descending inhibition produced by brain stem stimulation, is: to what extent is the inhibition being investigated a homogeneous and reproducible entity? Inhibition can result from a number of mechanisms using different transmitters. Thus, although slight differences in electrode placement may produce little apparent change in the inhibition from electrical stimulation, this could have significant effects on the reduction of this inhibition by a transmitter antagonist. The discordant results on the pharmacology of inhibition from raphé stimulation (discussed later) may well result from this difficulty. In this respect, stimulation in the PAG appears a better subject for pharmacological study since the response can be defined by circulatory parameters in addition to selective inhibition.

III. Tonic Descending Inhibition

In anesthetized or decerebrate cats the excitation of neurons of laminae I, IV and V by noxious cutaneous stimuli is under powerful tonic inhibition of supraspinal origin (Wall, 1967; Handwerker et al., 1975; Duggan et al., 1977b, 1981). This inhibition is selective since, with multi-receptive neurons, responses to innocuous mechanical stimuli to the skin are little changed by removal of tonic inhibition. Although the studies to be described have dealt largely with inhibition of transmission of impulses in unmyelinated primary afferents, tonic inhibition also affects reflex responses to impulses in myelinated afferents, as shown by the work of Engberg et al. (1968) on flexor reflex afferents.

Tonic inhibition is readily measured by reversibly blocking conduction in a spinal segment cephalic to the recording site by cooling. Because such cooling affects many descending tracts, it would seem unwise to regard tonic descending inhibition as a single process but likely to include inhibition from several

442

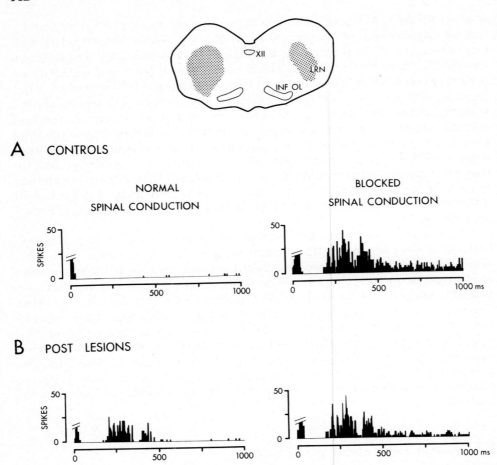

Figure 1. Reduction of tonic descending inhibition by bilateral lesions of the region of the lateral reticular nucleus. The histograms are the summed responses of a lamina V neuron to electrical stimulation of the ipsilateral tibial nerve. The stimuli (50 V, 0.5 msec pulses, 0.2 Hz) were adequate to excite unmyelinated primary afferents, and were delivered at time 0. Short-latency action potentials were superimposed on a field potential and not counted accurately, and hence this column has been truncated. Note the large increase in the number of action potentials evoked by impulses in unmyelinated primary afferents following cooling of the spinal cord at the thoraco-lumbar junction. Extensive electrolytic lesions were made at sites cephalic to that illustrated without reducing tonic inhibition. Lesioning the ipsilateral reticular nucleus (LRN) also caused no change in inhibition but, immediately after the contralateral ventral area of the LRN was lesioned, inhibition was reduced. The lower histograms were compiled at this time. The hatched areas include hemorrhage, probably from passage of needles in addition to coagulated areas. INF OL, inferior olive; XII, hypoglossal nucleus.

sources. Recent experiments on the source of tonic descending inhibition in the barbiturate-anesthetized cat suggest that this is not so, and that this inhibition derives largely from one area in the brain stem (Hall et al., 1981a, b).

Extensive lesions of areas of the brain stem which inhibit dorsal horn neurons when electrically stimulated, failed to reduce tonic descending inhibition. These regions included the PAG locus coereleus and subcoeruleus area, and midbrain and ponto-medullary raphé (Hall et al., 1981a, b). Tonic inhibition was reduced or abolished by bilateral lesions of the lateral reticular area of the caudal medulla. This is shown in Figure 1. The hatched area includes hemorrhage from needle passage and it is probably only the ventral parts which are important in tonic inhibition. In the light of the previous comment that circulatory responses accompanied selective inhibition from PAG stimulation, it may be significant that lesions reducing tonic descending inhibition always produced persistent hypotension. Electrolytic lesions destroy many cell types and fibers of passage, and hence only limited interpretation as to the cells of origin of tonic inhibition can be made. The lateral reticular area in the cat does have catecholamine-containing neurons (Blessing et al., 1980) and thus noradrenaline-containing descending fibers may be of importance in tonic descending inhibition.

IV. Mechanisms of Selective Inhibition

Little is known about how these inhibitions occur. It has been suggested that the firing pattern of neurons to a stimulus such as hair deflection, which evokes short bursts of spikes, will make this response less susceptible to inhibition than firing to a continuous stimulus such as noxious heat (McCreery et al., 1979). Thus, selectivity could arise from a somatic hyperpolarization. Two observations make this unlikely. Firstly, glycine and γ-aminobutyric acid (GABA), which hyperpolarize motoneurons (Werman et al., 1968; Curtis et al., 1968), when administered electrophoretically near the somata of laminae IV and V neurons, reduce their excitation by both noxious and non-noxious stimuli (Headley et al., 1978). Secondly on the same neuron, it can be shown that selective inhibition from PAG stimulation is changed to non-selective reduction of both noxious and non-noxious cutaneous stimuli when the stimulating electrodes are in a more ventral position.

Selective inhibition could result from a presynaptic action on the appropriate fibers or from a postsynaptic inhibition of superficial interneurons which do not receive large diameter primary afferents. In addition, if the distribution of primary afferents to lamina IV and V neurons is not random, and the inhibitory synapses are preferentially located adjacent to sites of small diameter afferent input, then postsynaptic inhibition could be selective. There is no evidence regarding the relative importance of these differing mechanisms.

Selective inhibition has been produced by administering compounds elective responses relatively selectively when administered in the SG (Duggan et al., 1977a; Headley et al., 1978), the approach used has been to administer antagonists electrophoretically, first in this area (while recording firing of a lamina IV or V cell with an independently manipulated micropipette), and then in 100 μm intervals progressively closer to cell bodies.

Enkephalin antagonists. Administered intravenously in doses adequate to antagonize the actions of enkephalins on dorsal horn neurons (Duggan et al., 1977a), naloxone did not reduce tonic descending inhibition (Duggan et al., 1977b). This inhibition has not been adequately studied with naloxone administered from micropipettes.

5-Hydroxytryptamine antagonists. There is doubt as to the adequacy of 5-HT antagonists acting at central 5-HT receptors (Curtis and Davis, 1962; Haigler and Aghajanian, 1974). In the SG, however, methysergide reduced the selective depression of nociceptive responses of laminae IV and V neurons produced by 5-HT administration (Griersmith and Duggan, 1980), and therefore this substance has been used in experiments on tonic descending inhibition.

Administered in the SG or near the bodies of dorsal horn neurons, methysergide had no effect on tonic descending inhibition (Griersmith et al., 1981). Topical application of a methysergide-containing solution (20 μM–20 mM) to the dorsum of the cord also failed to reduce this inhibition. Intravenous methysergide (1–2 mg/kg) did reduce descending inhibition, but also powerfully reduced cell firing at the spinal level. Cell responses after methysergide were not increased to the levels seen after removal of inhibition, but were depressed below controls. Thus, it is not possible to interpret this reduction of descending inhibition solely in terms of block of the action of synaptically released 5-HT since it may well have resulted from a depression of excitability of the cells of origin of descending inhibition or of interneurons along the pathway.

Amino acid antagonists. By immunohistochemical techniques researchers have found the GABA-synthesizing enzyme glutamate decarboxylase in the SG (McLaughlin et al., 1975). Since there is good evidence that GABA mediates presynaptic inhibition of transmission of impulses in large myelinated afferents of muscle origin (Curtis et al., 1977), similar effects on the terminals of unmyelinated primary afferents could mediate the effects of tonic descending inhibition.

Bicuculline antagonizes both the pre- and postsynaptic actions of GABA (Curtis et al., 1971, 1977) and hence this alkaloid was studied for effects on tonic descending inhibition. Bicuculline was administered electrophoretically in the SG and then progressively closer to the body of the neuron from which recordings were obtained. Concentrations of bicuculline adequate to block segmental inhibition did not reduce tonic descending inhibition (Duggan et al., 1981). Similar results were obtained with strychnine, a glycine antagonist (Curtis et al., 1968). Concentrations adequate to block segmental inhibition had no effect on tonic descending inhibition.

Thus no evidence was obtained to implicate inhibitory amino acids in tonic

Carstens, E., Yokota, T. and Zimmermann, M. (1979) Inhibition of spinal neuronal responses to noxious skin heating by stimulation of mesencephalic periaqueductal gray in the cat, *J. Neurophysiol.*, 42: 558-568.

Carstens, E., Fraunhoffer, M. and Zimmermann, M. (1981) Serotonergic mediation of descending inhibition from midbrain periaqueductal gray, but not reticular formation of spinal nociceptive transmission in the cat, *Pain*, 10: 149-167.

Cervero, F., Iggo, A. and Molony, V. (1977) Responses of spinocervical tract neurons to noxious stimulation of the skin, *J. Physiol. (Lond.)*, 267: 537-558.

Christensen, B.N. and Perl, E.R. (1970) Spinal neurons specifically excited by noxious or thermal stimuli: marginal zone of the dorsal horn, *J. Neurophysiol.*, 33: 293-307.

Curtis, D.R. and Davis, R. (1962) Pharmacological studies upon neurones of the lateral geniculate nucleus of the cat, *Brit. J. Pharmacol.*, 18: 217-246.

Curtis, D.R., Hosli, L., Johnston, G.A.R. and Johnston, I.H. (1968) The hyperpolarization of spinal motoneurons by glycine and related amino acids, *Exp. Brain Res.*, 5: 235-258.

Curtis, D.R., Duggan, A.W., Felix, D. and Johnston, G.A.R. (1971) Bicuculline, an antagonist of GABA and synaptic inhibition in the spinal cord, *Brain Res.*, 32: 69-96.

Curtis, D.R., Lodge, D. and Brand, S.J. (1977) GABA and spinal afferent terminal excitability in the cat, *Brain Res.*, 130: 360-363.

Duggan, A.W. and Griersmith, B.T. (1979) Inhibition of the spinal transmission of nociceptive information by supraspinal stimulation in the cat, *Pain*, 6: 149-161.

Duggan, A.W., Hall, J.G. and Headley, P.M. (1977a) Enkephalins and dorsal horn neurons of the cat: effects on responses to noxious and innocuous skin stimuli, *Brit. J. Pharmacol.*, 61: 399-408.

Duggan, A.W., Hall, J.G., Headley, P.M. and Griersmith, B.T. (1977b) The effect of naloxone on the excitation of dorsal horn neurons of the cat by noxious and non-noxious cutaneous stimuli, *Brain Res.*, 138: 185-189.

Duggan, A.W., Griersmith, B.T. and Johnson, S.M. (1981) Supraspinal inhibition of the excitation of dorsal horn neurons by impulses in unmyelinated primary afferents: lack of effect by strychnine and bicuculline, *Brain Res.*, 210: 231-241.

Engberg, I., Lundberg, A. and Ryall, R.W. (1968) Is the tonic decerebrate inhibition of reflex paths mediated by monoaminergic pathways? *Acta physiol. scand.*, 72: 123-133.

Fields, H.L., Basbaum, A.I., Clanton, C.H. and Anderson, S.D. (1977) Nucleus raphe magnus inhibition of spinal cord dorsal horn neurons, *Brain Res.*, 126: 441-453.

Griersmith, B.T. and Duggan, A.W. (1980) Prolonged depression of spinal transmission of nociceptive information by 5HT administered in the substantia gelatinosa: antagonism by methysergide, *Brain Res.*, 187: 231-236.

Griersmith, B.T., Duggan, A.W. and North, R.A. (1981) Methysergide and supraspinal inhibition of the transmission of nociceptive information in the anaesthetized cat, *Brain Res.*, 204: 147-158.

Guilbaud, G., Oliveras, J.L., Giesler, G. and Besson, J.-M. (1977) Effects induced by stimulation of the centralis inferior nucleus of the raphé on dorsal horn interneurons in cat's spinal cord, *Brain Res.*, 126: 355-360.

Haber, L.H., Martin, R.F., Chung, J.M. and Willis, W.D. (1980) Inhibition and excitation of primate spinothalamic neurons by stimulation in the region of nucleus reticularis gigantocellularis, *J. Neurophysiol.*, 43: 1578-1593.

Haigler, H.J. and Aghajanian, G.K. (1974) Peripheral serotonin antagonists: failure to antagonize serotonin in brain areas receiving a prominent serotonergic input, *J. Neural Transm.*, 35: 257-273.

Hall, J.G., Duggan, A.W., Johnson, S.M. and Morton, C.R. (1981a) Medullary raphé lesions do not reduce descending inhibition of dorsal horn neurons of the cat, *Neurosci. Lett.*, 25: 25-30.

Hall, J.G., Duggan, A.W., Johnson, S.M. and Morton, C.R. (1981b) Brain stem regions tonically inhibiting dorsal horn neurons, *Proc. Aust. Physiol. Pharmacol. Soc.*, 12: 6P.

Handwerker, H.O., Iggo, A. and Zimmermann, M. (1975) Segmental and supraspinal actions on dorsal horn neurones responding to noxious and non-noxious skin stimulation, *Pain*, 1: 147-165.

Headley, P.M., Duggan, A.W. and Griersmith, B.T. (1978) Selective reduction by noradrenaline and 5-hydroxytryptamine of nociceptive responses of cat dorsal horn neurons, *Brain Res.*, 145: 185-189.

Hodge, C.J., Apkarian, A.V., Stevens, R., Vogelsang, G. and Wisnicki, H.J. (1981) Locus coeruleus modulation of dorsal horn unit responses to cutaneous stimulation, *Brain Res.*, 204: 415-420.

Jurna, I. (1980) Effect of stimulation in the periaqueductal gray matter on activity in ascending axons of the rat spinal cord: selective inhibition of activity evoked by afferent Aδ and C fibre stimulation and failure of naloxone to reduce inhibition, *Brain Res.*, 196: 33-42.

Kumazawa, T. and Perl, E.R. (1978) Excitation of marginal and substantia gelatinosa neurons in the primate spinal cord: indications of their place in dorsal horn functional organization. *J. comp. Neurol.*, 177: 417-434.

Liebeskind, J.C., Guilbaud, G., Besson, J.-M. and Oliveras, J.L. (1973) Analgesia from electrical stimulation of the periaqueductal gray matter in the cat: behavioral observations and inhibitory effects on spinal cord interneurons, *Brain Res.*, 50: 441-446.

Lovick, T.A. (1981) Primary afferent depolarization of tooth pulp afferents by stimulation in nucleus raphé magnus and adjacent reticular formation in the cat: effect of bicuculline, *Neurosci. Lett.*, 25: 173-178.

McCreery, D.G., Bloedel, J.R. and Hames, E.G. (1979) Effects of stimulating in raphé nuclei and in reticular formation on response of spinothalamic neurons to mechanical stimuli, *J. Neurophysiol.*, 42: 166-182.

McLaughlin, B.J., Barber, R., Saito, K., Roberts, E. and Wu, J.Y. (1975) Immunocytochemical localisation of glutamate decarboxylase in rat spinal cord, *J. comp. Neurol.*, 164: 305-322.

Oliveras, J.L., Besson, J.M., Guilbaud, G. and Liebeskind, J.C. (1974) Behavioural and electrophysiological evidence of pain inhibition from midbrain stimulation in the cat, *Exp. Brain Res.*, 20: 32-44.

Rivot, J.P., Chaouch, A. and Besson, J.M. (1979) The influence of naloxone on the C-fiber response of dorsal horn neurons and their inhibitory control by raphé magnus stimulation, *Brain Res.*, 176: 355-364.

Wall, P.D. (1967) The laminar organization of dorsal horn and effects of descending impulses, *J. Physiol. (Lond.)*, 188: 403-423.

Wall, P.D., Merrill, E.G. and Yaksh, T.L. (1979) Responses of single units in laminae 2 and 3 of cat spinal cord, *Brain Res.*, 160: 245-260.

Werman, R., Davidoff, R.A. and Aprison, M.H. (1968) Inhibitory action of glycine on spinal neurons in the cat, *J. Neurophysiol.*, 31: 81-95.

West, D.C. and Wolstencroft, J.H. (1977) Location and conduction velocity of raphe spinal neurones in nucleus raphe magnus and raphe pallidus in the cat, *Neurosci. Lett.*, 5: 147-151.

Willis, W.D., Trevino, D.L., Coulter, J.D. and Maunz, R.A. (1974) Responses of primate spinothalamic tract neurons to natural stimulation of hindlimb, *J. Neurophysiol.*, 37: 358-372.

Willis, W.D., Haber, L.H. and Martin, R.F. (1977) Inhibition of spinothalamic tract cells and interneurons by brain stem stimulation in the monkey, *J. Neurophysiol.*, 40: 968-981.

Yezierski, R.P., Wilcox, T.K. and Willis, W.D. (1982) The effects of serotonin antagonists on the inhibition of primate spinothalamic tract cells produced by stimulation in nucleus raphé magnus or periaqueductal gray, *J. Pharmacol. exp. Ther.*, in press.

Brain Stem Control of Spinal Mechanisms
– B. Sjölund and A. Björklund, editors
© 1982 Elsevier Biomedical Press

20

Cellular Actions of Putative Transmitters of Descending Systems

W. ZIEGLGÄNSBERGER

Max-Planck-Institute for Psychiatry, Kraepelinstrasse 2, 8000 München, F.R.G.

I. Introduction

The principal focus of this rather selective overview will be on the neurophysiological characterization of neurotransmitters found in the dorsal horn of the spinal cord. Actions of amino acids (L-glutamate, gamma-aminobutyric acid, glycine) as "classical" neurotransmitters, amines (dopamine, norepinephrine, serotonin) as neuroactive agents which might induce changes in cell metabolism via adenylate cyclase-coupled events, and neuropeptides (substance P, enkephalins) as a class of neuroactive compounds that are increasing in number faster than sites and mechanisms can be even tentatively established, will be described. It is clear that the mere presence of a compound in nerve endings does not warrant any speculation about a role as an intercellular messenger mediating any particular type of pharmacological or behavioral effect. Several other criteria must be satisfied to establish a biologically active agent as a neurotransmitter (see, e.g., Werman, 1969). The most important criterion is that the agent should mimic the action of the neurotransmitter which is synaptically released after stimulation of the pre-synaptic nerves. To prove this identity of action, intracellular recordings are necessary. Only this technique offers information about the subthreshold events and the underlying ionic mechanism of action. Furthermore, with this method it is possible to make some predictions about the topographic sensitivity of the neuronal surface. These technically difficult studies have been performed so far with only a few groups of mammalian neurons, and have provided almost exclusively information about postsynaptic events near the soma. Recent investigations, however, suggest that some neuroactive agents might have selective dendritic and presynaptic sites of action (see below).

II. Amino Acids: L-Glutamate, Gamma-Aminobutyric Acid, Glycine

The experimental evidence that amino acids such as L-glutamate, gamma-aminobutyric acid (GABA) and glycine are involved in neural transmission in both invertebrates and vertebrates is quite substantial and has been reviewed with varying emphasis (for review see, e.g. Curtis and Johnston, 1974; Gerschenfeld, 1973; Krnjevic, 1974; Nistri and Constanti, 1979; Roberts et al., 1976). Some of the major characteristics of these amino acid neurotransmitters will be described as they emerge mainly from investigations in the mammalian spinal cord, with references to other sites where comparable investigations were performed.

Glutaminergic (and aspartergic) fibers may constitute the major central afferent and descending excitatory pathways in the mammalian CNS. Iontophoretic application of L-glutamate evokes a fast onset excitation of most neurons studied in the central nervous system (for review, see Curtis and Johnston, 1974; Curtis, 1979; Krnjevic, 1974; Nistri and Constanti, 1979). Cell bodies of dorsal root ganglion fibers, and glia cells, seem to be insensitive to L-glutamate. However, afferent terminals in the spinal cord of the cat are obviously depolarized by excitatory acting amino acids. The physiological relevance of this finding, however, remains to be established (Curtis et al., 1977). Very little data have been reported on L-glutamate or agonists induced inhibitory actions (see below). In most sites studied the polarization reaches a plateau (dose-dependent) during the application, whereas the neuronal excitability is increased. Due to the decrease in the input resistance associated with this depolarization, excitatory and inhibitory postsynaptic transients (EPSP/IPSP) were decreased in amplitude. The initiation of spikes, which increased at lower levels of depolarization, continuously decreased when higher concentrations of L-glutamate, sufficient to induce conductance changes, were applied (detectable with electrodes probably lodged in the soma of the neuron (see Zieglgänsberger and Puil, 1973; Zieglgänsberger and Champagnat, 1979, and references cited therein). This depolarization block is presumed to be due to an inactivation of the voltage-dependent sodium channels that occurs at these membrane potential levels. Small phoretic currents administered to dendritic regions of spinal neurons produced rapid onset depolarizations. These observations were interpreted as evidence of a dendritic localization of L-glutamate receptors. Conductance measurements performed at dendritic sites showed that, at times when the somatic conductance was not detectably altered, the conductance at the site of application was clearly increased (Zieglgänsberger and Champagnat, 1978, 1979). The initial rejection of L-glutamate as a neurotransmitter was based on the inability to reverse the EPSP and the L-glutamate response at the same membrane level (see Curtis et al., 1972). This discrepancy can be easily explained, however, by such a remote localization of the glutaminergic synapses.

Current research suggests that the L-glutamate-operated ionophore in the mammalian CNS regulates the permeability of the postsynaptic membrane preferentially for Na^+ ions. The depolarizing response of L-glutamate is not blocked by tetrodotoxin, indicating that this amino acid does not interfere with the voltage-sensitive Na-channel that is blocked by this neurotoxin (Curtis et al., 1972; Zieglgänsberger and Puil, 1972). This finding seems to be supported by experiments performed in vitro (see also Hösli and Hösli, 1978). Additional Ca^{2+} influx triggered by this depolarization might activate a K^+-conductance, and may be involved in the transient hyperpolarizations observed after L-glutamate application (see below). This picture is complicated, however, by the recent findings that ion movements, e.g. those linked with amino acid uptake and alterations of intra- and extracellular ion concentrations induced by prolonged activation of receptors, might also play a role (Heinemann and Pumain, 1980 and references therein). The possibility of the existence of an electrical component contained in some EPSPs (Edwards et al., 1976; Werman and Carlen, 1976) adds to these unanswered questions. Due to the complex geometry of the CNS, only approximate estimations of the L-glutamate reversal potential can be given (range -24 to -32 mV), as was also shown by Zieglgänsberger and Puil (1973; see also Zieglgänsberger and Champagnat, 1979). To our knowledge this has been the only attempt to obtain some information about this value from in vivo experiments.

Most depolarizing responses to L-glutamate in the vertebrate CNS do not desensitize. After termination of application there is a rapid repolarization which usually exceeds the control values for some 5–10 mV and lasts for several minutes. The decay rate of the amino acid action is most likely not regulated by mere diffusion (see Sonnhof et al., 1978). Other factors may contribute, such as (1) active uptake (low and high affinity, Na-dependent); (2) activation of pump mechanisms; (3) activation of K^+-conductance following Ca^{2+}-influx; (4) desensitization (seems to play a minor role); (5) actions on neighboring (inhibitory) neurons; and (6) peripheral receptors which mediate inhibitory responses might be reached. However, it was also shown that dendritic applications always caused depolarizations (see above), obviously excluding factors 5 and 6, in spinal neurons. There is evidence that, in the cerebellum, some low onset inhibitory reponses can be elicited by L-glutamate. To date no mechanism underlying this action has been established (Yamamoto et al., 1977). A predominantly indirect action of L-glutamate seems unlikely for the CNS primarily for two reasons: (1) microtopical application of tetrodotoxin (TTX) does not reduce the effect of L-glutamate; (2) intracellular injections of Cl^- do not alter L-glutamate actions. Although unlikely, a selective releasing action on, for example, terminals containing an excitatory neurotransmitter, cannot be excluded.

There is evidence that different L-glutamate receptors, as found in invertebrates, also exist on neurons of the mammalian CNS, and that these receptors are not homogeneously distributed over the surface of the neuron. However, due to the obviously insurmountable shortcomings of quantitative iontophoresis, and the complex geometry of the CNS, our knowledge of structure–activity relationships is still rather limited. For the analysis of glutaminergic pathways in the CNS it was postulated that a major breakthrough would be the development of a selective antagonist. Recently some substances have appeared to be promising candidates. Most of the compounds tested so far, however, have not been selective, and some of them displayed hyperpolarizing actions associated with a conductance increase (Krnjevic, 1974; Nistri and Constanti, 1979; Watkins, 1978).

Extra- and intracellular recordings, together with microiontophoretic or microtopical applications of *GABA* and its agonists and antagonists, have clearly demonstrated that inhibitory GABAergic transmission is operative at all levels of the neuraxis of the mammalian CNS (for review, see Hösli and Hösli, 1978; Nistri and Constanti, 1979). For obvious reasons no reliable kinetic data on the transmitter/receptor interaction in the CNS exist. In general, it is assumed that all pre- and postsynaptic effects of GABA in mammals involve increases in Cl^--permeability; however, this should not preclude a more subtle analysis (see, e.g., ten Bruggencate and Engberg, 1969, 1971). Shunting of both the pre- and postsynaptic membrane and the hyperpolarization render the cells less excitable to synaptic, chemical and electrical stimulation. Cells in cultured neuronal tissue displayed some features which were not detectable in mature, intact preparations. These responses could be due to: (1) non-physiological ionic driving forces; (2) conductances not present in later stages of development; or (3) voltage-sensitivity of the GABA responses. Despite the fact that cultured neurons might have some juvenile properties, they offer great advantages with respect to their accessibility for current noise analysis and for analysis of the elementary conductance values for single transmitter-operated channels (for references see, e.g., Barker and McBurney, 1978; McBurney and Barker, 1978). Some observations were reported that support the existence of at least two types of GABA receptor in the mammalian CNS which prefer different conformations (folded/extended) of GABA agonists and antagonists (for references, see Nistri and Constanti, 1979). It is not yet clear whether the depolarizing actions of GABA exerted on autonomic or sensory ganglia, or on several in vitro preparations, are mediated via different receptors or are due to different ion gradients sustained (like in central neurons) by active transport mechanisms for Cl^- ions. Like the hyperpolarizing actions of GABA, the depolarizing effects are also reversibly antagonized by picrotoxin and bicuculline in a non-competitive manner (for review, see Nistri and Constanti, 1979).

As was first predicted by Eccles et al. (1962), GABA is one of the most promising candidates in the spinal cord for mediating primary afferent depolarization (Curtis and Lodge, 1978; Gmelin, 1978; see also Levy, 1977), and is the transmitter for presynaptic inhibition of large diameter myelinated primary afferent fibers. There exists an inverse relationship between the excitability of terminals tested with the Wall technique, and the transmitter released from primary afferent terminals. The pharmacology of these presynaptic receptors is largely unknown. It is tacitly assumed that receptors on the terminal have similar pharmacological properties as those located at their cell bodies in the dorsal root ganglia, which therefore have been extensively studied as a model (see, e.g., Deschenes et al., 1976; Desarmenien et al., 1980, and references therein). These cell bodies are virtually insensitive to L-glutamate, acetylcholine and opioid peptides (Williams and Zieglgänsberger, 1981), but are markedly depolarized by GABA.

Glycine is found in most tissues. The uneven distribution of high concentrations of glycine in certain areas of the vertebrate nervous system suggests a distinct role (see Krnjevic, 1974; Curtis and Johnston, 1974). This amino acid is primarily confined to: (1) the ventral enlargements of the spinal cord, the site of most extensive interneuronal interactions between afferent fibers and efferent motor systems; (2) the pons and medulla regions where it might, in addition to interneuronal interactions, give rise to descending pathways, and (3) some retinal neurons. Glycine was considered not to be of major importance as a transmitter in the cerebellum and the cerebral cortex (but see Bernardi et al., 1979). In the areas of highest glycine concentrations, a high-affinity uptake system exists (for references see Nistri and Constanti, 1979). The selective uptake of glycine into terminals and brain homogenates supports the assumption that glycine is a neurotransmitter in these areas (Iversen and Bloom, 1972; Ljungdahl and Hökfelt, 1973). Compared to GABA, where formation in the terminals by glutamic acid decarboxylase (GAD) and the pre- and postsynaptic breakdown by GABA-transaminase (GABA-T), are well established, the metabolism of glycine and the possible clinical implications of glycinergic mechanisms are less well understood.

Electrophysiological studies have demonstrated that glycine, like GABA, fulfills the physiological critera for an ionotropic, inhibitory neurotransmitter (see Curtis and Johnston, 1974; Krnjevic, 1974). With regard to the activated ionophore, glycine and GABA cannot be distinguished. Both increase the conductance of the postsynaptic membrane to Cl^- ions, suggesting that this ionic channel is coupled to both amino acid receptors and that its kinetics are determined by the transmitter that is released (see Barker and McBurney, 1979). The actions of glycine on inhibitory spinal interneurons or motoneurons are selectively antagonized by strychnine, whereas GABA actions are antagonized by bicuculline and picrotoxin. It has been shown that glycine responses can be evoked with a shorter delay when the amino acid is applied close to the soma, suggesting a topographic distribution of inhibitory glycinergic synapses on the spinal motoneurons of the cat (Zieglgänsberger and Champagnat, 1979).

III. Amines: Dopamine, Norepinephrine, Serotonin

The *dopaminergic* neuronal system originates primarily from cell bodies clustered in various sites of the brain stem (A9, A10, A12). These three distinct systems are involved in extrapyramidal (nigrostriatal), behavioral and emotional (mesolimbic-mesacortical) and endocrine (tuberoinfundibular) functions (see Costa and Gessa, 1977). Dopaminergic neurons are also found scattered in the brain stem and other central and peripheral sites. Axons of the dopaminergic system show a most amazing divergence and are, therefore, probably not involved in clearly time-locked information transfer, but should be able to tune arrays of cells. It is interesting to note that dopamine release seems not to be restricted to, for example, striatal sites, but has also been demonstrated to occur from dendrites of the projection neuron (Groves et al., 1975). Investigations employing toxic agents like 6-hydroxydopamine (6-OHDA) (see Johnsson et al., 1975), suggest that dopaminergic transmission is involved at most diverse sites in the nervous system (for review see, e.g., McGeer et al., 1980). However, due to the fact that most dopaminergic terminals impinge on small cells, the ionic mechanism underlying the action(s) of dopamine is still largely unknown. Several extracellular studies have demonstrated that dopamine has primarily an inhibitory action on spontaneous, chemically or synaptically induced neuronal firing (for review, see Krnjevic, 1974). A synopsis of the most complex data obtained by various groups gives credence to the belief that stimulation of the descending dopaminergic system inhibits opioid-induced antinociception also at the spinal level. Depression of this system by dopamine antagonists potentiates the effect of the narcotic analgesics (see Bläsig, 1978; Heinz and Jurna, 1979; Jurna et al., 1978). There is evidence that this inhibitory action is due to a hyperpolarizing effect on the postsynaptic membrane (Herrling, 1981). However, other studies have shown depolarizing actions (Kitai et al., 1976) and also some novel mechanisms, where the firing rate decreases despite an obvious depolarizing action on the membrane potential that is associated with no detectable change in input resistance (Bernardi et al., 1978). It is not clear whether, at all sites tested, dopaminergic actions are not also partially mediated via adrenoreceptors. Dopamine and norepinephrine hyperpolarize hippocampal neurons and decrease membrane conductance (Herrling, 1981), unlike observations that were made in caudate neurons (Herrling and Hull, 1980). Such an increase in membrane input resistance might also explain the observed increased amplitude of evoked postsynaptic transients (see also below). Studies performed mostly in isolated superior cervica ganglia suggest that dopamine might have actions mediated via cyclic nucleotides as second messengers (see Bloom, 1975, 1976; Greengard, 1976, 1978).

Although the pharmacological systems of *norepinephrine* and dopamine overlap considerably, dopamine and norepinephrine responses can usually be distinguished by antagonists. Besides their different sites of origin, noradrenergic fibers are characterized by the presence of dopamine-beta-hydroxylase, the enzyme catalyzing the conversion of dopamine to norepinephrine. This enzyme is localized in storage vesicles and can be used as a histochemical marker for noradrenergic terminals. Fiber systems originating from areas A1, A2, A5 and A7, with a major contribution from cell bodies in the locus coeruleus, are the main sources of noradrenergic fibers for the CNS. A1 and A2 cell bodies project caudally into the spinal cord (see Nygren and Olson, 1977; Fleetwood-Walker and Coote, 1981, and references therein). Like dopaminergic fiber systems, noradrenergic fibers show an enormous degree of divergence (for review, see Moore and Bloom, 1979). By pharmacological manipulations, various pre- and postsynaptically located receptors (see Littauer et al., 1980) have been differentiated in the peripheral nervous system. However, a comparable differentiation of multiple receptors cannot easily be applied to the CNS.

The predominant effect of iontophoretically administered norepinephrine is a depression of spontaneous, chemically and synaptically induced firing. Neurons in the dorsal horn are also inhibited by iontophoretically applied norepinephrine (Belcher et al., 1978; Engberg and Ryall, 1966; Headley et al., 1978; see also Moore and Bloom, 1979). This action is most likely terminated by specific uptake mechanisms into nerve terminals. It is possible that some of the occasionally observed excitatory or biphasic effects are artifactual. In a most extensive study, Bloom's group (Siggins et al., 1971) has analyzed inhibitory noradrenergic actions in the cerebellum, and has provided convincing evidence in favor of an involvement of cAMP as a second messenger (also in vivo). Like spinal motoneurons of the cat (Marshal and Engberg, 1979, and see references therein), and hippocampal cells in vivo (Herrling, 1981) and in vitro (Segal, 1981), Purkinje cells were hyperpolarized by norepinephrine. Intracellular studies performed in hippocampal cells in vitro suggested that the hyperpolarizing actions of norepinephrine, which are associated with a decrease in input resistance, involve two mechanisms: (1) activation of Cl^- conductance; and (2) the activation of a Na/K pump, possibly mediated by cAMP (Segal, 1981, and see references therein). In vivo studies performed in spinal motoneurons (Marshal and Engberg, 1979) and in hippocampal cells showed an increase in input resistance following norepinephrine application (Herrling, 1981). This finding was attributed to a decrease of Na^+ and K^+ ion permeability or to Na-pump activation. The hyperpolarizing effect in the cerebellar neurons (in vivo), which was also associated with no change or an increase in membrane resistance, was potentiated by phosphodiesterase inhibitors (see Siggins, 1979). Comparable results were obtained in vivo in cultured Purkinje cells (Gähwiler, 1976).

Immunohistochemical techniques that employed antibodies against the characterizing enzyme of adrenergic neurons as marker (phenylethanolamine-N-methyltransferase), have demonstrated adrenaline in various parts of the mammalian CNS which are known to also contain noradrenergic cell bodies.

At present the physiological role of adrenaline in the CNS is totally obscure (see Moore and Bloom, 1979).

There is experimental evidence that *serotonin* plays a role as a neurotransmitter in invertebrates. Presumptive evidence exists that cyclic nucleotides are involved in the mediation of the effects. In vertebrates, serotoninergic mechanisms have now been implicated in sleep, sexual behavior, mood and mental illness and pain sensitivity (for review, see Essman, 1978). Most of the cell bodies containing serotonin in the mammalian CNS are located in the raphe and the reticular system of the brain stem. Our understanding of the anatomy of the serotoninergic system is still rather poor (Fuxe and Johnsson, 1974) and awaits new, more sensitive techniques which can also be used at the ultrastructural level (Chan-Palay et al., 1978; Pickel et al., 1976). Caudal parts of the raphe system give rise to descending pathways to the spinal cord, whereas the rostral parts send their fibers to diencephalic and telencephalic sites. The descending fibers end mainly in the lateral horn, but connections are also made with ventral and dorsal horn neurons (for references see Mayer and Price, 1976; Fields and Basbaum, 1978). Like the catecholaminergic fibers, serotoninergic fibers also ramify extensively. Microiontophoretic application of serotonin onto spinal neurons reduces the firing rate of dorsal horn neurons, a finding consistent with an inhibitory role of these pathways (Belcher et al., 1978; Headley et al., 1978; Randic and Yu, 1976) and serotonin's proposed role in nociceptive mechanisms (for review see, e.g., Mayer and Price, 1976; Fields and Basbaum, 1978; Yaksh and Wilson, 1979, and references cited therein). Recent data suggest that serotoninergic fibers also contain neuropeptides like substance P (see below), and that both substances might even be co-released (see Hökfelt et al., 1980). A co-release of neurotransmitters and neuropeptides might be postulated to occur at various central and peripheral sites of the nervous system. The functional implications of these mechanisms, however, are still obscure (see below). The biochemical pathways of serotonin metabolism are rather well understood, but turnover rates and control are largely unknown (see McGeer et al., 1980). The most general effect of phoretically applied serotonin is an inhibition of firing. In most areas of the CNS studied, this effect is blocked by antagonists like D-lysergic acid diethylamide (see Segal, 1980a, and references therein). Intracellular studies performed in vitro in hippocampal cells showed that the hyperpolarizing action of serotonin is associated with an increase in membrane conductance. It was suggested that serotonin activates K^+-channels in these cells (Segal, 1980a). The assumption of a postsynaptic action is based largely on the finding that L-glutamate actions are markedly reduced by serotonin (Jordan et al., 1978), and that the hyperpolarizing actions are also present in low-Ca/high-Mg medium (Segal, 1980b).

IV. Neuropeptides: Substance P, Enkephalins

More than 20 neuropeptides have been identified in the mammalian CNS. Some of them were previously known as neurohormones (see Gainer, 1977). There is evidence that some of these neuropeptides co-exist in neurons with other neurotransmitters (see Table 1 in Hökfelt et al., 1980).

Substance P was the first pharmacologically characterized neuropeptide. It has a widespread distribution in the peripheral and central nervous systems and seems to be involved in a variety of neuronal processes (see Skrabanek and Powell, 1977). Little is known about its synthesis, which might take place in the cell bodies of, for example, dorsal root ganglion cells, with subsequent transport to central and peripheral sites. There is evidence that the peptides are processed from a ribosomally synthesized precursor on their way to the release site(s). No mechanism of inactivation of substance P has yet been described. Substance P was demonstrated in small-diameter fibers of primary afferent neurons in the dorsal horn of the spinal cord (Barber et al., 1979; Chan-Palay and Palay, 1977; Cuello and Kanazawa, 1978; Hökfelt et al., 1975; Ljungdahl et al., 1978) and its analogue structure in the trigeminal complex (Dubner et al., 1976). The excitatory action of substance P on its target neurons has supported the assumption that substance P might be involved in somatosensory transmission, including nociception (see Henry, 1976; Lembeck and Zetler, 1962). In addition, in other sites in the CNS, substance P-reactive material was found in spinal neurons (see Table 1 in Nicoll, 1980b). Ultrastructural studies have shown substance P-reactive material to occur in synaptic vesicles (Barber et al., 1979; Chan-Palay and Palay, 1977; Cuello et al., 1977; Hökfelt et al., 1977; Pickel et al., 1977; Pelletier et al., 1977). There is evidence in favor of a co-existence of substance P and serotonin in some medullary neurons (Chan-Palay et al., 1978; Hökfelt et al., 1978) that presumably project to the spinal cord (for review, see Table 1 in Hökfelt et al., 1980). Substance P is released from neuronal tissue following depolarizing stimuli, both in vitro and in vivo, by a Ca-dependent mechanism (Gamse et al., 1979; Jessel and Iversen, 1977; Jessel et al., 1978; Mudge et al., 1979; Otsuka and Konishi, 1976; Yaksh et al., 1980). This release may occur not only at the terminal sites, but also at the peripheral endings of these fibers (see Nicoll et al., 1980b). When applied to neonatal animals, capsaicin, a pungent constituent of red pepper, depletes substance P only from sensory neurons. This depletion results in a functional impairment of sensory function, including nociception (preferentially for heat), and in degeneration of small-diameter fibers. In adult animals the evoked release of substance P is also restricted to sensory neurons, but it is not associated with a detectable degeneration of neuronal elements (for references, see Gamse et al., 1979, Holzer et al., 1979; Jancso et al., 1977; Williams and Zieglgänsberger, in press; Yaksh et al., 1980). Capsaicin induces a depolarization of dorsal root ganglion cells. These depolarizing responses showed a marked desensitization and were associated with conductance increase of the postsynaptic membrane. Both A- and C-fiber cell bodies were depolarized. In the latter cells the depolarizing action was only partially reversible. Pressure application of capsaicin to dorsal horn sites of the rat resulted in a transient excitation of most cells (multimodal input) in laminae 4 and 5. After capsaicin administration all neurons studied still responded to light touch, pressure and to locally applied glutamate, but could not be driven anymore by noxious heat stimulation (Williams and Zieglgänsberger, in press).

Using intracellular recordings from spinal neurons of the cat, studies have shown that the increase in excitability following iontophoretic substance P application is associated with depolarization (Konishi and Otsuka, 1974; Krnjevic, 1977; Zieglgänsberger and Tulloch, 1979a, and references cited therein). The ionic mechanism of the depolarization has not yet been established. An increase (Krnjevic, 1977), and no change (Zieglgänsberger and Tulloch, 1979a), in conductance have been reported. During the latter study evidence was obtained that dendritic sites also did not change their conductance following substance P administration. The most striking aspect of the effects produced by substance P was the extended time course of its action. The onset and offset of the excitatory effect of substance P often occurred over a period of several minutes. The excitatory effects in the various neuronal structures tested were variable and tended to decrease with repeated application (for review, see Nicoll et al., 1980b). Some synthetic substance P derivates seem to possess antagonistic properties in neurons of the locus coeruleus (Engberg et al., 1981). The use of a series of substance P analogues having different biological activities may partially substitute for a substance P antagonist to indicate some specificity of action. There is some evidence that the effects produced by substance P are mediated through a specific receptor. This was deduced after substance P binding sites were demonstrated in a membrane fraction from rabbit brain (Nakata et al., 1978), and the binding affinity of a series of SP analogues correlated well with their biological activity.

The use of isolated preparations eliminates some of the problems associated with iontophoresis of substance P. Bath application of known amounts of substance P has been used to study spinal motoneurons of frog and rat isolated spinal cords (Konishi and Otsuka, 1974), sympathetic ganglia (Dun and Karczmar, 1979), and myenteric ganglia (Katayama et al., 1979). The depolarization observed in the isolated spinal cord and in the myenteric ganglia was usually associated with an increase in membrane conductance. In spinal cord cells, the depolarization was determined to be a direct action since it was not changed in a solution where synaptic transmission was blocked. Furthermore, a series of analogues was used to test the specificity of this effect. The depolarization of guinea pig myenteric neurons produced by substance P was associated with a decrease in membrane conductance, probably for K^+ ions (Katayama et al., 1979). The specificity of action was tested using two relatively inactive substance P analogues. In addition, unlike in spinal neurons, the effective concentration of substance P on myenteric neurons compared

Engberg, G., Svensson, T.H., Rosell, S. and Folkers, K. (1981) A synthetic peptide as an antagonist of substance P, *Nature (Lond.)*, 293: 222-223.

Essman, W.B. (1978) *Serotonin in Health and Disease, Vols. 1-5*, Spectrum Publ., New York.

Fields, H.L. and Basbaum, A. (1978) Brain stem control of spinal pain transmission neurons, *Ann. Rev. Physiol.*, 40: 193-221.

Fields, H.L., Emson, P.C., Leigh, B.K., Gilbert, R.F.T. and Iversen, L.L. (1980) Multiple opiate binding sites on primary afferent fibers, *Nature (Lond.)*, 283: 351-353.

Fleetwood-Walker, S.M. and Coote, J.H. (1981) Contribution of noradrenaline, dopamine and adrenaline-containing axons to the innervation of different regions of the spinal cord, *Brain Res.*, 206: 95-106.

Frederickson, R.C.A. (1977) Enkephalin pentapeptides – A review of current evidence for a physiological role in vertebrate neurotransmission, *Life Sci.*, 21: 23-42.

Fuxe, K. and Johnsson, G. (1974) Further mapping of central 5-hydroxytryptamine neurons: studies with the neurotoxic dihydroxytryptamines. In E. Costa, G.L. Gessa and M. Sandler (Eds.), *Advances in Biochem. Pharmacol., Vol. 10*, Raven Press, New York, pp. 1-12.

Gainer, H. (1977) *Neurobiology of Peptides*, Plenum Press, New York.

Gähwiler, B.H. (1976) Inhibitory action of noradrenaline and cyclic AMP in explant of rat cerebellum, *Nature (Lond.)*, 259: 483-484.

Gähwiler, B.H. (1980) Excitatory action of opioid peptides and opiates on cultured hippocampal pyramidal cells, *Brain Res.*, 194: 193-203.

Gall, C., Brecha, N., Karten, H.J. and Chang, K.J. (1981) Localization of enkephalin-like immunoreactivity to identified axonal and neuronal populations of the rat hippocampus, *J. comp. Neurol.*, in press.

Gamse, R., Molnar, A. and Lembeck, F. (1979) Substance P release from spinal cord slices by capsaicin, *Life Sci.*, 25: 629-636.

Gamse, R., Holzer, P. and Lembeck, F. (1980) Decrease of substance P in primary afferent neurons and impairment of neurogenic plasma extravasation by capsaicin, *Brit. J. Pharmacol.*, 68: 207-213.

Gerschenfeld, H.M. (1973) Chemical transmission in invertebrate central nervous system and neuromuscular junctions, *Physiol. Rev.*, 53: 1-119.

Glazer, E.J. and Basbaum, A.I. (1980) Ultrastructural localization of leucine enkephalin in the superficial dorsal horn of the cat, *Soc. Neurosci. Abstr.*, 6: 523.

Gmelin, G.W. (1978) Electrophoretic studies on presynaptic inhibition in the mammalian spinal cord. In R.W. Ryall and J.S. Kelly (Eds.), *Iontophoresis and Transmitter Mechanisms in the Mammalian Central Nervous System*, Elsevier/North-Holland, Amsterdam, pp. 267-269.

Goodman, R.R., Snyder, H.J., Kuhar, M.J. and Young, W.S. (1980) Differentiation of delta and mu opiate receptor localization by light microscopic autoradiography, *Proc. nat. Acad. Sci. U.S.A.*, 77: 6239-6243.

Greengard, P. (1976) Possible role for cyclic nucleotides and phosphorylated membrane proteins in postsynaptic actions of neurotransmitters, *Nature (Lond.)*, 234: 100-103.

Greengard, P. (1978) *Cyclic Nucleotides, Phosphorylated Proteins and Neuronal Function*, Raven Press, New York.

Groves, P.M., Wilson, C.J., Young, S.J. and Rebec, G.V. (1975) Self-inhibition by dopamine neurons, *Science*, 190: 522-529.

Haas, H.L. and Ryall, R.W. (1981) Is excitation by enkephalins of hippocampal neurons in the rat due to presynaptic facilitation or to disinhibition? *J. Physiol. (Lond.)*, 303: 315-330.

Headley, P.M., Duggan, A.W. and Griersmith, B.T. (1978) Selective reduction by noradrenaline and 5-hydroxytryptamine of nociceptive responses of cat dorsal horn neurons, *Brain Res.*, 145: 185-189.

Heinemann, U. and Pumain, R. (1980) Extracellular calcium activity changes in cat sensorimotor cortex induced by iontophoretic application of amino acids, *Exp. Brain Res.*, 40: 247-250.

Heinz, G. and Jurna, I. (1979) The anti-nociceptive effect of reserpine and haloperidol mediated by

468

the nigrostriatal system: antagonism by naloxone, *Naunyn-Schmiedeberg's Arch. Pharmacol.*, 306: 97-100,

Henderson, G., Hughes, J. and Kosterlitz, H.W. (1978) In vitro release of leu- and met-enkephalin from the corpus striatum, *Nature (Lond.)*, 271: 677-679.

Henriksen, S.J., Bloom, F.E., McCoy, F., Ling, N. and Guillemin, R. (1978) Beta-endorphin induced nonconvulsive limbic seizures, *Proc. nat. Acad. Sci. U.S.A.*, 75: 5221-5225.

Henry, J.L. (1976) Effects of substance P on functionally identified units in cat spinal cord, *Brain Res.*, 114: 439-451.

Herkenham, M. and Pert, C.B. (1980) In vitro autoradiography of opiate receptors in rat brain suggest loci of "opiatergic" pathways, *Proc. nat. Acad. Sci. U.S.A.*, 77: 5532-5536.

Herrling, P.L. (1981) The membrane potential of cat hippocampal neurons recorded in vivo displays four different reaction-mechanisms to iontophoretically applied transmitter agonists. *Brain Res.*, 212: 331-343.

Herrling, P.L. and Hull, C.D. (1980) Iontophoretically applied dopamine depolarizes and hyperpolarizes the membrane of cat caudate neurones, *Brain Res.*, 192: 441-462.

Hökfelt, T., Kellerth, J.O., Nilsson, G. and Pernow, B. (1975) Substance P: localization in the central nervous system and in some primary sensory neurons, *Science*, 190: 889-890.

Hökfelt, T., Johansson, O., Kellerth, J.O., Ljungdahl, A., Nilsson, G., Nygards, A. and Pernow, B. (1977) Immunohistochemical distribution of substance P. In U.S. von Euler and B. Pernow (Eds.), *Substance P*, Raven Press, New York, pp. 117-145.

Hökfelt, T., Ljungdahl, A., Steinbusch, H., Verhofstad, A., Nilsson, G., Brodin, E., Pernow, B. and Goldstein, M. (1978) Immunohistochemical evidence of substance P-like immunoreactivity in some 5-hydroxytryptamine-containing neurons in the rat central nervous system, *Neuroscience*, 3: 517-538.

Hökfelt, T., Johansson, O., Ljungdahl, A., Lundberg, J.M. and Schultzberg, M. (1980) Peptidergic neurones, *Nature (Lond.)*, 284: 515-521.

Holzer, P., Jurna, I., Gamse, R. and Lembeck, L. (1979) Nociceptive threshold after neonatal capsaicin treatment, *Europ. J. Pharmacol.*, 53: 511-514.

Hösli, L. and Hösli, E. (1978) Action and uptake of neurotransmitters in CNS tissue culture, *Rev. Physiol. Biochem. Pharmacol.*, 81: 135-188.

Hughes, J., Smith, T.W., Kosterlitz, H., Fothergill, L., Morgan, B. and Morris, H. (1975) Identification of two related pentapeptides from the brain with potent opiate agonist activity, *Nature (Lond.)*, 258: 577-579.

Hunt, S.P., Kelly, J.S. and Emson, P.C. (1980) The electron microscopic localization of methionine-enkephalin within the superficial layers (I and II) of the spinal cord, *Neuroscience*, 5: 1871-1890.

Illes, P., Zieglgänsberger, W. and Herz, A. (1979) Normorphine inhibits neurotransmission in the mouse vas deferens by a calcium-dependent mechanism, *Neurosci. Lett.*, 3: 238.

Iversen, L.L. and Bloom, F.E. (1972) Studies of the uptake of [^{3}H]-GABA and [^{3}H]-glycine in slices and homogenates of rat brain and spinal cord by electron microscopic autoradiography, *Brain Res.*, 41: 131-143.

Iversen, L.L., Lee, C.M., Gilbert, R.F., Hunt, S. and Emson, P.C. (1980) Regulation of neuropeptide release, *Proc. roy. Soc. B*, 210: 91-111.

Jancso, G., Kiraly, E. and Jancso-Gabor, A. (1977) Pharmacologically induced selective degeneration of chemosensitive primary sensory neurones, *Nature (Lond.)*, 270: 741-743.

Jessel, T.M. and Iversen, L.L. (1977) Opiate analgesics inhibit substance P release from rat trigeminal nucleus, *Nature (Lond.)*, 268: 549-551.

Jessel, T.M., Iversen, L.L. and Cuello, A.C. (1978) Capsaicin-induced depletion of substance P from primary sensory neurones, *Brain Res.*, 152: 183-188.

Johnsson, G., Malmfors, T. and Sachs, C. (Eds.), (1975) *6-Hydroxydopamine as a Denervation Tool in Catecholamine Research*, North-Holland Publ., Amsterdam.

Jordan, L.M., Kenshalo, D.R., Martin, R.F., Haber, L.H. and Willis, W.D. (1978) Depression of primate spino-thalamic tract neurons by iontophoretic application of 5-hydroxytryptamine, *Pain*, 5: 135-142.

Jurna, I., Heinz, G., Blinn, G. and Nell, T. (1978) The effect of substantia nigra stimulation and morphine on alpha-motoneurons and the tail-flick response, *Europ. J. Pharmacol.*, 51: 239-250.

Katayama, Y., North, R.A. and Williams, J.T. (1979) The action of substance P on neurons of the myenteric plexus of the guinea pig small intestine, *Proc. roy. Soc. B*, 206: 191-208.

Kitai, S.T., Sugimori, M. and Koscis, J.D. (1976) Excitatory nature of dopamine in the nigro-caudate pathway, *Exp. Brain Res.*, 24: 351-363.

Konishi, S. and Otsuka, M. (1974) The effects of substance P and other peptides on spinal neurons of the frog, *Brain Res.*, 65: 397-410.

Krnjevic, K. (1974) Chemical nature of synaptic transmission in vertebrates, *Physiol. Rev.*, 54: 418-540.

Krnjevic, K. (1977) Effects of substance P on central neurons in cats. In U.S. von Euler and B. Pernow (Eds.), *Substance P*, Plenum Press, New York, pp. 217-230.

LaMotte, C. and de Lanerolle, N. (1981) Substance P, enkephalin and serotonin: ultrastructural basis of pain transmission in primate spinal cord, *Pain*, 1: 19.

LaMotte, C., Pert, C.B. and Snyder, S.H. (1976) Opiate receptor binding in primate spinal cord: distribution and changes after dorsal root section, *Brain Res.*, 112: 407-412.

Lembeck, F. and Zetler, G. (1962) Substance P: a polypeptide of possible physiological significance especially within the nervous system, *Int. Rev. Neurobiol.*, 4: 159-215.

Levy, R.A. (1977) The role of GABA in primary afferent depolarization, *Progr. Neurobiol.*, 9: 211-267.

Littauer, U.Z., Dudai, Y., Silman, I., Teichberg, V.I. and Vogel, Z. (Eds.), (1980) *Neurotransmitters and their Receptors*, John Wiley, New York, 569 pp.

Ljungdahl, A. and Hökfelt, T. (1973) Autoradiographic uptake patterns of [^{3}H]-GABA and [^{3}H]-glycine in central nervous tissue with special reference to the cat spinal cord, *Brain Res.*, 62: 587-595.

Ljungdahl, A., Hökfelt, T., Nilsson, G. and Goldstein, M. (1978) Distribution of substance P-like immunoreactivity in the central nervous system of the rat. II. Light microscopic localization in relation to catecholamine-containing neurons, *Neuroscience*, 3: 945-976.

MacDonald, R.L. and Nelson, P.G. (1978) Specific-opiate-induced depression of transmitter release from dorsal root ganglion cells in culture, *Science*, 199: 1449-1451.

Marshal, K.C. and Engberg, I. (1979) Reversal potential for noradrenaline-induced hyperpolarization of spinal motoneurons, *Science*, 205: 422-424.

Mayer, D.J. and Price, D.D. (1976) Central nervous system mechanisms of analgesia, *Pain*, 2: 379-404.

McBurney, R.N. and Barker, J.L. (1978) GABA-induced conductance fluctuations in cultured spinal neurones, *Nature (Lond.)*, 274: 596-597.

McGeer, P.L., Eccles, J.C. and McGeer, E. (1980) *Molecular Neurobiology of the Mammalian Brain*, Plenum Press, New York.

Moore, R.Y. and Bloom, F.E. (1979) Central catecholamine neurone systems: anatomy and physiology of the norepinephrine and epinephrine system, *Ann. Rev. Neurosci.*, 2: 113-168.

Mudge, A., Leeman, S. and Fischbach, G. (1979) Enkephalin inhibits release of substance P from sensory neurons in culture and decreases action potential duration, *Proc. nat. Acad. Sci. U.S.A.*, 76: 526-530.

Nagy, J.I., Vincent, S.R., Staines, W.M.A., Fibiger, H.C., Reisine, T.D. and Yamamura, H.I. (1980) Neurotoxic action of capsaicin on spinal substance P neurons, *Brain Res.*, 186: 435-444.

Nakata, Y., Kusuka, Y., Segawa, T., Yajima, H. and Kitgawa, K. (1978) Substance P: regional distribution and specific binding to synaptic membranes in rabbit central nervous system, *Life Sci.*, 22: 259-268.

Nicoll, R.A., Siggins, G.R., Ling, N., Bloom, F.E. and Guillemin, R. (1977) Neuronal actions of endorphin and enkephalins among brain regions: a comparative microiontophoretic study, *Proc. nat. Acad. Sci. U.S.A.*, 74: 2584-2588.

470

Nicoll, R.A., Alger, B.E. and Jahr, C.E. (1980a) Enkephalin blocks inhibitory pathways in the vertebrate CNS, *Nature (Lond.)*, 287: 22-25.

Nicoll, R.A., Schenker, C. and Leeman, S.E. (1980b) Substance P as a transmitter candidate, *Ann. Rev. Neurosci.*, 3: 227-263.

Nistri, A.A. and Constanti, A. (1979) Pharmacological characterization of different types of GABA and glutamate receptors in vertebrates and invertebrates, *Progr. Neurobiol.*, 13: 117-235.

North, R.A. (1979) Opiates, opioid peptides and single neurones, *Life Sci.*, 24: 1527-1546.

Nygren, L.G. and Olson, L. (1977) A new major projection from locus coeruleus: the main source of noradrenergic nerve terminals in the ventral and dorsal columns of the spinal cord, *Brain Res.*, 132: 85-93.

Osborne, H., Höllt, V. and Herz, A. (1978) Subcellular distribution of enkephalins and endogenous opioid activity in rat brain, *Life Sci.*, 22: 611-618.

Otsuka, M. and Konishi, S. (1976) Release of substance P-like immunoreactivity from isolated spinal cord of newborn rat, *Nature (Lond.)*, 264: 83-84.

Pert, C.B. and Snyder, S.H. (1974) Opiate receptor binding of agonists and antagonists affected differentially by sodium, *Molec. Pharmacol.*, 10: 868-879.

Pelletier, G., Leclerc, R. and Dupont, A. (1977) Electron microscope immunohistochemical localization of substance P in the central nervous system of the rat, *J. Histochem. Cytochem.*, 25: 1373-1380.

Pepper, Ch.M. and Henderson, G. (1980) Opiate and opioid peptides hyperpolarize locus coeruleus neurons in vitro, *Science*, 209: 394-396.

Pickel, V.M., Tong, H.J. and Reis, D.J. (1976) Monoamine synthetizing enzymes in central dopaminergic, noradrenergic and serotoninergic neurons, *J. Histochem. Cytochem.*, 24: 792-806.

Pickel, V.M., Reis, D.J. and Leeman, S.E. (1977) Ultrastructural localization of substance P in neurons of rat spinal cord, *Brain Res.*, 122: 534-540.

Price, D.D., Hull, C.D. and Buchwald, N.A. (1971) Intracellular responses of dorsal horn cells to cutaneous and sural nerve A and C fiber stimuli, *Exp. Neurol.*, 33: 291-309.

Randic, M. and Miletic, V. (1977) Effect of Substance P in cat dorsal horn neurones activated by noxious stimuli, *Brain Res.*, 128: 164-169.

Randic, M. and Yu, H.H. (1976) Effects of 5-hydroxytryptamine and bradykinin in cat dorsal horn neurones activated by noxious stimuli, *Brain Res.*, 111: 197-203.

Roberts, E., Chase, T.N. and Tower, D.B. (Eds.) (1976) *GABA in Nervous System Function*, Raven Press, New York.

Ruda, M.A. (1981) Ultrastructural demonstration of direct enkephalinergic input onto medullary and spinal dorsal horn projection neurons, *Pain*, 1: 19.

Sar, M.W., Stumpf, W., Miller, R., Chang, K.J. and Cuatrecasas, P. (1978) Immunohistochemical localization of enkephalin in the rat brain and spinal cord, *J. comp. Neurol.*, 182: 17-38.

Sastry, B.R. (1978) Morphine and met-enkephalin effects on sural A-delta afferent terminal excitability, *Europ. J. Pharmacol.*, 50: 269-273.

Sastry, B.R. (1979a) Presynaptic effects of morphine and methionine-enkephalin in feline spinal cord, *J. Neurophysiol.*, 18: 367-375.

Sastry, B.R. (1979b) Substance P effects on spinal nociceptive neurons, *Life Sci.*, 24: 2169-2178.

Satoh, M., Zieglgänsberger, W. and Herz, A. (1976) Actions of opiates upon single unit activity in the cortex of naive and tolerant rats, *Brain Res.*, 115: 99-110.

Satoh, M., Akaike, A. and Takagi, H. (1979) Excitation by morphine and enkephalin of single neurons of nucleus reticularis paragigantocellularis in the rat: a probable mechanism of analgesic action of opioids, *Brain Res.*, 169: 406-410.

Segal, M. (1980a) The serotoninergic receptor in the rat hippocampus. In U.Z. Littauer, Y. Dudai, I. Silman, V.I. Teichberg and Z. Vogel (Eds.), *Neurotransmitters and their Receptors*, John Wiley and Sons, New York, pp. 89-100.

Segal, M. (1980b) The action of serotonin in the rat hippocampal slice preparation, *J. Physiol. (Lond.)*, 303: 423-439.

Segal, M. (1981) The action of norepinephrine in the rat hippocampus: intracellular studies in the slice preparation, *Brain Res.*, 206: 107-128.

Siggins, G.R. (1979) Neurotransmitters and neuromodulators and their mediation by cyclic nucleotides. In Y.E. Ehrlich, J. Volavka, L.G. Davis and E.G. Brunngraber (Eds.), *Modulators, Mediators and Specifiers in Brain Function*, Plenum, New York, pp. 41-64.

Siggins, G.R. and Zieglgänsberger, W. (1981) Morphine and opioid peptides reduce inhibitory synaptic potentials in hippocampal pyramidal cells in vitro without alteration of membrane potential, *Proc. nat. Acad. Sci. U.S.A.*, in press.

Siggins, G.R., Oliver, A.P., Hoffer, B.J. and Bloom, F.E. (1971) Cyclic adenosine monophosphate and norepinephrine: effects on transmembrane properties of cerebellar Purkinje cells, *Science*, 171: 192-194.

Skrabanek, P. and Powell, D. (1977) Substance P. In D.F. Horrobin (Ed.), *Annual Research Reviews*, Eden, Montreal, pp. 181.

Sonnhof, U., Grafe, P., Richter, D.W., Paretek, N., Krummikel, G. and Linder, M. (1978) Investigations of the effects of glutamate on motoneurones in the isolated frog spinal cord. In R.W. Ryall and J.S. Kelly (Eds.), *Iontophoresis and Transmitter Mechanisms in the Mammalian Central Nervous System*, Elsevier/North-Holland, Amsterdam, pp. 391-393.

ten Bruggencate, G. and Engberg, I. (1969) The effect of strychnine on inhibition in Deiter's nucleus induced by GABA and glycine, *Brain Res.*, 14: 536-539.

ten Bruggencate, G. and Engberg, I. (1971) Iontophoretic studies on Deiter's nucleus of the inhibitory actions of GABA and related amino acids and the interactions of strychnine and picrotoxine, *Brain Res.*, 25: 431-448.

Watkins, J.C. (1978) Excitatory amino acids. In E.G. McGeer, J.W. Olney and P.L. McGeer (Eds.), *Kainic Acid as a Tool in Neurobiology*, Raven Press, New York, pp. 37-69.

Werman, R. (1969) An electrophysiological approach to drug-receptor mechanisms, *Biochem. Physiol.*, 30: 997-1017.

Werman, R. and Carlen, P. (1976) Unusual behaviour of the IA EPSP in cat spinal motoneurons, *Brain Res.*, 112: 395-401.

Williams, J.T. and Zieglgänsberger, W. (1981a) Mature spinal ganglion cells are not sensitive to opiate receptor mediated actions, *Neurosci. Lett.*, 21: 211-216.

Williams, J.T. and Zieglgänsberger, W. (1981b) Neuropeptides in the primary afferent system of the spinal cord. In E. Costa and M. Trabucchi (Eds.), *Regulatory Peptides: Functional and Pharmacological Aspects*, Raven Press, New York.

Yaksh, T.L. and Rudy, T.A. (1978) Narcotic analgesics: CNS sites of action as revealed by intracerebral injection technique, *Pain*, 4: 299-359.

Yaksh, T.L. and Wilson, P.R. (1979) Spinal serotonin terminal system mediates antinociception, *J. Pharmacol. exp. Ther.*, 208: 446-453.

Yaksh, T., Farb, D.H., Leeman, S.E. and Jessel, T.M. (1979) Intrathecal capsaicin depletes substance P in the rat spinal cord and produces prolonged thermal analgesia, *Science*, 206: 481-483.

Yaksh, T.L., Jessel, T.M., Gamse, R., Mudge, A.W. and Leeman, S.E. (1980) Intrathecal morphine inhibits substance P release from mammalian spinal cord in vivo, *Nature (Lond.)*, 286: 155-157.

Yamamoto, C., Yamashita, H. and Chujo, T. (1977) Inhibition and excitation induced by glutamic acid on cerebellar interneurons, *Jap. J. Physiol.*, 27: 225-234.

Zieglgänsberger, W. (1980) Peptides in the regulation of neuronal function. In F.E. Bloom (Ed.), *Peptides: Integrators of Cell and Tissue Function*, Raven Press, New York, pp. 219-233.

Zieglgänsberger, W. and Bayerl, H. (1976) The mechanism of inhibition of neuronal activity by opiates in the spinal cord of cat, *Brain Res.*, 115: 111-128.

Zieglgänsberger, W. and Champagnat, J. (1978) L-Glutamate and glycine receptive sites on the somadendritic membrane of lumbar motoneurons of the cat. In R.W. Ryall and J.S. Kelly (Eds.), *Iontophoresis and Transmitter Mechanisms in the Mammalian Central Nervous System*, Elsevier/North-Holland, Amsterdam, pp. 103-105.

Zieglgänsberger, W. and Champagnat, J. (1979) Cat spinal motoneurons exhibit topographic sensitivity to glutamate and glycine, *Brain Res.*, 160: 95-104.

Zieglgänsberger, W. and Fry, J. (1978) Actions of opioids on single neurons. In A. Herz (Ed.), *Developments in Opiate Research*, Marcel Dekker, New York, pp. 193-239.

Zieglgänsberger, W. and Puil, E.A. (1972) Tetrodotoxin interference of CNS excitation by glutamic acid, *Nature New Biol.*, 239: 204-205.

Zieglgänsberger, W. and Puil, E.A. (1973) Actions of glutamic acid on spinal neurons, *Exp. Brain Res.*, 17: 35-49.

Zieglgänsberger, W. and Tulloch, I.F. (1979a) Effects of substance P on neurons in the dorsal horn of the spinal cord of the cat, *Brain Res.*, 166: 273-282.

Zieglgänsberger, W. and Tulloch, I.F. (1979b) The effects of methionine- and leucine-enkephalin on spinal neurons of the cat, *Brain Res.*, 167: 53-64.

Zieglgänsberger, W., French, E.D., Siggins, G.R. and Bloom, F.E. (1979) Opioid peptides may excite hippocampal pyramidal neurons by inhibiting adjacent inhibitory interneurons, *Science*, 205: 415-417.

Zieglgänsberger, W., Gessler, M., Rust, M. and Struppler, A. (1981) Neurophysiologische Grundlagen der spinalen Opiatanalgesie, *Anaesthetist*, 30: 342-346.

Brain Stem Control of Spinal Mechanisms
– B. Sjölund and A. Björklund, editors
© 1982 Elsevier Biomedical Press

21

Putative Transmitters of Descending Systems – Studies of Local Administration and Liberation

TONY L. YAKSH and DONNA L. HAMMOND

Departments of Neurosurgery and Pharmacology, Mayo Foundation, Rochester, MN 55905, U.S.A.

I. Introduction

In spinalized animals, the systemic administration of morphine results in a powerful inhibition of spinal reflexes (Wikler, 1950) and a reduction in the discharge of dorsal horn neurons evoked by noxious stimuli (Le Bars et al., 1975). These results first suggested that opiates exerted an action at the level of the spinal cord. Later studies reported that iontophoresis of opiates in the substantia gelatinosa inhibited the discharge of more deeply situated neurons evoked by high intensity somatic stimulation (Duggan et al., 1977), and offered more support for the concept that opiates exerted an action in the spinal cord. That such local actions of opiates would have relevance to the behavior of an intact, unanesthetized animal in response to noxious stimuli is supported by the results of studies in which opiates have been administered directly into the spinal cord by means of chronic indwelling catheters (Yaksh and Rudy, 1976). Thus, a powerful analgesia, as determined by a variety of simple and complex analgesiometric measures, is produced by the intrathecal injection of opiates in rat, cat, primate and man (Yaksh and Rudy, 1977; Yaksh and Reddy, 1981; Ventafridda et al., 1979; Wang et al., 1979).

The concept that opiates act at the level of the spinal cord received further credence with the report of high density opiate binding in the spinal cord dorsal horn (Atweh and Kuhar, 1977). The observation that dorsal rhizotomy reduced this binding (LaMotte et al., 1976) led to the suggestion that some of the actions of opiates in the spinal cord could be attributed to the reduction in the release of neurotransmitters from primary afferent terminals evoked by noxious stimulation and the accompanying reduction in the response of second order spinal cord neurons to these stimuli*. The demonstration of opiate ligand

---

* Recent reports have failed to identify enkephalin-containing nerve terminals in the dorsal horn adjacent to primary afferent terminals (Hunt et al., 1980). Whether this failure to see an anatomi-

binding in the spinal cord and the suggestion of receptors in the spinal cord was followed by the discovery of endogenous substances, notably the pentapeptides methionine- and leucine-enkephalin, which possess a pharmacology similar to that of the opiate alkaloids (Hughes et al., 1975). The complexity of the synthetic and metabolic pathways and the forms which such endogenous opiates may take are as yet only partially understood. However, populations of neurons exhibiting methionine- and leucine-enkephalin-like immunoreactivity have been visualized in various regions of the brain and in the substantia gelatinosa of the spinal cord (Hökfelt et al., 1977; Uhl et al., 1979). Thus, it appears probable that exogenous administration of opiates mimics the physiological effects of activating these enkephalin-containing neurons.

The inhibition of spinal reflex activity (Tsou and Jang, 1964) and the elevation of nociceptive threshold produced by intracerebral administration of opiates attest to a supraspinal action of opiates as well. Thus, microinjection of microgram doses of morphine in the periaqueductal gray (PAG) results not only in an elevation of an animal's threshold as measured by an operant task such as shock titration, but also a blockade of spinal reflex activity as measured by the tail flick test (Fig. 1). Subsequent studies have demonstrated that the microinjection of morphine in the PAG and other brain stem structures (Hayes et al., 1979) will also inhibit the discharge of dorsal horn neurons in response of noxious stimuli. These observations, and corollary observations with electrical stimulation of the brain stem (Fields et al., 1977; Guilbaud et al., 1977) and microinjection of the excitatory transmitter glutamate in the PAG (Behbehani and Fields, 1979), suggest that supraspinal manipulations alter the spinal processing of nociceptive information by the activation of descending modulatory pathways.

Early Swedish literature had previously pointed to a modulatory effect on spinal cord function of alterations in monoaminergic tone produced by systemic administration of a variety of precursors or inhibitors (Andén et al.,

---

cal proximity between receptors and afferents and the terminals of an enkephalin-containing cell indicates that a non-enkephalin-containing opiate is acting on the primary afferents, or whether the enkephalin cells may exert their effects on opiate receptors thought to be in primary afferents by a hormone-like spread, remains to be determined.

Figure 1. A, graph shows effects of microinjections of 5.0 µg/0.5 µl of morphine sulfate into the PAG in the site indicated in the schematic on the tail flick (top) and hot plate (bottom) escape latency. These responses were measured concurrently in the same experiment. The ordinate presents escape latency in seconds and the abscissa is time in minutes after the intracerebral injection of morphine. At the time indicated, naloxone (1 mg/kg, i.p.) was injected. B, graph shows the effects of microinjecting (5 µg/0.5 µl) morphine sulfate into three different sites in the same rat implanted with chronic intracerebral cannulae on the discrete trial shock titration response threshold. The ordinate represents the shock level in steps and the abscissa represents the time in minutes after the intracerebral injection of morphine. Sites of injection are presented in adjacent schematic sections. (Adapted from Yaksh et al., 1976.)

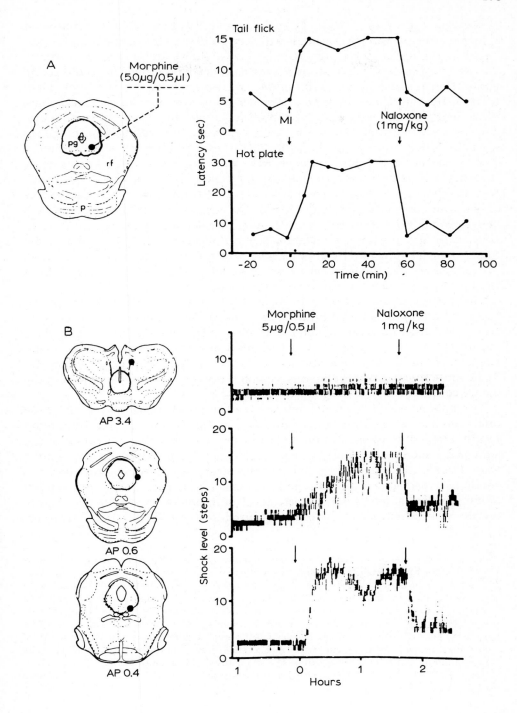

1966; Engberg et al., 1968). Dahlström and Fuxe's (1965) description of spinopetal monoaminergic systems which originated in the medulla and terminated in the spinal cord, provided the neural substrates for these observed physiological effects. Later studies, which employed methods for the discrete application of monoamines to the spinal cord, served to more definitively identify the effects produced by local activation of spinal monoaminergic receptors. Thus, iontophoretic administration of either serotonin or norepinephrine produces a profound inhibition of the discharge of dorsal horn nociceptors (Headley et al., 1978; Belcher et al., 1978). Intrathecal administration of serotonin and α-adrenergic, but not β-adrenergic, receptor agonists elevates nociceptive threshold, as determined by measures of reflex activity such as the tail flick test (Reddy et al., 1980; Yaksh and Wilson, 1979) and more complex measures of behavior such as the hot plate test or the shock titration paradigm (Yaksh and Reddy, 1981). As observed with intrathecally administered opiates, intrathecally administered monoamines elevated nociceptive threshold as defined by such supraspinally organized tests as the hot plate or shock titration. This indicates that the local activation of spinally located receptors can inhibit the rostral transmission of a sensory message.

These observations clearly indicate that activation of spinal monoaminergic receptors alters spinal cord processing of nociceptive information, as does intracerebral microinjection of opiates. In view of the data discussed, the following question may be formulated: is the effect of various brain stem manipulations on spinal function specifically mediated by the activation of spinopetal monoaminergic pathways and an accompanying release of monoamines in the spinal cord?

Two approaches have been employed to examine this question. First, if the effects on nociceptive threshold produced by morphine or electrical stimulation focally applied at various brain stem loci are dependent on activation of the spinopetal monoaminergic pathways and spinal monoaminergic receptors, then local antagonism of spinal noradrenergic and serotonergic receptors would be expected to attenuate the behavioral effects produced by supraspinal administration of morphine or electrical stimulation of brain stem loci. Figure 2 presents a schematic of the paradigm used to study the effects of intrathec-

---

Figure 2. Top, schematic representation of the animal preparation employed to examine the pharmacology of the effects produced on spinal reflex function by supraspinal manipulations. Rats are implanted with intracerebral electrodes or cannulae and an intrathecal catheter. Following recovery, stimulation or the microinjection of morphine is made into the various brain regions which alter spinal reflex function. The antagonist is administered intrathecally. Bottom, the effect is expressed as the mean and S.E. of the maximum percent effect (MPE), as measured on the tail flick (A) and hot plate (B), of rats receiving an injection of morphine sulfate (5 µg/0.5 µl) into the PAG at time 0 (first arrow). At the second arrow, each animal received in different experiments an intrathecal injection of 15 µl of either saline (●—●), methysergide bimaleate (15 µg: ▽—▽), phentolamine-HCl (15 µg: ▲—▲), or both methysergide and phentolamine (15 µg each: □—□). (Adapted from Yaksh, 1978.)

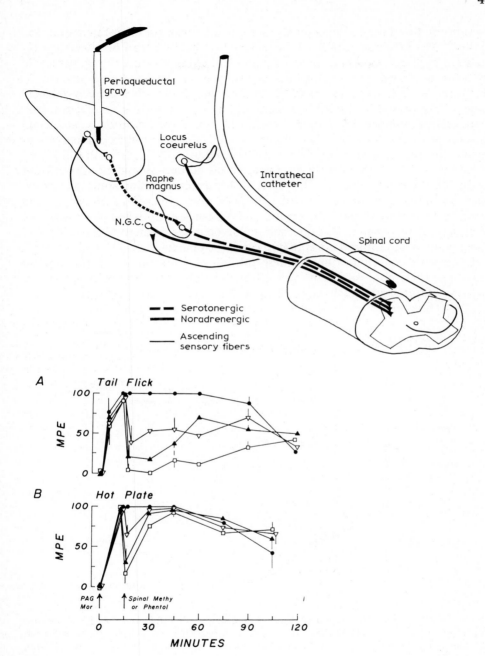

478

ally administered antagonists on the actions of morphine microinjected in the PAG of unanesthetized animals. In the bottom panel it can be seen that intrathecal application of both methysergide and phentolamine antagonized the analgesia produced by the morphine microinjection. These results provide direct support for the concept that the action on spinal reflex activity of morphine microinjected in the PAG is mediated by a joint activation of serotonergic and noradrenergic receptors located in the spinal cord. Similarly, electrical stimulation of the nucleus raphe magnus has been reported to produce a significant inhibition of spinal reflex activity (Oliveras et al., 1975; Proudfit and Anderson, 1975). Although there appear to be no norepinephrine-containing neurons in the raphe magnus, the effect of this stimulation on spinal reflex activity was also antagonized by intrathecally administered serotonergic and noradrenergic antagonists (Hammond and Yaksh, unpublished observations).

The second approach to this question involved measurement of the release of endogenous serotonin and norepinephrine into superfusates of the spinal cord. If supraspinal manipulations which inhibit the discharge of nociceptive neurons in the spinal cord exert this effect through an activation of the spinopetal monoaminergic pathways, then an increase in the release of these

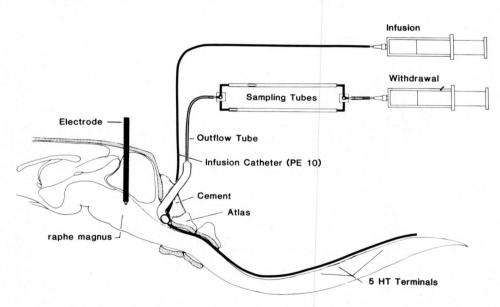

Figure 3. Schematic representation of the system employed for superfusing in situ the spinal cord of the anesthetized rat. A polyethylene 10 catheter used for infusion is inserted through the cisterna magna to the caudal level of the lumbar cord. An outflow cannula is placed into the cisterna magna. Artificial CSF is perfused at the rate of 100 µl/min and collected by a withdrawal syringe using iced sampling tubes. Modification of release from spinal cord is achieved in this schematic by the placement of an electrode into the raphe magnus. In other experiments, microinjection cannulae were placed into the PAG.

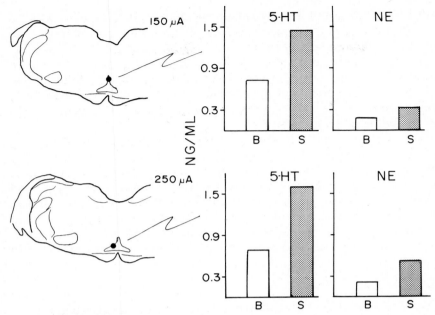

Figure 4. Release of serotonin and norepinephrine into spinal cord superfusates of two representative rats following electrical stimulation of the nucleus raphe magnus. On the left side of the figure the sites of stimulation have been indicated on coronal sections of the medulla using black circles. After collection of a 25-min sample of superfusate to determine the basal efflux of serotonin and norepinephrine, the raphe magnus was stimulated at 25 Hz using 0.5 msec square wave pulses of either 150 or 250 µA for 25 min. During stimulation, another sample of superfusate was collected to determine the release of serotonin and norepinephrine evoked by raphe stimulation. Quantitation of the amines was by high pressure liquid chromatography with electrochemical detection. The right side of the figure presents the release of serotonin (5-HT) and norepinephrine (NE) expressed as ng/ml superfusate under basal conditions (B; open bars) and during stimulation of the raphe magnus (S; stippled bars).

neurotransmitters should occur as indicated by their extracellular levels in the spinal cord. To examine the release of materials from the spinal cord, we have developed a method for in situ superfusion of the spinal cord of intact anesthetized rats and cats. Figure 3 includes a schematic representation of this technique. In preliminary experiments, it was demonstrated that microinjection of morphine in the PAG resulted in a significant increase in the efflux of serotonin into spinal cord superfusates. The release of norepinephrine was not examined in this study (Yaksh and Tyce, 1979). As mentioned earlier, electrical stimulation of brain stem regions is known to produce analgesia (Liebeskind et al., 1973; Oliveras et al., 1975). Recently, a significant increase in the efflux of both serotonin and of norepinephrine into spinal cord superfusates following stimulation of the nucleus raphe magnus has been demonstrated (Hammond et al., 1981). Figure 4 displays these results obtained in two animals, where serotonin and noradrenaline were measured simultaneously in the spinal superfusate before and during stimulation of the raphe magnus. These results suggest that electrical stimulation of the raphe magnus activates *both* serotonergic and noradrenergic pathways. Such findings showing joint activation of both monoamine circuits are consistent with the ability of intrathecally administered serotonergic and noradrenergic antagonists to attenuate the analgesia elicited from this site*.

These results clearly indicate that supraspinal manipulations known to alter spinal sensory processing produce an activation of descending monoaminergic pathways. The pharmacology of the spinal inhibition produced by these manipulations suggests the involvement of both serotonergic and noradrenergic spinal receptors. Direct activation of these receptors produces physiological effects which resemble those produced by the supraspinal manipulations. Furthermore, these supraspinal manipulations produce a measurable release of endogenous serotonin and norepinephrine into spinal cord superfusates.

II. Evidence for the Activation of Intrinsic Modulatory Systems: Release of Monoamines and Opioid Materials From Mesencephalon and Spinal Cord

Microinjection studies performed in the PAG and in the spinal cord, along with characterization of the pharmacology of their effects**, have indicated that opiate-sensitive synapses exist in these regions and that their activation alters the rostral transmission of nociceptive information. The coincident location of these synapses with the distribution of enkephalin-containing neurons suggests the presence of a modulatory system which serves to control spinal function. An essential question concerns what stimuli normally activate these intrinsic substrates. We have recently focused our attention on the ability of

---

* Although noradrenergic neurons are not reported in the raphe magnus, a dense noradrenergic projection to the raphe magnus does exist (Poitras and Parent, 1978; Levitt and Moore, 1979). Electrical stimulation of the raphe magnus may antidromically activate these projections and thereby produce an activation of the spinopetal noradrenergic system. Alternately, raphe stimulation may activate spinothalamic collaterals and so activate this system. As will be discussed later, somatic stimulation produces a release of serotonin and norepinephrine into spinal cord superfusates. Thus, raphe stimulation may, by means of activating spinothalamic tract collaterals, mimic the effects of peripheral input and activate both monoaminergic systems.

** Thus, it has been shown that the analgesic effect produced by intracerebral and intrathecal opiates is characterized by a dose dependent effect of the agonists, a dose dependent inhibition by several different antagonists, and a decreased structure–activity relationship involving stereospecificity (Yaksh and Rudy, 1978; Yaksh, 1981).

somatic input to alter the physiological and behavioral response of an animal to painful stimuli. Thus, McCreery and Bloedel (1976) observed that the discharge of spinothalamic neurons having their receptive field in the lumbar dermatomes could be inhibited by pinch applied to the ear. More recently, Le Bars and colleagues (1979) have demonstrated that the activity of dorsal horn neurons is subject to a powerful modulatory control by somatic stimulation of areas other than the principal receptive field and proposed the existence of a diffuse noxious inhibitory control (DNIC). Transcutaneous nerve stimulation and acupuncture are examples of the ability to alter the responsiveness of an organism to otherwise aversive stimuli by the activation of as yet undefined categories of primary afferents. The proposals of Melzack and Wall (1965) have directed attention towards the concept of a modulation of spinal sensory processing by various populations of primary afferents. These observations suggested to us that it would be worthwhile to investigate the ability of somatic stimuli to activate the intrinsic modulatory systems. While such studies could be carried out employing an electrophysiological approach (e.g. examining the discharge of neurons), such an approach would not permit us to easily assess whether the modulatory influences were mediated by an activation of monoaminergic and/or enkephalinergic neurons. Therefore, we elected to examine the effects of somatic stimulation on the release of monoamines into spinal cord superfusate (Tyce and Yaksh, 1981) and on the release of methionine-enkephalin-like immunoreactivity (MELI) from the spinal cord and from the PAG (Yaksh and Elde, 1981), two regions where opiate receptors are known to exert a powerful control over an animal's response to nociceptive stimulation. Cats were anesthetized and prepared for perfusion of the mesencephalic aqueduct by placement of an inflow cannula into the caudal third ventricle and an outflow cannula into the mouth of the aqueduct. In addition, a concentric arrangement of two cannulas was threaded through the cisterna magna and into the spinal cord subarachnoid space. The inflow cannula was threaded to the level of the caudal lumbar enlargement while the outflow cannula was passed to the level of the thoracic spinal cord. Thus, artificial CSF was perfused through the mesencephalic aqueduct and also through the spinal cord subarachnoid space. Thus, both the mesencephalic PAG and the lumbar spinal cord of each cat were perfused with artificial CSF. The sciatic nerves were stimulated bilaterally to investigate the effects of sensory input. In these experiments, we formulated three questions concerning the release of both the monoamines and the enkephalins. (1) What is the nature of the fiber population whose activation results in a release of monoamines and MELI? (2) Would the release of these substances from the lumbar spinal cord be segmentally organized, or would it involve supraspinal connections? In these experiments the release evoked by sciatic nerve stimulation was examined in the presence and absence of a cervical cold block. (3) Would the release of these substances from the lumbar spinal cord be activated in a somatotopic fashion? In these experiments, stimulation of an input distant to the lumbar dermatomes was achieved by supramaximal stimulation of the infraorbital branch of the trigeminal nerve.

Figure 5 demonstrates the resting and stimulus-evoked release of serotonin and norepinephrine into superfusates of the lumbar spinal cord of the cat. During low intensity stimulation of the sciatic nerve (associated with activity in Aβ fibers and no detectable effects on blood pressure or pupil size), there was no change in the levels of serotonin and norepinephrine in the superfusate. In contrast, high intensity stimulation (associated with activation of Aβ and Aδ/C fibers, mydriasis and a rise in blood pressure) resulted in a significant increase in the levels of serotonin and norepinephrine. In the presence of a cervical cold block, high intensity stimulation of the sciatic nerves failed to increase the re-

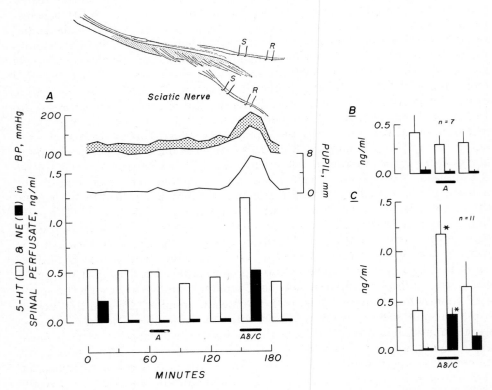

Figure 5. A, results obtained in one experiment showing: blood pressure (BP, mm Hg), pupil size (pupil, mm), and levels of serotonin (5-HT) and norepinephrine (NE) in the spinal superfusate. At intervals indicated by the black bars, the sciatic nerve was stimulated bilaterally at low intensities (A) or high intensities (Aδ/C) at the rate of 1 per second, every other second. B and C, the effects produced in 7 and 11 animals, respectively, by A fiber or Aδ/C fiber stimulation of the sciatic nerve. In this figure and Figures 6 and 7, * $P < 0.05$; S, stimulating electrodes; R, recording electrodes. (From Tyce and Yaksh, 1981, with permission.)

lease of serotonin and norepinephrine or to alter blood pressure or pupil size (Fig. 6). The failure to alter pupil size or blood pressure suggested that the cold block was adequate to inhibit the rostral transmission of sensory information relevant to the afferent arm of the sympathetic reflex. The failure to evoke a release of serotonin and norepinephrine suggests that a supraspinal connection was critical to the activation of the bulbospinal monoaminergic pathways. Finally, supramaximal stimulation of the infraorbital branch of the trigeminal nerve produced a significant increase in the levels of serotonin and norepinephrine in the superfusate which was nearly totally absent in the presence of a cervical cold block.

Studies of the release of MELI revealed certain differences in the hodology of

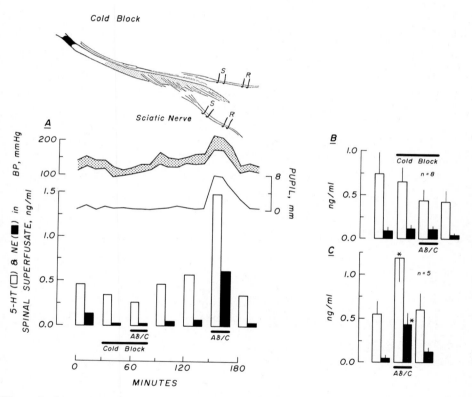

Figure 6. A, results obtained in one animal showing: blood pressure (BP, mm Hg), pupil size (pupil, mm), and levels of serotonin (5-HT) and norepinephrine (NE) in the spinal superfusate during high intensity stimulation of the sciatic nerve (Aδ/C) at times indicated by the short black bar as a function of a cold block applied to the cervical cord during the intervals indicated by the long black line. B and C, the levels of 5-HT and NE (ng/nl; mean ± S.E.) evoked by high intensity stimulation of the sciatic nerve (Aδ/C). In B, a cold block was applied to the cervical cord during the interval indicated by the black bar. (From Tyce and Yaksh, 1981, with permission.)

the two intrinsic modulatory systems. As indicated by Figure 7, stimulation of the sciatic nerve at Aβ and Aδ/C fiber intensity resulted in an increase in the levels of MELI in lumbar spinal cord superfusates and also in the aqueductal perfusate. Unlike the monoamines, a cervical cold block did not alter either the resting release or the evoked release of this immunoreactivity from the spinal cord. However, such a cold block inhibited the release of immunoreactivity in the aqueductal perfusate evoked by high intensity sciatic nerve stimulation. This suggested that, unlike the monoamines, the release of MELI in the lumbar cord was segmentally organized, while that which was released from the

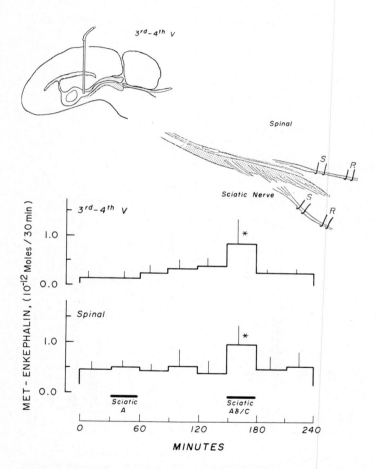

Figure 7. Levels of methionine-enkephalin-like immunoreactivity (MELI: Met-enkephalin; pmol/30 min, mean ± S.E., n = 5) in ventricular (top) and spinal (bottom) perfusates. During the interval indicated by the black bar stimulation of the sciatic nerve was carried out at low (A) and high (Aδ/C) intensities as described in Figure 5. * $P < 0.05$. (From Yaksh and Elde, 1981, with permission.)

Brain Stem Control of Spinal Mechanisms
– B. Sjölund and A. Björklund, editors
© 1982 Elsevier Biomedical Press

22

The Role of Brain Stem–Spinal Systems in Genital Stimulation: Induced Inhibition of Sensory and Motor Responses to Noxious Stimulation

BARRY R. KOMISARUK

Institute of Animal Behavior, Rutgers University, Newark, NJ 07102, U.S.A.

I. Introduction

Through our studies on the role of afferent activity from the genitalia in the control of sexual behavior in female rats, we have identified a sensory stimulus that has a potent antinociceptive effect. This stimulus is distention of the vaginal canal, which is produced by probing against the vaginal cervix with a glass rod (Komisaruk and Wallman, 1977). The present paper provides evidence that, in rats, vaginal stimulation (VS) strongly antagonizes responses to noxious stimulation and that its effects are mediated by at least three mechanisms: (a) monoaminergic pathways that descend to the spinal cord; (b) an opiate-sensitive process, and (c) an intrinsic spinal system.

II. Modulation of Sensorimotor Activity by Genital Stimulation in Female Rats

Vaginal stimulation (VS) plays a significant role in copulatory behavior in rats in that it prolongs (Kuehn and Beach, 1963; Bermant and Westbrook, 1966; Diakow, 1975) and intensifies (Komisaruk and Diakow, 1973) the female's immobile mating stance (lordosis), which normally occurs during penile insertion and ejaculation. The lordosis posture elevates the rump, exposing the female's genitalia to the male, and the immobilization facilitates intromission and ejaculation (Komisaruk, 1978). Furthermore, immobilization after ejaculation facilitates sperm transport in the female (Matthews and Adler, 1977). VS alone, applied by probing against the cervix with a glass rod, has a strong immobilizing effect (Komisaruk and Diakow, 1973), inhibits the righting response (Naggar and Komisaruk, 1977), and induces extension of the legs and digits (Komisaruk, 1978). VS also produces a marked suppression of flexor responses to noxious stimulation, e.g. inhibiting leg flexion to foot pinch (Komisaruk and Larsson, 1971; Komisaruk et al., 1976) (Fig. 1). Furthermore, VS facilitates lordosis in response to stimulation of the genital skin (Komisaruk and Diakow, 1973). Thus, VS potentiates certain extensor responses and simultaneously suppresses certain flexor responses. In addition, VS suppresses vibrissa retraction to ear pinch, and the eyeblink response to corneal stimulation (Komisaruk and Larsson, 1971). A supraspinal indicator of nociception, vocalization in response to tail shock, is also suppressed by VS, whereas rats' ability to vocalize in response to non-noxious stimulation, e.g. lifting, is not suppressed by VS (Komisaruk and Wallman, 1977).

These findings raise the question of the mode of action of VS. Are its effects due to suppression of the rat's motor responsiveness, or its sensory responsiveness, or both? What are the loci of action of the suppression of responses to noxious stimulation?

We tested the motor hypothesis by direct electrical stimulation of the pyramidal tract at current intensities just suprathreshold to elicit muscular movements of the face or limbs (Komisaruk and Wallman, 1977). VS had no inhibitory effect on these movements, indicating that the inhibitory effect of VS acts proximal to the final common motor pathway.

III. Antinociceptive Action of Vaginal Stimulation in Rats

We then determined whether VS would suppress sensory responses to noxious stimulation. Single- and multi-unit responses of thalamic neurons to noxious and innocuous stimuli were recorded from the ventrobasal complex of the thalamus. Neurons in this nuclear complex have also been shown to respond to noxious stimuli in rats (Mitchell and Hellon, 1977) and in monkeys (Foreman et al., 1977). Thalamic neuronal responses to pinching the foot were markedly suppressed by VS. Furthermore, neuronal populations and even single neurons that responded to both noxious and innocuous sensory stimulation were differentially suppressed by VS. That is, neuronal responses to innocuous stimulation were unaffected by VS, whereas neuronal responses to noxious stimulation were markedly attenuated by VS (Fig. 2). Our analysis of this differential effect is summarized in Figure 3 (Komisaruk and Wallman, 1977).

Foreman et al. (1977) observed that, in the monkey, distention of the urinary bladder or rectum exerts an inhibitory effect on spinothalamic neuron firing activity. In the rat, the urinary bladder, rectum, and vaginal canal receive afferent innervation from the pelvic nerve (Komisaruk et al., 1972), and mechanical distention of the rectum also inhibits leg withdrawal responses to foot pinch (Komisaruk and Larsson, 1971). This selective suppression of nociceptive, but not innocuous tactile afferent, activity by VS parallels our ob-

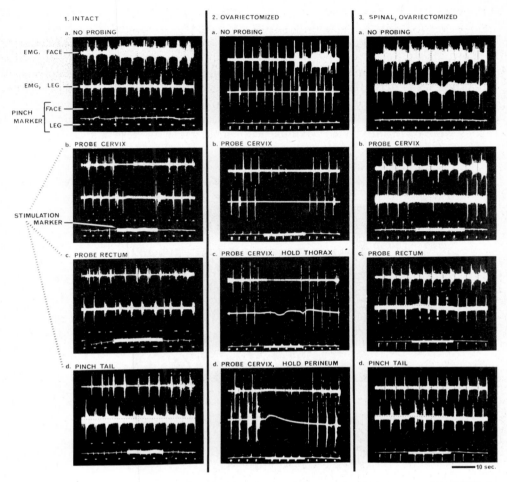

Figure 1. Vaginal stimulation suppresses responses to noxious stimuli as measured by EMG. In 1a, pinching the ear (at markers) produces stimulus-bound ipsilateral retraction of the vibrissae, and pinching the foot (at markers) produces stimulus-bound leg withdrawal. These responses are suppressed or blocked during VS (probing against the cervix) (1b). This effect was also obtained in ovariectomized, hormonally untreated rats (2a, b). As a control stimulus for probing the cervix, pinching the tail had no suppressive effect on leg or vibrissa responses (1c). The responses were also blocked by cervical probing when the rat was held by the perineum rather than the tail during the probing (2c). In chronically-prepared spinal rats (6 weeks after mid-thoracic spinal transection) leg withdrawal responses (3a) were blocked by cervical probing (3b), whereas the cranial nerve-mediated vibrissa retraction response (3a) was unaffected (3b). The control stimulus of pinching the tail did not suppress either response. (From Komisaruk and Larsson, 1971, with permission.)

496

servation that, at the same time that withdrawal reflexes are suppressed by VS, there is actually a facilitation of the extensor-dominated lordosis response to tactile stimulation of the surface of the genital skin (Komisaruk and Diakow, 1973).

The VS-induced suppression of afferent responses to noxious stimulation implies that VS is actually analgesic, rather than that it simply blocks the rats' capability of performing a motor response to noxious stimulation. We therefore hypothesized that rats would perform an operant response which provided VS if they were confronted with noxious skin shock. The rats were suspended in a

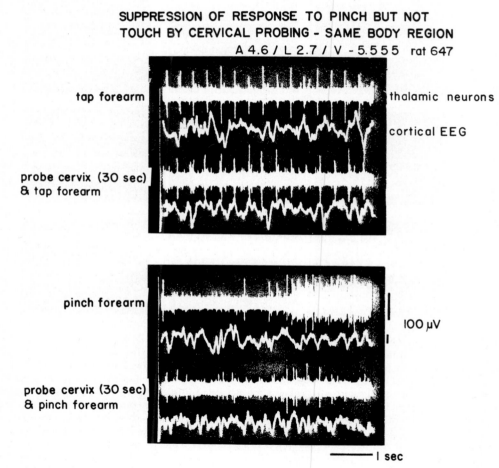

Figure 2. Selective antinociceptive effect of VS. At a single recording site in the ventrobasal complex, the stimulus-bound neuronal response to repetitive light tap of the forearm was unaffected by cervical probing (upper figure) whereas the stimulus-bound response to pinch of the forearm (middle of trace, lower figure) was suppressed by cervical probing. Urethane, 1.6 g/kg. (From Komisaruk, 1974, with permission.)

harness and obtained VS by pressing a lever placed in front of them. The onset of skin shock was signalled by a light. All groups received inescapable noxious skin shock. The operant response latencies were significantly shorter in the experimental group which could obtain VS in conjunction with the noxious skin shock, than in the control groups, which could obtain either external genital

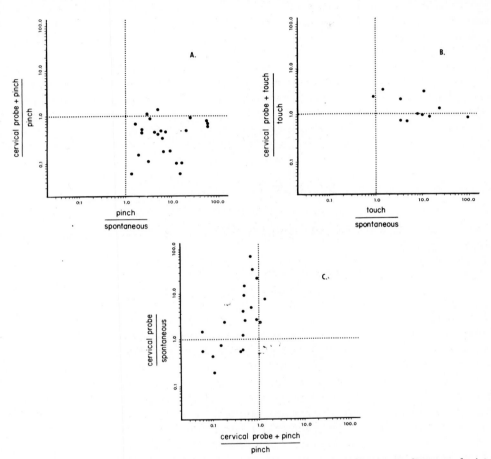

Figure 3. Summary of the antinociceptive effect of VS. Each point in the scatter diagrams depicts firing rate ratios at a single recording site. In A, all pinch: spontaneous firing rate ratios are greater than 1, i.e. all sites were activated by pinch. However, when cervical probing was applied in conjunction with pinch, the firing rates were lower than during pinch alone in almost all cases, demonstrating the suppressive effect of the cervical probing on responses to pinch. By contrast (B), the responses to touch were relatively unaffected by cervical probing. Graph C shows that the suppressive effect of cervical probing on response to pinch is not due simply to a non-specific reduction in firing activity of neurons that respond to pinch, because the spontaneous activity of the majority of these neurons was actually increased by cervical probing. Thus, cervical probing does not have a general depressive effect, but rather differentially attenuates neuronal responses to noxious but not innocuous tactile stimulation. (From Komisaruk and Wallman, 1977, with permission.)

skin stimulation or no other stimulation in conjunction with the noxious skin shock. In this experimental design, note that the rats pressed the lever, i.e. performed the operant response, before the VS was applied. Thus, they performed a response for VS before they could have become immobilized by it. We interpret these findings as demonstrating that VS antagonizes the aversive property of skin shock (Ross et al., 1979). Taking this interpretation together with the findings that VS suppresses thalamic sensory responses to noxious, but not innocuous, stimulation, we conclude that VS indeed produces an analgesic state.

In order to study the factors which mediate the actions of VS, we developed a convenient indicator of the effect of VS. This is the relationship between force exerted against the vaginal cervix and the threshold to elicit vocalization in response to tail shock (Crowley et al., 1976). As the force applied to the vaginal cervix is increased using a calibrated spring-loaded probe, the vocalization threshold increases from a mean of 0.25 ± 0.05 mA at 50 g force, to a mean of 0.68 ± 0.10 mA at 800 g force. This appears to be an antinociceptive effect, because VS does not inhibit vocalization elicited by non-noxious (lifting) stimulation (Komisaruk and Wallman, 1977).

IV. Mechanisms of Antinociceptive Action of Vaginal Stimulation

IV.1. Role of the monoaminergic systems

Systemic studies. Using vocalization threshold as a nociceptive indicator, we assessed the effects of various monoamine treatments on the response to VS. Our findings provide consistent evidence that VS activates an α-adrenergic mechanism which attenuates responses to noxious stimulation. Our findings for the role of a serotonergic mechanism are less consistent.

Our initial studies involved systemic administration of monoamine synthesis inhibitors. Systemic administration of the tyrosine hydroxylase inhibitor, α-methyltyrosine (200 mg/kg) significantly reduced forebrain levels of norepinephrine (NE) and dopamine (DA) and significantly reduced the vocalization threshold produced by VS to 60% of control levels. Specific inhibition of NE synthesis by administration of the DA-β-hydroxylase inhibitor, disulfiram, significantly reduced the vocalization threshold produced by VS to 66% of control levels. Additon of the NE precursor, dihydroxyphenylserine, to α-methyltyrosine-treated rats significantly and strongly potentiated the threshold-elevating effect of VS to 175% of control levels. None of these treatments significantly changed baseline (non-VS) vocalization thresholds (Crowley et al., 1977a).

The role of serotonin is more difficult to interpret because of conflicting findings between the effects of the putative serotonin receptor blocker cinanserin

(25 mg/kg), which strongly attenuated the effect of VS to 47% of control levels, versus the presumed stimulation of serotonin receptors with 100 µg/kg of lysergic acid diethylamide, or enhanced serotonin release with H 75/12, both of which also attenuated the effect of VS, to 58% and 45% of controls, respectively (Crowley et al., 1977a). It is possible that conflicting results for serotonin are due to partial agonistic effects of the receptor blockers or differential effects on separate components of the system, as in the case of adrenergic control of blood pressure occurring at multiple sites in the CNS (Bolme et al., 1972).

Despite the inconsistencies in the serotonergic studies, the effects of adrenergic agonists and antagonists are consistent with the effects of adrenergic synthesis blocker and precursor treatment. The antinociceptive effect of VS was doubled by the adrenergic agonist clonidine (100 µg/kg) and by the catecholamine releasing agent, H 77/77. Conversely, the α-adrenergic receptor blocking agent, phentolamine (10 mg/kg or 25 mg/kg), significantly attenuated the effect of VS to 69% of control levels. The β-adrenergic antagonist, sotalol (40 mg/kg or 80 mg/kg), had no significant effect (Crowley et al., 1977a).

The dopaminergic system seems to play a role in mediating the threshold elevating effect of VS, which is consistent with the immobilizing effect of VS. That is, the DA receptor blocker, pimozide (1 mg/kg), which potentiates immobilization (Chiodo et al., 1979), potentiated the effect of VS (vocalization threshold: 170% of control level). The DA receptor agonist, apomorphine (3.5 mg/kg), which antagonizes the immobilizing effect of VS (unpublished observations) and stimulates compulsive locomotion (Andén et al., 1976), reduced the effect of VS to 51% of the control level (Crowley et al., 1977a). In this regard, it may be helpful to conceptualize the dopaminergic system as a "go" system and the effect of VS as an antagonistic, analgesic "stop" system. Further support for this concept is provided by our finding that VS significantly delayed the depletion of striatal DA after synthesis inhibition with α-methyltyrosine, suggesting that VS inhibits the activity of nigrostriatal DA neurons (Crowley et al., 1977a).

Spinal studies. We assessed the possible role of descending spinopetal monoaminergic systems in mediating the effect of VS, through the use of direct administration of monoaminergic receptor blocking agents or neurotoxins directly to the spinal cord, and by measurement of monoamines in cord or superfusate of the cord after VS (Steinman et al., 1980).

The α-adrenergic receptor blocking agent, phentolamine, or the serotonergic receptor blocking agent, methysergide, were injected perispinally, i.e. intrathecally, into the lumbar area via chronically implanted polyethylene catheters, according to the method of Yaksh and Rudy (1976). Drugs were injected in 20 µl of saline solution followed by a 10 µl saline flush. Then we assessed the effect of these local spinal drug treatments on the ability of VS to elevate the vocalization threshold, or on the latency to flick the tail away from a radiant heat source. Threshold determinations were started 15 min after drug administration. On both the vocalization test and the tail flick test, the

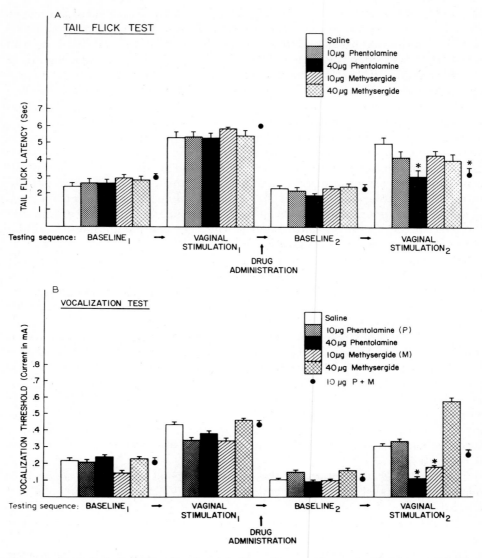

Figure 4. Perispinal (intrathecal) administration of an α-adrenergic blocking agent (phentolamine), a serotoninergic blocking agent (methysergide), or a combination of these, attenuates the suppressive effect of VS on responses to noxious stimulation. Before drug administration, all groups showed uniformly low baselines, and uniform elevations in threshold during VS (200 g force). Fifteen minutes after drug administration, all baselines were again uniformly low. When VS was again applied, there was a significant attenuation of the threshold elevation (by comparison with the saline control group on this test) in the 40 μg phentolamine and the 10 μg phentolamine + 10 μg methysergide groups on the tail flick test. On the vocalization test, there was a significant attenuation of the threshold elevating effect of VS in the 40 μg phentolamine and in the 10 μg methysergide groups. (From Steinman et al., in preparation, with permission.)

effect of VS was significantly attenuated by injection of 40 µg phentolamine, as seen in Figure 4. Methysergide (10 µg) significantly attenuated the effect of VS on the vocalization test only. Combined injection of 10 µg phentolamine plus 10 µg methysergide had an additive effect, significantly attenuating the effect of VS on the tail flick test. The antagonistic effect of 10 µg methysergide on the antinociceptive effect of VS is consistent with that of systemically injected cinanserin, which also antagonized the effect of VS on vocalization threshold. However, these findings are difficult to reconcile with the elevation in vocalization threshold produced by 40 µg methysergide, unless perhaps at this high dose methysergide acts as a partial agonist.

As an alternative approach to the local administration of monoaminergic receptor blocking agents, we administered monoamine neurotoxins to the spinal cord. Microinjection of 6-hydroxydopamine (6-OHDA), a toxin for catecholaminergic neurons (Kostrezewa and Jacobowitz, 1974), were made bilaterally into the spinal cord at the level of the cisterna magna (10 µg in 1 µl) and the rats were tested 16 days later. The effect of VS on vocalization threshold was significantly attenuated to 60% of vehicle control levels, and the level of NE measured in the spinal cord was reduced from a mean control level of 198 ng/g in the controls to a mean of 42 ng/g in the 6-OHDA rats (Crowley et al., 1977a). These findings further support a role for NE mediating the antinociceptive effect of VS.

In a separate experiment, 5,7-dihydroxytryptamine (5,7-DHT), a neurotoxin for serotonergic neurons (Breese, 1975), was injected intrathecally and three days later the effects of VS on the vocalization threshold were determined. Doses of 4 µg or 10 µg of 5,7-DHT prevented VS from significantly elevating vocalization threshold (i.e. the increases in vocalization threshold induced by VS were 6% and 18%, respectively, compared to 91% in the saline controls) (Steinman and Komisaruk, 1981).

If VS acts via NE and serotonin, then these transmitters would be expected to be released at neuron terminals in response to VS. Therefore, the spinal cord was superfused with artificial cerebrospinal fluid, and superfusates of the spinal cord were collected and assayed for NE and serotonin using high pressure liquid chromatography. Superfusion samples were collected in chloralose-anesthetized rats for 30 min before VS, for 30 min during VS (a total of 10 probing episodes, 1.5 min each, every 3 min) and then for 30 min after the end of VS. A control group received no VS. Figure 5 shows that VS significantly increased the levels of NE and serotonin in the spinal superfusate. Release of NE persisted into the post-VS period. These findings provide further evidence that the antinociceptive effect of VS is mediated at least in part by VS-induced release of NE and serotonin at nerve terminals in the spinal cord (Steinman et al., 1980). In support of this, it is noteworthy that Allen et al. (1981) showed a significant increase in uptake of 2-deoxyglucose (2-DG) in dorsal raphe and mesencephalic reticular formation after VS. Thus, VS may utilize monoaminergic systems that have been shown in other contexts to exert antinociceptive effects (see Yaksh and Rudy, 1978; Basbaum and Fields, 1978, for review).

With regard to the noradrenergic mechanism, clonidine has been reported to inhibit motor responses to noxious stimulation (Spaulding et al., 1979). However, clonidine has also been reported to increase flexor reflex responsiveness in the acutely spinalized rat (Andén et al., 1970; Bolme et al., 1974). Similarly, clonidine has been reported, by Forssberg and Grillner (1973), to facilitate locomotion in the acute spinal cat. Kawasaki et al. (1978) account for the apparent discrepancy in acutely spinalized rats by demonstrating, with EMG recordings of the extensor muscle of the tail, that low dosages of clonidine (e.g. 60 µg/kg) inhibit the EMG response to tail pinch, whereas higher dosages of clonidine (500 µg/kg) in the range of those used by earlier authors (Andén et al., 1970; Bolme et al., 1974) (up to 300–1000 µg/kg) actually potentiated the EMG response to tail pinch. Furthermore, pretreatment with phentolamine blocked the inhibitory but not the excitatory effect of clonidine on the tail flick reflex. Bolme et al. (1972) point out that "short-latency" flexor reflex pathways

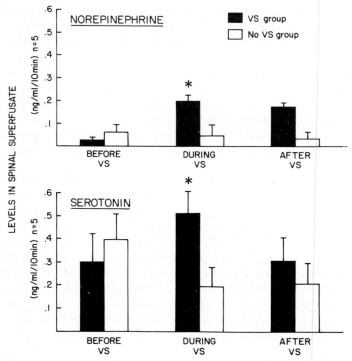

Figure 5. VS releases NE and serotonin into spinal cord superfusate. The levels of NE and serotonin collected in spinal superfusate during a 30 min period when VS was applied were significantly elevated 10- and 2-fold, respectively, over the pre-VS levels. The control group receiving no VS showed no significant changes. The NE level remained elevated in the 30 min sampling period after VS. (From Steinman et al., in preparation, with permission.)

may be activated separately from "long-latency" pathways although both utilize NE, in the sense that DOPA depresses transmission in the "short-latency" pathways, and the "long-latency" pathway is released when the former pathways are inhibited by DOPA (Andén et al., 1966). Our earlier findings that the catecholamine synthesis inhibitor α-methyltyrosine antagonizes the effect of VS on vocalization threshold but not on the flexor reflex response to foot shock (Crowley et al., 1977a), further indicate the differential sensitivity to NE that is observed when different indicators are used.

IV.2. Role of opiate systems

There is extensive evidence that descending spinopetal serotonergic and noradrenergic pathways mediate analgesia, including opiate-induced analgesia (for reviews, see Yaksh and Rudy, 1978; Basbaum and Fields, 1978). For example, microinjection of morphine into the periaqueductal gray induces analgesia that is antagonized by phentolamine or methysergide injected intrathecally into the spinal cord (Yaksh, 1979). Morphine injected into the periaqueductal gray increased the release of serotonin into spinal superfusate. Morphine administered locally to the locus coeruleus increased nociceptive thresholds (Yaksh, 1979), and morphine injected systemically increased the levels of normetanephrine, a metabolite of NE, in spinal cord, but not after cord transection at C1 (Shiomi and Takagi, 1974). These findings raise the question of whether VS may activate an opiate system which in turn activates the descending noradrenergic and serotonergic spinopetal systems. We therefore determined whether the effect of VS on elevating the vocalization threshold would be antagonized by administration of naloxone or induction of morphine tolerance. Naloxone (10 mg/kg) did not affect the ability of VS to elevate the vocalization threshold (Crowley et al., 1977b). Furthermore, rats made tolerant to morphine by 35 days of morphine treatment also showed no attenuation of the VS-induced increase in vocalization threshold. Thus, on this measure, VS did not show cross-tolerance to morphine. However, Hill and Ayliffe (1981) reported that 10 mg/kg naloxone did attenuate the effect of VS on elevating the latency of tail flick to radiant heat and the latency to withdraw the tail from hot water. Thus, we repeated the experiment, this time using both tail flick and vocalization threshold measures. In this study, we confirmed both our earlier study as well as that of Hill and Ayliffe (1981). That is, naloxone did not significantly attenuate the effect of VS on the vocalization threshold, but it did attenuate the effect of VS on the tail flick latency. In addition, 8 of 8 rats showed a 6+ sec tail flick latency before naloxone administration, but only 3 of 8 rats showed a 6+ sec tail flick latency after receiving 10 mg/kg naloxone i.p. (Steinman and Komisaruk, in preparation). These findings suggest that an opiate–monoaminergic system mediates the VS-produced increase in tail flick latency, but VS may bypass the opiate component in producing an increase in vocalization threshold to tail shock.

There is evidence that descending monoaminergic pathway that are opiate-sensitive and mediate analgesia course through the dorsolateral funiculus (DLF). The DLF contains descending serotonergic axons whose cell bodies are located in the raphe nuclei (Dahlström and Fuxe, 1965; Basbaum and Fields, 1978), and descending noradrenergic axons whose cell bodies are located in nuclei A1–3 (Nygren and Olsen, 1977). Electrical stimulation of these nuclear regions produces analgesia (see Basbaum and Fields, 1978, for review). Furthermore, lesions of the DLF have been shown to antagonize analgesia produced by: electrical stimulation in the vicinity of the raphe nuclei (Basbaum et al., 1976), morphine microinjections into the periaqueductal gray (Murfin et al., 1976), and by systemic morphine administration (Hayes et al., 1978), in addition to opiate-dependent front paw shock-induced analgesia (Mayer and Watkins, 1981).

In collaboration with Patricia Faris, Linda Watkins and David Mayer, we have obtained preliminary results in a study designed to determine whether DLF lesions disrupt the effect of VS, which indicate that the opioid-related increase in tail flick latency that is produced by VS is attenuated by DLF lesions, but the opioid-independent vocalization threshold increase produced by VS is not. It is possible that opiates mediate the effects of VS on monoaminergic systems that descend in the DLF, whereas descending monoaminergic systems that do not utilize the DLF can be activated by VS independently of the opiates. These indications of an involvement of an opiate mechanism in the effect of VS are consistent with the findings of Pert (personal communication) that VS reduces the level of β-endorphin measured in central gray.

IV.3. Intraspinal system

In addition to the evidence that monoaminergic and opiate mechanisms play a role in mediating the effects of VS, it is important to note that, even in rats with complete spinal transection at the midthoracic level, VS can still attenuate the leg withdrawal response to foot pinch (Komisaruk and Larsson, 1971). Despite the significant effects of the manipulations described above, only bilateral transection of the pelvic nerve, which conveys afferent activity from the vaginal canal (Komisaruk et al., 1972), has been found to abolish the VS blockage of the leg withdrawal response to foot pinch. Thus, there is a third, intraspinal, component of the inhibitory effect of VS, but the mechanism of action of this, perhaps most powerful, component of the inhibitory effects of VS is not known. Adrenergic innervation of the spinal cord via autonomic fibers that enter the cord as recurrent sympathetic fibers has been described by McNicholas et al. (1980), and this might mediate such an effect in the spinal animal. Whether intraspinal inhibitory neurotransmitters are released by VS to suppress afferent and/or efferent activity remains to be determined.

The inhibitory effects of opiates (Yaksh and Rudy, 1977) and monoamines administered locally to the spinal cord (e.g. Belcher et al., 1978; Headley et al.,

1978; Engberg and Ryall, 1966; Phillis, 1968; Engberg and Thaller, 1970; Engberg and Marshall, 1971; Jordan et al., 1978) that have been identified thus far may account for only a part of the total inhibitory effect of VS.

V. Conclusion

The apparent existence of multiple mechanisms by which responses to noxious stimulation can be blocked may complicate the task of identifying the underlying mechanisms, but should also be viewed optimistically as providing for multiple, and therefore perhaps additive, opportunities for intervening in the suppression of nociceptive activity. Apparently, VS exerts inhibitory effects on nociceptive activity, but it can also inhibit movement that is not under nociceptive control. Its antinociceptive effects appear to involve monoaminergic and opiate mechanisms.

In addition, it should be noted that although the effect of VS in suppressing responses to noxious stimulation is most powerful at the tail, it extends to all parts of the body as far rostrally as the tip of the snout. Is this whole body effect due to some unique synaptic configuration of pelvic nerve afferents and/or their projections in releasing inhibitory transmitters? Is there a specific neurotransmitter that is unique to the pelvic nerve?

The dynamic aspects of genital stimulation are also of interest. The ability of genital stimulation to produce intense somatic and visceral motor activity that is characteristic of orgasm, or its equivalent in infrahuman species, may be due to the ability of rhythmical genital afferent stimulation to recruit massive neuronal discharges throughout the body. This could be due primarily to the configuration and dynamic spatial–temporal effects initiated by genital afferent activity rather than to a particular neurotransmitter. In this regard, it is curious that virtually nothing is known about the neurophysiological and central neuroanatomical basis of the remarkable sensorimotor effects which characterize orgasm. Perhaps an understanding of the mechanism underlying such effects as the extensor dominance and attenuation of specific sensory activity produced by vaginal stimulation in the present context may be of relevance toward an understanding of the mechanism underlying orgasm.

In addition to the mechanism of action of genital stimulation, the question of the adaptive significance of the antinociceptive effect of genital stimulation, whether it plays a role in copulatory behavior and/or parturition, and its generality across species, including humans, raises interesting problems for further research, which could extend to possible therapeutic application.

Acknowledgements

Contribution from the Institute of Animal Behavior. Excellent technical assistance from Ms. W. Cunningham and Ms. C. Banas is appreciated. Portions of the research reported in this paper were supported by National Science Foundation Grant BNS-7824504.

References

Allen, T.O., Adler, N.T., Greenberg, J.H. and Reivich, M. (1981) Vaginocervical stimulation selectively increases metabolic activity in the rat brain, *Science*, 211: 1070-1072.

Andén, N.-E., Jukes, M.G.M., Lundberg, A. and Vyklicky, L. (1966) The effect of DOPA on the spinal cord. 1. Influence of transmission from primary afferents, *Acta. physiol. scand.*, 67: 373-386.

Andén, N.-E., Corrodi, H., Fuxe, K., Hökfelt, B., Rydin, D. and Svensson, T. (1970) Evidence for a central noradrenaline receptor stimulation by clonidine, *Life Sci.*, 9: 513-523.

Andén, N.-E., Grabowska, M. and Strombom, U. (1976) Different alpha-adrenoreceptors in the central nervous system mediating biochemical and functional effects of clonidine and receptor blocking agents, *Naunyn-Schmiedeberg's Arch. Pharmacol.*, 292: 43-52.

Basbaum, A. and Fields, H.L. (1978) Endogenous pain control mechanisms: review and hypothesis, *Ann. Neurol.*, 4: 451-462.

Basbaum, A.I., Marley, N. and O'Keefe, J. (1976) Spinal cord pathways involved in the production of analgesia by brain stimulation. In: J.J. Bonica and D. Albe-Fessard (Eds.), *Advances in Pain Research and Therapy, Vol. 1*, Raven Press, New York, pp. 511-515.

Belcher, G., Ryall, R.W. and Schaffner, R. (1978) The differential effects of 5-hydroxytryptamine, noradrenaline and raphe stimulation on nociceptive and non-nociceptive dorsal horn interneurons in the cat, *Brain Res.*, 151: 307-321.

Bermant, G. and Westbrook, W.H. (1966) Peripheral factors in the regulation of sexual contact by female rats, *J. comp. physiol. Psychol.*, 61: 244-250.

Bolme, P., Fuxe, K. and Lidbrink, P. (1972) On the function of central catecholamine neurons – their role in cardiovascular and arousal mechanisms, *Res. Commun. Chem. Path. Pharmacol.*, 4: 657-697.

Bolme, P., Corrodi, H., Fuxe, K., Hökfelt, T., Lidbrink, P. and Goldstein, M. (1974) Possible involvement of central adrenaline neurons in vasomotor and respiratory control. Studies with clonidine and its interaction with piperoxane and yohimbine, *Europ. J. Pharmacol.*, 28: 89-94.

Breese, G.R. (1975) Chemical and immunochemical lesions. In L.L. Iversen, S.D. Iversen, and S.H. Snyder (Eds.) *Biochemical Principles and Techniques in Neuropharmacology*, Plenum Press, New York, pp. 137-189.

Chiodo, L.A., Antelman, S.M., Caggiula, A.R. and Lineberry, C.G. (1979) Reciprocal influences of activating and immobilizing stimuli on the activity of nigrostriatal dopamine neurons, *Brain Res.*, 189: 385-390.

Crowley, W.R., Jacobs, R., Volpe, J., Rodriguez-Sierra, J.F. and Komisaruk, B.R. (1976) Analgesic effect of vaginal stimulation in rats: modulation by graded stimulus intensity and hormones, *Physiol. Behav.*, 16: 483-488.

Crowley, W.R., Rodriguez-Sierra, J.F. and Komisaruk, B.R. (1977a) Monoaminergic mediation of the antinociceptive effect of vaginal stimulation in rats, *Brain Res.*, 137: 67-84.

Crowley, W.R., Rodriguez-Sierra, J.F. and Komisaruk, B.R. (1977b) Analgesia induced by vaginal stimulation in rats is apparently independent of a morphine-sensitive process, *Psychopharmacology*, 54: 223-225.

Dahlström, A. and Fuxe, K. (1965) Evidence for the existence of monoamine-containing neurons in the central nervous system. I. Demonstration of monoamines in the cell bodies of brain stem neurons, *Acta physiol. scand.*, Suppl. 232: 1-55.

Diakow, C. (1975) Motion picture analysis of rat mating behavior, *J. comp. physiol. Psychol.*, 89: 704-712.

Engberg, I. and Marshall, K.C. (1971) Mechanism of noradrenaline hyperpolarization in spinal cord motoneurons of the cat, *Acta physiol. scand.*, 83: 142-144.

Engberg, I. and Ryall, R.W. (1966) The inhibitory action of noradrenaline and other monoamines on spinal neurons, *J. Physiol. (Lond.)*, 185: 298-322.

Engberg, I. and Thaller, A. (1970) Hyperpolarizing actions of noradrenaline in spinal motoneurons, *Acta physiol. scand.*, 80: 34A-35A.

Foreman, R.D., Schmidt, R.F. and Willis, W.D. (1977) Convergence of muscle and cutaneous input onto primate spinothalamic tract neurons, *Brain Res.*, 124: 555-560.

Forssberg, H. and Grillner, S. (1973) The locomotion of the acute spinal cat injected with clonidine i.v., *Brain Res.*, 50: 184-186.

Hayes, R.L., Price, D.D., Bennett, G.J., Wilcox, G.L. and Mayer, D.J. (1978) Differential effects of spinal cord lesions on narcotic and non-narcotic suppression of nociceptive reflexes: further evidence for the physiologic multiplicity of pain modulation, *Brain Res.*, 155: 91-101.

Headley, P.M., Duggan, A.W. and Griersmith, B.T. (1978) Selective reduction by noradrenaline and 5-hydroxytryptamine of nociceptive responses of cat dorsal horn neurons, *Brain Res.*, 145: 185-189.

Hill, R.G. and Ayliffe, S.J. (1981) The antinociceptive effect of vaginal stimulation in the rat is reduced by naloxone, *Pharmacol. Biochem. Behav.*, 14: 631-632.

Jordan, L.M., Kenshalo, D.R., Martin, R.F., Haber, L.H. and Willis, W.D. (1978) Depression of primate spinothalamic tract neurons by iontophoretic application of 5-hydroxytryptamine, *Pain*, 5: 135-142.

Kawasaki, K., Takesue, H. and Matsushita, A. (1978) Modulation of spinal reflex activities in acute spinal rats with alpha-adrenergic agonists and antagonists, *Jap. J. Pharmacol.*, 28: 165.

Komisaruk, B.R. (1974) Neural and hormonal interactions in the reproductive behavior of female rats. In W. Montagna and W.A. Sadler (Eds.), *Reproductive Behavior*, Plenum Publ., New York, pp. 97-129.

Komisaruk, B.R. (1978) The nature of the neural substrate of female sexual behaviour in mammals and its hormonal sensitivity: review and speculations. In J.B. Hutchison (Ed.), *Biological Determinants of Sexual Behaviour*, John Wiley, New York, pp. 349-393.

Komisaruk, B.R. and Diakow, C. (1973) Lordosis reflex intensity in rats in relation to the estrous cycle, ovariectomy, estrogen administration, and mating behavior, *Endocrinology*, 93: 548-557.

Komisaruk, B.R. and Larsson, K. (1971) Suppression of a spinal and a cranial nerve reflex by vaginal or rectal probing in rats, *Brain Res.*, 35: 231-235.

Komisaruk, B.R. and Wallman, J. (1977) Antinociceptive effects of vaginal stimulation in rats: neurophysiological and behavioral studies, *Brain Res.*, 137: 85-107.

Komisaruk, B.R., Adler, N.T. and Hutchison, J. (1972) Genital sensory field: enlargement by estrogen treatment in female rats, *Science*, 178: 1295-1298.

Komisaruk, B.R., Ciofalo, V. and Latranyi, M.B. (1976) Stimulation of the vaginal cervix is more effective than morphine in suppressing a nociceptive response in rats. In J.J. Bonica and D. Albe-Fessard (Eds.), *Advances in Pain Research and Therapy, Vol. 1*, Raven Press, New York, pp. 439-443.

Kostrezewa, R.M. and Jacobowitz, D.M. (1974) Pharmacological actions of 6-hydroxydopamine, *Pharmacol. Rev.*, 26: 199-388.

Kuehn, R.E. and Beach, F.A. (1963) Quantitative measurement of sexual receptivity in female rats, *Behaviour*, 21: 282-299.

Matthews, M. and Adler, N.T. (1977) Facilitative and inhibitory influences of reproductive behavior on sperm transport in rats, *J comp. physiol. Psychol.*, 91: 721-741.

Mayer, D.J. and Watkins, L.R. (1981) The role of endorphins in endogenous pain control systems.

508

In H.M. Emrich (Ed.), *Modern Problems of Pharmacopsychiatry: The Role of Endorphins in Neuropsychiatry*, Karger AG, Basel.

McNicholas, L.F., Martin, W.R., Sloan, J.W. and Nozaki, M. (1980) Innervation of the spinal cord by sympathetic fibers, *Exp. Neurol.*, 69: 383-394.

Mitchell, D. and Hellon, R.F. (1977) Neuronal and behavioural responses in rats during noxious stimulation of the tail, *Proc. roy. Soc. B*, 197: 169-194.

Murfin, R., Bennett, G.J. and Mayer, D.J. (1976) The effects of dorsolateral spinal cord (DLF) lesions on analgesia from morphine microinjected into the periaqueductal gray matter (PAG) of the rat, *Soc. Neurosci. Abstr.*, 2: 946.

Naggar, A.N. and Komisaruk, B.R. (1977) Facilitation of tonic immobility by stimulation of the vaginal cervix in the rat, *Physiol. Behav.*, 19: 441-444.

Nygren, L.-G. and Olson, L. (1977) A new major projection from locus coeruleus: the main source of noradrenergic nerve terminals in the ventral and dorsal columns of the spinal cord, *Brain Res.*, 132: 85-93.

Paalzow, G. and Paalzow, L. (1976) Clonidine antinociceptive activity: effects of drugs influencing central monoaminergic and cholinergic mechanisms in the rat, *Naunyn-Schmiedeberg's Arch. Pharmacol.*, 292: 119-126.

Phillis, J.W., Tebecis, A.K. and York, D.H. (1968) Depression of spinal motoneurons by noradrenaline, 5-hydroxytryptamine, and histamine, *Europ. J. Pharmacol.*, 4: 471-475.

Ross, E.L., Komisaruk, B.R. and O'Donnell, D. (1979) Evidence that probing the vaginal cervix is analgesic in rats, using an operant paradigm, *J. comp. physiol. Psychol.*, 93: 330-336.

Shiomi, H. and Takagi, H. (1974) Morphine analgesia and the bulbospinal noradrenergic system: increase in the concentration of normetanephrine in the spinal cord of the rat caused by analgesics, *Brit. J. Pharmacol.*, 52: 519-526.

Spaulding, T.C., Venafro, J.J., Ma, M.G. and Fielding, S. (1979) The dissociation of the antinociceptive effect of clonidine from supraspinal structures, *Neuropharmacology*, 18: 103-105.

Steinman, J.L. and Komisaruk, B.R. (1981) Spinal serotonin mediates a supraspinal component of analgesia produced by vaginal stimulation in rats, *Soc. Neurosci. Abstr.*, 7: 583.

Steinman, J.L., Komisaruk, B.R., Yaksh, T. and Tyce, G.M. (1980) Vaginal stimulation-produced analgesia is mediated by spinal norepinephrine and serotonin in rats, *Soc. Neurosci. Abstr.*, 6: 454.

Yaksh, T.L. (1979) Direct evidence that spinal serotonin and noradrenaline terminals mediate the spinal antinociceptive effects of morphine in the periaqueductal gray, *Brain Res.*, 160: 180-185.

Yaksh, T.L. and Rudy, T.A. (1976) Chronic catheterization of the spinal subarachnoid space, *Physiol. Behav.*, 17: 1031-1036.

Yaksh, T.L. and Rudy, T.A. (1977) Studies on the direct spinal action of narcotics in the production of analgesia in the rat, *J. Pharmacol. exp. Ther.*, 202: 411-428.

Yaksh, T.L. and Rudy, T.A. (1978) Narcotic analgesics: CNS sites and mechanisms of action as revealed by intracerebral injection techniques, *Pain*, 4: 299-359.

Brain Stem Control of Spinal Mechanisms
– B. Sjölund and A. Björklund, editors
© 1982 Elsevier Biomedical Press

23

Neuropeptides in Human Cerebrospinal Fluid – Relation to Pain

LARS TERENIUS

Department of Pharmacology, University of Uppsala, Box 573, 751 23 Uppsala, Sweden

I. Introduction

There are several reasons why spinal and lower brain stem mechanisms are important targets for studies of pain and the endogenous modulation of pain. The first synapse between a nociceptive afferent fiber and second order projection neurons in the dorsal horn is not only a site for signal transfer, but also for modulation of the nociceptive signal. An early formulation of modulation of nociceptive input at the spinal level was the gate-control theory of Melzack and Wall (1965). This theory was of considerable heuristic value and stimulated neuroanatomic and neurophysiologic characterization of the dorsal horn. Another important development was the regional localization of the opiate receptor sites in the CNS (Tsou and Jang, 1964; Yaksh et al., 1976). Strong sensitivity to morphine and, consequently, high levels of opiate receptors were identified in both the dorsal spinal cord and brain stem areas, i.e. the nuclei raphe magnus and gigantocellularis. Very soon after the discovery of the endogenous opioids, studies of their CNS distribution were made with immunohistochemical techniques. It was found that enkephalin-staining neurons were present in a large number of nuclei of the brain and also in the dorsal spinal cord. Every brain area previously known to be affected by the opiates contained these neurons, and it was also clear on a quantitative basis that areas known to be of importance in the transmission and processing of nociceptive signals were rich in these neurons (Hökfelt et al., 1977a). At the spinal level enkephalin interneurons terminate within the terminal field of the thin non-myelinated primary afferents, which probably transmit nociceptive stimuli and contain substance P (Hökfelt et al., 1977b).

Another important line of research stems from the observation of Reynolds (1969) that electrical stimulation of CNS areas close to the cerebral aqueduct (periaqueductal gray matter) produced surgical anesthesia in the rat. This ac-

509

tion could at least partly be ascribed to the activation of descending systems involving serotonin (5-HT) and ultimately modulating the signal transfer at the level of the dorsal horn. Since naloxone could at least partly reverse the analgesia, an endorphinergic link was implicated (Fields and Basbaum, 1978).

In summary, neuronal systems utilizing enkephalin, substance P and 5-HT have been found to be involved in the transmission and modulation of nociceptive signals.

II. On the Nature of Clinical Pain

In recent years, it has become almost a truism that clinical pain in man cannot be equated with experimentally induced pain. Clinical pain is a much more complex phenomenon, strongly overlayering other CNS activities, e.g. as reflected by increases in cerebral blood flow over wide brain areas (Lassen et al., 1978). In chronic pain, as in any other chronic disorder, the patient is afflicted with a sense of helplessness and despair. The disorder can be characterized as a disease state, and it has several clinical similarities with affective disorders (Engel, 1958; Sternbach, 1974).

At the time the endorphins were discovered and were found to be present in "pain pathways", the next and obvious question was to define their physiologic and pathophysiologic roles in pain control. It was already known that the narcotic antagonist naloxone had practically no effect in a healthy volunteer, suggesting that tonic activation of opiate receptors was not of great consequence. The situation might be quite different in clinical pain. Besides using naloxone tests, we set out to analyze the content of endorphin in cerebrospinal fluid (CSF). CSF was chosen, rather than blood or urine, because the endorphins were found to be produced not only in the CNS but also in peripheral tissues (cf. Terenius, 1981). The procedure (Terenius and Wahlström, 1975) was to fractionate CSF in a simple chromatographic system and test fractions for opiate receptor affinity. This approach was quite straightforward, although at the time the chemical identity of the tested fractions was not clear. Along with the rapid progress in structure identification of endorphins we calibrated our chromatographic system with reference peptides and found, somewhat to our surprise, that the endorphins we were isolating and testing were not identical to those characterised in brain extracts, such as enkephalin, β-endorphin or dynorphin. In the meantime a number of clinical correlations were established with levels of the chromatographic fractions we were testing, named Fractions I and II (FI and FII) for simplicity. These observations have led us into research activities along several lines: (a) establishment of the chemical identity of CSF endorphins; (b) the significance of endorphins in clinical pain (and other conditions not discussed here) as reflected by CSF measurements; and (c) extension of these studies to measurements of other substances, such as substance P and 5-HT, which also are involved in pain and pain modulation. These studies have led to the formulation of a disease model for chronic benign pain which seems to have therapeutic implications. Several of these research lines will be reviewed here.

III. Chemical characteristics and measurements of CSF endorphins

It has already been mentioned that we have adopted a receptor-assay for CSF endorphins. This assay will react to all agents with opiate receptor affinity irrespective of structure. Figure 1 illustrates a typical result from fractionation of CSF with a Sephadex G 10-column. Fractions from the column were run in the receptor-assay. For analytical assays the CSF is ultrafiltered prior to the chromatographic separation. This excludes the peak, which elutes early (and is unusually large in the sample shown in Figure 1). The column separates one fraction eluting ahead of salts (FI) and one fraction eluting later than the salts (FII); the area where salt elutes cannot be tested directly because of the high ionic strength. The FII actually shows evidence for some separation into two components. It can also be noted that there is very little receptor-active material in the area where enkephalins elute. Although not shown here, we know that enkephalins form a very small fraction of the total assayable endorphin activity. β-Endorphin would elute ahead of FI and it would occur in very small amounts. Thus, if we exclude activity eluting in the void volume, which is probably artifactual, most of the CSF endorphins having opiate receptor affinity elute in the FI and FII fractions.

We have collected considerable information about the structural characteristics of the active substances in FI and FII. It is clear that completely different substances elute in the two fractions. In FI we find a complex mixture of peptides and three or four major components which separate on electrophoresis or molecular sieving chromatography. One of these components seems related to dynorphin (Wahlström and Terenius, 1980). All peptides are more basic than enkephalin. In FII the two peaks also separate on electrophoresis. These components are of much smaller moleculer weight, chemically related to the enkephalins, extended at the C-terminus by a few amino acids, and more basic (Nyberg, Wahlström and Terenius, unpublished observations). Thus, a whole family of peptides, probably deriving from a common precursor, is present in the CSF. We know that these peptides are metabolically quite stable and we therefore have reason to believe that, since these substances reach the CSF in considerable quantities, they may also bathe opiate receptors and therefore play a functional role by themselves. Another possibility is that they just represent spill-over products which are more metabolically stable than, for example, the enkephalins. In order to investigate these possibilities, we are presently studying the release of endorphins and other neuropeptides into the CSF of rats or cats under various experimental conditions. The animals are

512

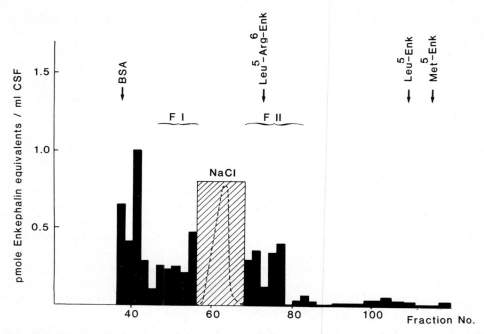

Figure 1. Elution profile of material reacting in a radioreceptor-assay using tritium-labeled dihydromorphine as the radioligand. A sample of 50 ml CSF was run through a Sephadex G 10 column, (5 cm × 100 cm) and eluted in 0.2 M acetic acid. The flow rate was 1 ml/min and the fraction size, 20 ml. The column was calibrated with bovine serum albumin (BSA) and enkephalin (ENK) peptides, as indicated. The position of the salt fraction was determined by conductometry. The elution positions of FI and FII are also indicated (Nyberg and Terenius, unpublished observations.)

perfused over the cerebral ventricles or the spinal canal, and the perfusate is collected under periods of resting or strong afferent stimulation of back extremities. Substantial increases in FI and FII levels are observed in cats and a strong increase in FI is observed in rats on afferent stimulation (Jhamandas et al., 1982). In addition, studies in man indicate that acupuncture-like stimulation increases FI endorphins (Sjölund et al., 1977). Therefore, in all probability, the release of these endorphins from the spinal cord to the CSF is neuronally mediated. It therefore becomes so much more important to obtain a proof of the chemical identity of these substances.

IV. Clinical Pain and CSF Endorphins

We have applied CSF endorphin analysis to two different problems with relevance to clinical pain. One is acute postsurgical pain. Due to ethical considerations, we have not used naloxone in such patients. On the other hand, chemical analysis of CSF endorphins was carried out in a series of patients undergoing a standard laparotomy for conditions not involving pain prior to operation. After recovery from anesthesia, these patients were allowed to self-administer pethidine, a short-acting narcotic analgesic, so they remained comfortably pain-free. Each patient would soon find his individual minimum dosage rate, and by repeated blood sampling we could show that the individually established minimum effective steady-state plasma (or CSF) concentration of pethidine varied between patients by a factor of 3 to 5. Each patient maintained an essentially stable steady-state for at least 36 h. If the steady-state level is related to the preoperative FI endorphin level, we observe a statistically significant inverse relationship, i.e. patients with low endorphin levels titrate to higher pethidine levels than do patients with high endorphin levels (Tamsen et al., 1980, 1982). This provides indirect evidence that activity in endorphin systems determines our propensity to tolerate clinical pain.

Fairly extensive studies have provided evidence that measurement of CSF endorphins may be one tool for the taxonomy of chronic pain. Early studies (Terenius and Wahlström, 1975; Sjölund et al., 1977) indicated that patients with chronic neurogenic pain showed lower FI endorphins than healthy volunteers. A more extensive study (Almay et al., 1978) verified this observation. However, in this latter study it was observed that not every patient with chronic pain showed low endorphin levels, but that this condition seemed to be characteristic of chronic neurogenic pain – where pain derives from a lesion of the nervous system itself (Table I). It was also noted that several other clinical characteristics of these patients related to the FI endorphin levels (Table II). Of particular interest is the relation between depth of depression and endorphin level. Another observation which probably is highly relevant is that endorphins reduced with increasing duration of illness. It is also apparent from

TABLE I

DISTRIBUTION OF CASES IN DIFFERENT CLINICAL CATEGORIES WITH REGARD TO FRACTION I ENDORPHIN AND SUBSTANCE P LEVELS IN CSF

(From Sjölund et al., 1977; Almay et al., 1978; Terenius, 1981, with permission.)

Clinical diagnosis	Fraction I (pmol/ml CSF)*			Substance P (fmol/ml CSF)		
	< 0.6	0.6–1.2	> 1.2	< 50	50–120	> 120
Healthy volunteers	3	12	4	–	14	–
Neurogenic pain	29	2	2	6	–	–
Other organic pain	2	3	3	–	–	3
Psychogenic pain	3	9	10	–	2	–
Depressive disorders		3	12	–	–	–

* Calculated as Met-enkephalin equivalents.

TABLE II

FRACTION I ENDORPHIN LEVELS IN THE CSF OF PA-
TIENTS WITH CHRONIC PAIN (n = 44), AND CLINICAL AND
LABORATORY VARIABLES

(cf. Terenius, 1981.)

Correlation	Variable
Positive	Thresholds to experimental pain
	Tolerance limits to experimental pain
	Depression scores
	5-HIAA levels in CSF
Negative	Duration of disorder (neurogenic pain)
Yes	EEG response to visual stimuli (V.E.P.)
	Personality variables
No	Sex, age, self-rated severity of pain

Table I that substance P levels tend to be lower in patients with chronic
neurogenic pain. In a patient with somatogenic pain of peripheral origin, "organic pain", the levels are high. Finally, we have observed that low levels of FI
endorphins are usually associated with low 5-HT levels (Almay et al., 1980). It
therefore seems as if CSF analysis, particularly of endorphin FI and substance
P, may provide a biochemical tool to assess the status of a pain patient and to
offer a potential method for subdiagnosis. Perhaps more importantly, these observations suggest limitations and possibilities in strategies for control of
these disorders.

V. A Disease Model for Chronic Neurogenic Pain

Inspection of Table I reveals that reduced levels of FI endorphins are characteristic of neurogenic pain, while patients with, for instance, "psychogenic
pain" and depression tend to have higher levels, maybe even above the range
in healthy individuals. The accompanying low levels of substance P suggest
that the input from thin non-myelinated C-fibers is low. These data suggest
that there is no excessive activity in afferent fibers, which we usually associate
with pain. Another observation fits with this model. Morphine is known to be
the most efficient drug in severe clinical pain of general organic origin (surgical trauma, cancer, arthritis, etc.). On the other hand, it is by tradition never
used in chronic neurogenic pain. The reason is partly the addiction potential,
but we have also learned by experience that morphine is not active. We have re-

cently confirmed this in two patients with chronic neurogenic pain who were allowed to self-administer pethidine as described above. Both patients reached higher steady-state levels than demanded in postoperative pain and they still did not report any pain relief (unpublished observation).

We therefore propose that chronic neurogenic pain is characterized by a deficiency in pain inhibitory mechanisms and also in the afferent pathways leading to activation of these systems. Morphine is inactive since it can only inhibit signal traffic in pathways activated from peripheral nociceptors. Thus, according to this model, chronic neurogenic pain is a deficiency syndrome and should probably be treated by restitution rather than ablation. One way to achieve this is by activating the afferent input by strong somatic stimulation, such as classic acupuncture, electrical stimulation of acupuncture needles, or electroacupuncture via surface electrodes (transcutaneous nerve stimulation). This approach has a purely empirical basis but is found to be effective. Many of the published reports on the therapeutic efficacy of these procedures are hard to evaluate. To some extent this is due to the problems of designing proper trials, for instance placebo treatment is hard to come by. One study with a follow-up period of three months and a thorough design is of particular interest, since patients were classified according to similar criteria to those we applied in Table I. The therapeutic outcome in this series is summarized in Table III. It is clear that patients with neurogenic pain do best, while the psychogenic pain patients respond poorly. The latter observation strongly argues against any strong influence of psychological factors in the therapeutic response. Thus, the best responders are those with neurogenic pain previously demonstrated to

TABLE III

RESPONSE RATE TO TRANSCUTANEOUS NERVE STIMULATION IN PATIENTS WITH CHRONIC PAIN

The terminology of Table I is followed. (Data from Eriksson et al., 1979.)

Kind and site of pain	No. of patients entering study	No. of patient continuing treatment after 3 months
Neurogenic pain		
Neuralgia	43	27 (63%)
Rhizalgia	22	14 (64%)
Dorsalgia	7	6 (86%)
Central pain	18	12 (67%)
Organic pain		
Cancer	11	5 (45%)
Ischemia	5	1 (20%)
Psychogenic pain	17	3 (17%)

516

have a biochemical deficiency. Low frequency transcutaneous nerve stimulation has been found to elevate FI endorphins (Sjölund et al., 1977), and the long-term consequences of such therapy is a return to normal levels of FI endorphins, 5-HT and probably substance P (unpublished observations). Chronic neurogenic pain can therefore be considered as a systems disorder which needs an integrated therapeutic approach. There may be some analogy to the use of electroshock in affective disorders.

This model of the disorder should also lead to searches into possible improvements of therapy. Drugs acting on the 5-HT system have therapeutic effects (Johansson et al., 1980). Recently we have also attempted to study the mechanisms of acupuncture analgesia in experimental animals. Antibodies to endorphins and substance P have been injected locally into various sites within the CNS. It was observed that anti-enkephalin antibody given intrathecally can almost completely reverse acupuncture (Han et al., 1982), emphasizing the role of spinal processes, as also suggested from experiments in humans (Sjölund et al., 1977).

Measurements of neuropeptides in the CSF have therefore been instrumental in providing insight into the possible mechanisms of pain and pain modulation, particularly in conditions of disease.

Acknowledgement

The work is supported by the Swedish Medical Research Council.

References

Almay, B.G.L., Johansson, F., Von Knorring, L., Terenius, L. and Wahlström, A. (1978) Endorphins in chronic pain. I. Differences in CSF endorphin levels between organic and psychogenic pain syndromes. *Pain*, 5: 153-162.

Almay, B.G.L., Johansson, F., Von Knorring, L., Terenius, L. and Wahlström, A. (1980) Relationships between CSF levels of endorphins and monoamine metabolites in chronic pain patients, *Psychopharmacology*, 67: 139-142.

Engel, G.L. (1958) "Psychogenic" pain and the pain prone patient, *Amer. J. Med.*, 26: 899-918.

Eriksson, M.B.E., Sjölund, B.H. and Nielzén, S. (1979) Long-term results of peripheral conditioning stimulation as an analgesic measure in chronic pain. *Pain*, 6: 335-347.

Fields, H.L. and Basbaum, A.I. (1978) Brainstem control of spinal transmission neurons, *Ann. Rev. Physiol.*, 40: 217-248.

Han, J.S., Xie, G.X., Zhou, Z.F., Folkesson, R. and Terenius, L. (1982) Enkephalin and β-endorphin as mediators of electroacupuncture analgesia in rabbits: an antiserum microinjection study, *Advanc. Biochem. Psychopharmacol.*, in press.

Hökfelt, T., Elde, R., Johansson, O., Terenius, L. and Stein, L. (1977a) The distribution of enkephalin immunoreactive cell-bodies in the rat central nervous system, *Neurosci. Lett.*, 5: 23-31.

Hökfelt, T., Ljungdahl, Å., Terenius, L., Elde, R. and Nilsson, G. (1977b) Immunohistochemical analysis of peptide pathways possibly related to pain and analgesia: enkephalin and substance P, *Proc. nat. Acad. Sci. U.S.A.*, 74: 3081-3085.

Jhamandas, K., Yaksh, T.L., Bergström, L. and Terenius, L. (1982) Release of endogenous opioids from spinal cord in vivo following sciatic nerve stimulation. In H. Takagi (Ed.), *Advances in Endogenous and Exogenous Opioids*, Kyoto.

Johansson, F., Von Knorring, L., Sedvall, G. and Terenius, L. (1980) Changes in endorphins and 5-hydroxyindoleacetic acid in cerebrospinal fluid as a result of treatment with a serotonin reuptake inhibitor (zimelidine) in chronic pain patients, *Psychiat. Res.*, 2: 167-172.

Lassen, N.A., Ingvar, D.H. and Skinhøj, E. (1978) Brain function and blood flow, *Sci. Amer.*, 239: 50-59.

Melzack, R. and Wall, P.D. (1965) Pain mechanisms: a new theory, *Science*, 150: 971-979.

Reynolds, D.V. (1969) Surgery in the rat during electrical analgesia induced by focal brain stimulation, *Science*, 164: 444-445.

Sjölund, B., Terenius, L. and Eriksson, M. (1977) Increased cerebrospinal fluid levels of endorphins after electroacupuncture, *Acta physiol. scand.*, 100: 382-384.

Sternbach, R.A. (1974) *Pain Patients: Traits and Treatment*, Academic Press, New York.

Tamsen, A., Hartvig, P., Dahlström, B., Wahlström, A. and Terenius, L. (1980) Endorphins and on-demand pain relief, *Lancet*, i: 769-770.

Tamsen, A., Sakurada, T., Wahlström, A., Terenius, L. and Hartvig, P. (1982) Postoperative demand for analgesics in relation to individual levels of endorphins and substance P in cerebrospinal fluid, *Pain*, in press.

Terenius, L. (1981) Endorphins and pain, *Front. Horm. Res.*, 8: 162-177.

Terenius, L. and Wahlström, A. (1975) Morphine-like ligand for opiate receptors in human CSF, *Life Sci.*, 16: 1759-1764.

Tsou, K. and Jang, C.S. (1964) Studies on the site of analgesic action of morphine by intracerebral microinjection, *Sci. Sin.*, 8: 1099-1109.

Wahlström, A. and Terenius, L. (1980) Chemical characteristics of endorphins in human cerebrospinal fluid, *FEBS Lett.*, 118: 241-244.

Yaksh, T.L., Yeung, J.C. and Rudy, T.A. (1976) Systematic examination in the rat of brain sites sensitive to the direct application of morphine: observation of differential effects within the periaqueductal gray, *Brain Res.*, 114: 83-103.

Subject Index